CIRCLES
FROM THE SKY

CIRCLES FROM THE SKY

PROCEEDINGS OF THE FIRST INTERNATIONAL CONFERENCE ON THE CIRCLES EFFECT AT OXFORD

together with post-conference additions

Edited by
Dr. GEORGE TERENCE MEADEN

Sponsored by the Circles Effect Research Group (CERES) and the Tornado and Storm Research Organisation (TORRO)

SOUVENIR PRESS

First published 1991 by Souvenir Press (Educational & Academic) Ltd.
43 Great Russell Street, London WC1B 3PA
and simultaneously in Canada

ISBN 0 285 63036 9

Printed and bound in Great Britain by
The Dowland Press Ltd., Frome, Somerset

CONFERENCE PROCEEDINGS

CONTENTS

Conference Chairmen: Professors Christopher Church, John T. Snow, G. Terence Meaden.

Conference Organisers Dr. Derek M. Elsom and G. T. Meaden.

Conference held at Oxford Polytechnic, Oxford, 23rd June 1990.

FOREWORD

In this volume we issue the latest information on crop-circles research as reported and interpreted by the world's most reliable researchers on the subject. In addition to the proceedings of the first international conference on the circles effect, the subject matter has been updated to 1991 by the inclusion of important papers which give the most recent circles news and analysis together with a long illustrated summary of the spectacular findings of the 1990 season. This includes the amazing Alton Barnes circles group - the most extraordinary and best-known of all complex cases, the analyses of which are bringing us ever nearer to a total solution to this puzzling phenomenon.

The Oxford conference was convened by CERES, the world's only professional scientific organization researching the circles mystery. Due to its

Figure 1. Professors Hiroshi Kikuchi and Yoshi-Hiko Ohtsuki with G. Terence Meaden at the Oxford Conference.

skilled research team and the excellence of its survey details CERES had by the spring of 1991 established a 1700-circle data bank. What is more, since its beginnings in 1980 CERES has attracted into its research orbit a large number of professional scientists from Britain, America, Japan, Australia, Germany, France and Sweden. Research is advancing on several fronts, for besides the obvious observational and analytical work useful research is being undertaken into experimental and theoretical projects, not only in physics and meteorology but also in archaeology, anthropology, prehistory, religious history, mythology, and psychology.

As I wrote in *The Circles Effect and its Mysteries* in 1989, "what began as an ingenuous desire (in 1980) to ascertain when and how plain single circles could be formed (the only ones known at the beginning) has, in the wake of a multitude of unforeseeable discoveries, evolved into an arduous, complex study – one which will have far-reaching consequences in disciplines well removed from the one in which the investigation began". 1991 will see an amazing surge in crop-circle research as new lines of enquiry are opened up following the publication of this book and another one entitled *The Goddess of the Stones.*

PREFACE

CROP CIRCLES AND THE VORTICES THAT MAKE THEM
– the remarkable discoveries continue

The recent discovery of the circles effect is a major event for the natural sciences, concerning as it does a visually-exciting atmospheric phenomenon which, amazingly, has gone unrecognized all these years.

Not unnaturally it has attracted the attention of the world, and especially in England vast numbers of people are actively seeking circles every spring and summer. As a result, season by season, reporting improves and the evidence mounts, painstakingly gathered by the efforts of enthusiasts who track down new circles which they survey and photograph. The keenest researchers interview farmers and locals in an attempt to certify circle formation dates, and thence determine whenever possible the atmospheric conditions at the time of circle creation. Gradually, the clues combine, and advances are made – small steps at a time. When assessed dispassionately, they all point towards a meteorological solution, complex and difficult though it may be – and the valid experts, the professional vortex scientists, agree.

The importance of this work for meteorological science is increasingly acknowledged across the world. Today we have proof of this by the attendance at the world's first conference on circles research of many visitors from abroad, and they number, among the speakers, American and Japanese professors of physics and meteorology, attracted to Britain by this stimulating subject still in its exhilaratory, pioneering period.

Whenever and wherever it happens the circles effect in its exotic forms is both an eye-catching and memorable experience, at once baffling and beguiling. Despite the extensive publicity given to the complex formations they are nevertheless not at all common; single circles remain by far the most frequent type of event that occurs. Yet even the plain single circle, examined closely, is an impressive work of art, offering intriguing problems for the curious. Its sharp perimeter, spiral centre, twisted straws, layered beds, all are witness to an extraordinary event that happened swiftly, mysteriously, and on most occasions unseen and unheard. Whereas the creative event is undoubtedly rapid, spinning itself out in a matter of seconds, the resulting traces linger much longer. At times, the circles survive for weeks on end awaiting the harvest when the reaper – or in these days the combine-harvester – arrives. At other times the circles are destroyed quickly, sometimes within hours if the harvest is ripe and the farmer is ready.

How is it then, if the circles have been seen by countrydwellers since time immemorial, they were not brought to the attention of inquisitive scientists before 1980?

The primary reason is that the busy farmer and hardworking labourer never suspected that science could attach importance to the subject. For some farmers it was such a familiar sight that it was ignored. All too often circles were not discovered until harvest time – that ultimate and rewarding occasion when the hard-pressed farmer is reaping the fruits of his labours. At the same time, it is the day of destruction, that adverse moment for the circles when by gathering the grain the stalks are destroyed. In cruel seconds fate eliminates those very stems which had been storing the secret, the stems which had yielded to the stresses of the mystery vortices and preserved until then their precious, fragile clues.

In all events, the relatively few farmers who paused to reflect on these puzzling circles had their private explanations for their origin. Why search further when the culprits are so obvious? All too often, the circles were blamed on nature's events, particularly birds and animals.

In recent years too, improvements in crop variants and changes in agricultural practices may have rendered certain species more vulnerable to permanent damage when struck by circle-making phenomena. Perhaps the circles are easier to see these days than formerly, the crops presenting a more uniform appearance in quality, height and colour. Even so, the circles remain rare in most parts of the globe, and recur regularly at comparatively few sites.

Now that the attention of the world is directed at the subject, the numbers of circle sites and circle totals are mounting quickly – but not necessarily because more circles are forming. Rather, it is because the totals relate to a rise in circle-hunting hours expended by an increasing number of observers. The sensational claims of publicity-seeking non-scientists to the effect that circle numbers correlate with some other developing phenomenon, like 'the growing hole in the ozone layer' or to various unspecified 'paranormal/extraterrestrial effects', are valueless guesses unsupported by sound reasoning.

By contrast this first conference on the circles effect is a public attempt by professional physicists and mathematicians to grapple with the elements of the problem. We welcome too those dedicated amateurs whose spirit of enthusiasm and will to co-operate transcend desires for financial gain and personal glory. The conference and the book of the conference are for scientists and for those with a scientific spirit who thirst for knowledge, the

the amateurs who genuinely inquire after the truth. Conference and book are not for the distorters of reality, the reckless, the poltergeist hunters, for whom self-interest and book sales to a gullible public are the main concern. They are for open-minded, educated people seeking wisdom in a vital subject, as yet in its pioneering stage. There is no embellishment of the evidence here, no sensationalism. The testimony of the circles is legitimate, impressive, instructive, while yet perplexing and problematic.

The stamp of a good puzzle perpetually delights. The circle-agent arrives unheralded, spinning its marks unseen. Then off it goes, like the whirlwinds in Martin Chuzzlewit, departing, as Dickens put it, "doubtless to join other whirlwinds". It vanishes into thin air, leaving behind provocative traces for us to admire, the rings and circles which constitute 'the circles effect' and they call to us to use our powers of logic and scientific knowledge to demystify this apparent enigma.

For this, conventional application of the scientific method is called for, and the laws of science are not found wanting.

'Tis strange – but true; for truth is always strange;
Stranger than fiction'. G. G. BYRON

G. T. MEADEN

THE ORIGIN OF THE CIRCLES – A CHALLENGE TO SOLVE

In the space of ten years this difficult study has grown from a small-scale inquiry into a project having immense scientific potential with a huge following both serious and popular.

Field investigations start before the end of April when the crops are mature enough to submit to permanent damage when struck by the fast spinning air of the vortex, and work continues until harvest time when the combines destroy the fragile evidence and the crop circles disappear for another season. Besides cereals and other crops and vegetation, the vortex leaves its traces in earth, sand, snow and frost-covered grass. Occasionally it scours or blasts circular hollows into the ground or snow, so even in the absence of damageable material the potential for outdoor research is maintained.

All such studies are part of the research programme of CERES, The Circles Effect Research Unit of TORRO whose ultimate aim is to understand the vortex behaviour at the heart of the problem. This scientific body is the leading group in circles research. It seeks information concerning all localized occurrences in which rotatory forces come from a skyward direction, especially when they cause damage or unusual effects to crops, buildings, gardens, automobiles, animals and people, whether by night or by day. Electromagnetic phenomena are included too, for we have gathered a certain quantity of direct evidence and a vast amount of circumstantial evidence which link the circles-effect vortex to optical and electrical manifestations having certain affinities with the ball-lightning phenomenon.

Therefore, to assemble into a single archive every bit of information relevant to the subject, CERES established in 1987 an international data bank for the centralization of information and photographs on both the primary question of the circles effect and on ancillary vortex-related phenomena involving unusual noises (humming, whining, crackling, etc), electrical effects (interference to radio-communications, television, vehicle performance), and luminosity (especially low, hovering, spinning, pulsating, and descending lights or balls-of-light).

Readers who can provide data are invited to get in touch with CERES, as also those who feel they can help in the future by acting as spotters and investigators of crop circles *anywhere in England or the rest of the globe.* On the world scale we expect that other countries suffer similar vortex-phenomena where topography, the conditions of the air, and frontal types are similar, but a comparable rate of circle frequencies to that of the south of England demands that the land be equally crop-covered too. In Southern England these conditions combine superbly every summer, and render Wiltshire the most prolific area in the world for the formation of these exquisite circles. This is the home of CERES, the organization which is getting to the heart of the problem with its dedicated scientific research, its international databank, its summer circle-watches, its international lecture circuit, and now its first international conference. These manifold aspects of the circles effect are discussed in the opening address given by *Dr. Meaden.*

The conference draws together the leading scientifically-minded researchers in the field of circles study including the first theoreticians to apply their knowledge to the problem. All are exponents of the scientific method, and have, in common with professional scientists throughout the world, a belief in the adequacy of the application of the laws of physics to new phenomena as well to old. In this they differ from non-scientific speculators who, whenever they encounter observations they cannot understand, comfort themselves by inventing pseudo-scientific nonsense which also confuses other non-specialists. This is especially true of 'ufology', a domain which suffers chronically from the temptation to attribute unexplained events to the possibility, if not probability, of the intervention of extraterrestrial forces or 'intelligence'. *Paul Fuller and Jenny Randles* refreshingly do the opposite. They argue that Meaden's explanation for the origin of the circles effect and its parent vortex 'solves the UFO problem' and that ufologists should now study meteorology.

Professor John Snow and Dr. Tokio Kikuchi are the first practical theoreticians to apply themselves to the difficult problem of explaining the origin of the circles. They agree with Meaden's 10-year old statement that natural atmospheric vortices are at the core of the problem. Several vortex mechanisms are considered in their paper, including that of vortex breakdown which would project fast-moving ring-vortices towards the ground to swirl out the observed spiraliform traces. Counterflowing rings can arise when the main vortex contacts the surface, as noted in laboratory experiments when smoke-ring vortices make contact with a surface boundary. These scientists conclude by confirming what Meaden has been saying for years, namely that "an explanation of the circles effect provides a new topic in boundary layer meteorology".

The paper by J. T. Snow and T. Kikuchi is followed by George Bathurst's which looks to spherical vortices as producing similar effects; he further suggests how interference at the crop-canopy boundary can trigger the multiplets and rings. *Frederick C. Taylor* pilot and circles hunter, demonstrates the importance of aerial reconnaissance in circles research by showing 15 minutes of video film taken by himself in the last three seasons (1987-1989). To this is added last-minute footage of the stupendous triple-ringed quintuplet of 13 May 1990 and the quadruple-ringed sextuplet.

David Reynold's talk concerns a rare and most impressive kind of circle consisting of a huge number of outward-radiating spikes disposed about the periphery of a giant circle some 70 metres across. This amazing discovery, made in 1989, is difficult to explain unless it is the result of a ring-vortex 'exploding' in mid-air.

The remaining papers are chiefly concerned with the electrical aspects of the circle-making vortices by which they are regarded as 'plasma vortices'. *Professor Ohtsuki* begins by describing Japanese radar observations of what may have been a plasma vortex out at sea. The plasma was spotted by radar from two ships, one of them a scientific research vessel. At first nothing was seen by direct observation, only by radar, but later the position indicated by the radar image was confirmed by the sighting of a large moving lightform. Next, Professor Ohtsuki relates the progress he is making on producing plasma vortices in the laboratory and shows slides of luminous plasma which he has created by microwave interference in air at normal temperature and pressure!

Professor Hiroshi Kikuchi is an authority on ionization and electromagnetic effects in the atmosphere. He recognizes that the marvellous problems posed by the circles-effect vortices require the creation of new theories in order to account for the evident electromagnetic properties. In particular, work is needed on collision-dominant plasmas involving ionizations, 'dirty' plasmas containing charged dust particles or aerosols, and electro-magneto-hydrodynamics combining plasma physics with meteorology. He himself has contributed to such research by introducing useful new ideas like electric reconnection, critical ionization velocity and ponderomotive force. In the context of circles research he concentrates on how initial EHD helical turbulence evolves into tubular vortices, especially in the presence of an axial electric field and the Earth's magnetic field. Thus he arrives at associating EHD vortices with circles phenomena and is able to comment on some of the electrical effects reported for some circles.

Finally, there is *Professor Christopher Church* who, like John Snow, is one of America's leading tornado meteorologists. Their expertise in understanding the phenomena of natural atmospheric vorticity is a welcome quality for chairmen of such a technical conference as this.

G. T. MEADEN, D. M. ELSOM

CIRCLES FROM THE SKY
- A NEW TOPIC IN ATMOSPHERIC RESEARCH

By G. TERENCE MEADEN

Abstract: Research over the last decade has established that the distinctive circular-symmetric traces left in grass, standing corn and other vegetation have their origin in the descent of energetic atmospheric vortices of previously-unrecognized type. This paper explores some of the conditions under which the vortices and circles form, and summarizes the main features of the huge variety of circles and annular rings which have been discovered.

Although in the absence of crops or other damageable material able to serve as tracers, durable circles cannot form, the occurrence of unusual descending damaging winds can still be detected by their effects on people, animals, buildings, cars etc. Happenings like these have previously been reported by a puzzled public but have never been explained hitherto. Evidence is also given to show that the vortices are accompanied by electrical effects, so that at night luminous phenomena may be visible. These seem able to explain nocturnal lights, R.F. emissions, television and radio interference, motor vehicle breakdowns, and radar ghost images which have been reported at various times but never previously understood. The electrical effects seem to be due to a low-density of charged particles carried along by the primary vortex which is therefore in a 'cool' plasma condition, and are additionally responsible for the ionizing and electromagnetic effects associated with secondary vortices and rings.

BRIEF HISTORY OF THE CIRCLES EFFECT

Ten years ago, in summer 1980, I was looking at my first circles in the corn. The place was a field of oats near Bratton beneath the steep grassy slopes upon which the famous White Horse of Westbury is cut into the underlying chalk.

Fig. 1: The *Wiltshire Times* photograph which first attracted my attention to the circles. Bratton 1980.

My attention had been drawn to the circles by a front-page photograph in the *Wiltshire Times,* and later again by a telephone call from Ian Mrzyglod of Bristol who had been to survey the two circles (Figure 1). He had also met the farmer John Scull who declared that he had never seen such neat circular areas of damage before. Although these were the first circles to be brought to the attention of the scientific community via my report in *J. Meteorology* (Vol.6, 1981), for many farmers *in circle-prone regions* the sight was nothing new. For them, circles were recurring phenomena scarcely worthy of concern or interest. Such marks appeared from time to time in one field or another, and the origin of most were assigned, unconsciously or not, to natural or animal causes (see later section). On the other hand the majority of farmers in Britain, including even near-neighbours to some of the more-highly 'circle-prone' farmers, never seemed to suffer from this 'circles effect'. For many of these people news of the circles came as much as an unexpected surprise as it did to the scientists.

As for the affected farms, like John Scull's in Wiltshire, the fields were mown at harvest-time and the circles erased, the harvesters unaware that the circular formations could be of interest to anyone in the world. But in 1980 as I encountered the circles problem for the first time and contemplated its origins, my appetite for investigative research was whetted. A difficult and challenging puzzle with its multifold ramifications lay before me – a physicist and meteorologist with a lifetime addiction to solving mysteries and problems.

And so began the laborious quest for a solution. Increasingly, as the years passed and the complexity of the problem grew, I came to devote more and more time to it, until, as now, my whole life has become centred around this one great project which I hope to pursue, with enthusiasm and enjoyment, until it is resolved, despite the heavy financial burden entailed.

For ten years I have worked on the circles mystery, for the first seven years largely in scientific isolation. Advances were slow at first. Finding new circle-sites has always been an onerous task due to the rarity of the phenomenon and the brevity of the mature-cropfield season (which for Britain is principally from early May to late August), but enough progress had been made by the end of 1987 that I was able to start explaining to other scientists something of the atmospheric-vortex origins of this perplexing affair.

This began with my Oxford lecture to the Second TORRO Conference in June 1988 (reported in the influential London *Observer* the next day), my lecture to the URSI Conference in Tokyo in September 1989 which was filmed by Japanese television, and my lecture to the Department of Applied Mathematics and Theoretical Physics in Cambridge University this March. A paper in January 1989 in *Weather,* a journal of the Royal Meteorological Society, also announced the circles and their vortices as a major new topic in boundary-layer meteorology well worthy of funded research. Most meteorologists in recognizing the fundamental importance of the problem have accepted the issues raised by the circles phenomenon with real interest, although there are still a few who have not had the mental agility or competence to understand how vortices with a descending component can be involved. The paper by Professor John Snow and Dr Tokio Kikuchi given at this conference should answer any remaining doubts.

Several gifted scientists are now doing pioneering work on the problem – indeed, four full professors are helping us with this conference today (Professors J. T. Snow, Hiroshi Kikuchi, Y.-H. Ohtsuki and Christopher Church) – and a great number of amateurs are at work too, most of them performing valuable observational work. Circle types, circle totals, and circle sites are escalating in numbers as observer numbers rise, and discoveries are coming thick and fast. At the same time retrospective research has uncovered proof of around one hundred pre-1980 circles. The oldest which dates back to the year 1678 caused initial dismay to the paranormal and extraterrestrial hopefuls who had been recklessly claiming, on baseless guesswork, that the problem was a modern, post-1980 one.

WHAT A TYPICAL CORNFIELD CIRCLE LOOKS LIKE

Despite having visited many hundreds of Nature's circles, the finding of a freshly-formed circle is still an exciting moment for me. Every time, it provides an exhilaration which is only exceeded by a visit to the interior of the site itself.

Upon arrival, one cannot help but sense that a powerful agent has been present; one that laboured unseen, spinning out its microcosmic arena before vanishing and leaving behind such an intriguing trace for us to contemplate – this voiceless witness to a shortlived visitation of 'something which must have come down from the sky'.

What does a typical cornfield circle look like?

(Turn to Figure 2 overleaf).

Most commonly it is a circular area of damage in which stalks of growing corn have been pushed over as if by an intense rotating force imbued with axial symmetry. Often the pliable stems are not broken but simply bent over just above ground level. In most cases a conspicuous spiral trace is discernible, extending outwards from a centre to a diameter of several metres at which a sharp perimeter-boundary typically appears. The smallest and largest circle diameters measured to date are 0.3 and 61 metres respectively (1 foot and 200 feet!). In Figure 3 we see contrasting examples in the same field. The main part of the big circle has a diameter of 32 metres, the small circles are two metres across. If we consider the sizes of ring diameters (see later), as opposed to circle diameters, the biggest known ring is 92 metres, or 300 feet!

Both senses of rotation are found. At some sites, year after year, only clockwise traces have been noted. At others, both senses of rotation appear. More rarely a radially-directed effect is discerned, often in association

Fig.2: A typical cornfield circle with spiral pattern in the bed of a flat-bottomed circle with steep sides. Woolstone, Glos.

Fig.3: Circle extremes. Diameters 2 and 32 metres. West Overton, Wiltshire.

with severe downward blasts.

Many circle beds are complex affairs as only a detailed site inspection can reveal. Double layering, double centering, S-shaped swirling, different layers turning in different senses, spiked perimeters, and so on (Figure 4).

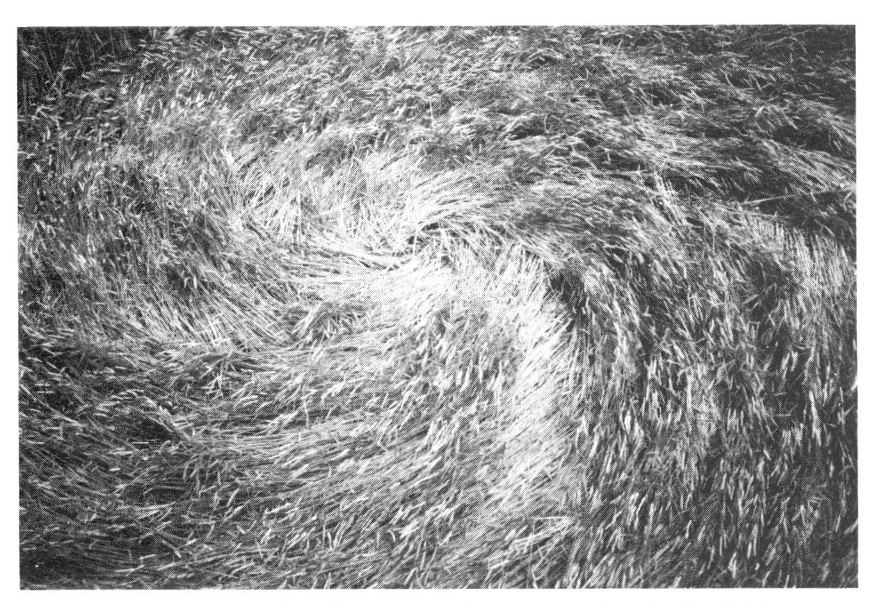

Fig.4: Strong swirling flow in a circle in a Hampshire barley-field.

Usually the corn is laid down firmly, either clockwise or anticlockwise. The manner in which the stalks lie and all the other evidence accumulated over the years strongly indicate that the horizontal flattening agent is a vortex *which must have originated from above.* Sometimes the circle-centre is not flattened, but remains upright, as a sort of pyramid courageously sentinel in a swirling bed of straw (Figures 5 and 6). This particular clue which the author had first noticed in June 1987 was spotted in at least ten circles in the 1989 season. It indicates that for these cases at least the damaging part of the vortex partakes of the character of a *ring-vortex.* More often, instead of a standing pyramid of straight and bent stalks, there are signs that a pre-existing pyramid has been knocked flat by subsequent oscillation or drift of the principal outward-swirling agent. On these occasions snapped stems are often found.

Although it is true that most vortices known to meteorologists are *ascending* ones, it is indisputable that to produce the circles effect the circle-making agent must be a *descending* vortex, as I emphasised in the *Weather* paper (1989) and have repeatly said throughout the 1980's. As we shall show, we have reliable eye-witness evidence in support of this with regard both to circle-formation and to other cases of 'spinning-downward pressures'. The problem for the atmospheric scientist is to determine how the breakdown of the common spin-up vortex condition can evolve into a state of downward vortex-motion. We shall return to this later, but only briefly for this is

Fig.5: A wheat circle having a prominent central pyramid or cone of straw at Beckhampton, Wiltshire 1989. This is strong evidence of a descending ring-vortex. The author is holding out his coat to demonstrate the magnitude of the pyramid. Photograph by Dr. Tokio Kikuchi.

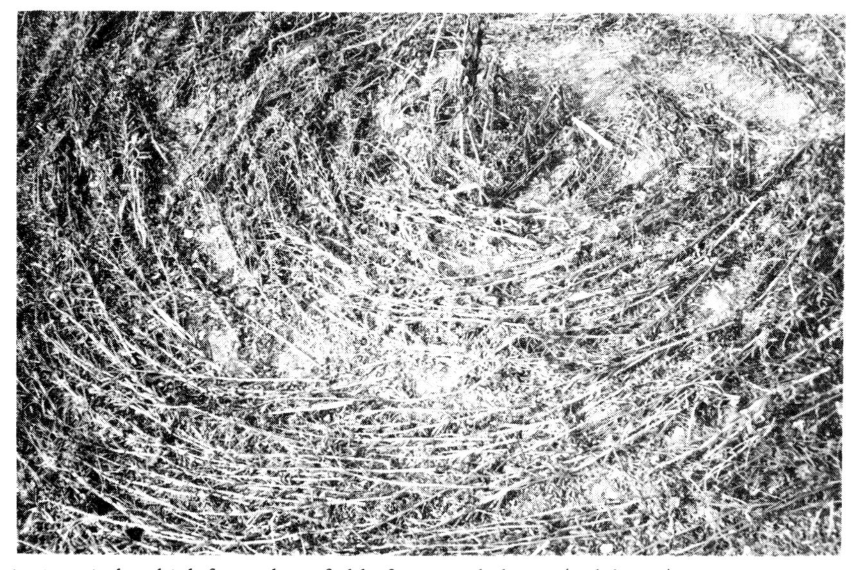

Fig.6: A circle which formed in a field of ripe cattle beans (tick beans). Again a pyramidal centre is left standing following the vortex descent. Beckhampton 1989.

primarily the job of Professor Snow in the next lecture. First let us erase doubts which some armchair critics may still have regarding certain fundamental aspects of the circles problem.

THE CIRCLES ARE NOT A HOAX

At the beginning of the 1990 season some 850 genuine circles were listed in the comprehensive databank of CERES. About one hundred of these pre-date the discovery of the genuine circles at Bratton in August 1980. Since then, all the circles *visited by the author* have been checked out as genuine. The majority of the remaining few not seen by the author are likely to be genuine too but it has to be admitted that just a very few of these might be experiments, deceptions or practical jokes.

For example, the fabrication of a set of five was organized in 1983 by representatives of the *Daily Mirror* in the hope of tricking the *Daily Express* into sensationalizing their phoney event (but the newspaper was not taken in by this – nor was anyone else who took a look at the fake markings). In addition, a few singles have been made for experimental reasons or for television documentaries, and no more than a very few others made by potential tricksters. In every case an artificial or counterfeit circle can be immediately recognized by experienced circle-watchers. The manufactured circles never display the complex layering effects and twin centres with radiating spirals so often found in the real thing. The stalks in the beds look bruised, the earth beneath is trodden down. Moreover, there is an instrumental test known only to a few circle investigators which can be applied to any circle as an independent check on its authenticity.

We must insist that no-one from among any remaining 'doubters' should adversely comment about circles until he or she has personally visited the circle-rich countryside that is Wessex with the object of inspecting genuine circles in the company of an expert. What is more, no-one who has not studied genuine circles in the field should accept to referee scientific papers on the subject. Everyone I have met, and that includes many good scientists, who have inspected real circles have been completely convinced by the legitimacy of the circles problem.

The total number of genuine circles listed for England and Scotland in 1989 is 303. Excluded from this total as 'experimental' or jocular were the quintuplet circles reported from near Polperro, Cornwall, and also the Mansfield circle (Notts) about which much doubt currently exists. Although I was not able to visit every circle of the British cropfield-circle season, I did visit or fly over 267 of them before harvesting. All the complex formations were personally visited. As a result I can say that none of them had been interfered with or embellished in any way. The instrumental security-check was applied in the majority of cases to the more interesting features of the quintuplet and ringed systems, the hooked system at Longwood, and the complex circles at Winterbourne Stoke (see later). I do not agree with the suggestion made by Paul Fuller and Jenny Randles in their paper (p.105) that some pre-1990 complex circle formations are suspected of having been modified by pranksters. Nevertheless, caution must continue to be exercised this year and in future years because of the tremendous publicity to which the circles effect is now subjected.

SOME FARMERS' BELIEFS

Prior to the 1980's why did affected farmers accept circle-damage in their fields without undue fuss?

We believe that the majority of farmers thought that natural causes were responsible for the pre-1980 circles. As Paul Fuller's study showed (Fuller 1988, see also Fuller and Randles' paper in this book) many farmers (21%) in the survey blamed the weather for the circles whereas many more (32%) accused hoaxers. The survey related to the 1980's, but in pre-1980 days it is more probable that most farmers of this century who did not hold the weather responsible set the blame on animals instead.

For instance, there were occasions when upon visiting a circle a farmer found hedgehogs or deer or foxes inside. Such findings may have initiated the countryside stories of circles being made by families of ambulating hedgehogs, or rutting deer, or vixens and cubs. Again, it is known that crows enjoy eating the soft grain of unripe cereals. In order to bring the heads of the corn to the ground for their dinner, the birds glide with outstretched wings into an open space within the field, or instead attack the edge of the field. Thus it is that farmers must sometimes have seen these big birds broadening existing circles, with the result that the crows came to be accused of creating the circles instead of solely widening them.

Added to this is the fact that many circles are found only at the moment of the harvest, so the circles get destroyed at the very instant of their discovery. In so many cases the circles turn up in remote areas, far from roads, villages and farmhouses. Indeed it is so often the mower who finds the circles, rather than the owner of the field, and the former is paid by the latter to reap, not meditate upon one of nature's great mysteries. Besides, the degree of damage inflicted by a circle-making vortex is minute compared with the typical seasonal damage caused by rain, hail and storm. Most farmers were therefore not unduly worried about the small areas lost to the circles.

THE THEORETICIANS ARRIVE

An assault upon the theoretical problems raised by the circles effect is now underway, for there is no possibility that the effect is a hoax, nor that the circles are non-natural in any fashion (as if, for example, they result from vortices generated by aircraft, cf Meaden 1989a). Indeed, every observer who responsibly examines flattened circles on site is impressed by the swirling spiral outflow, the multi-layered interwoven beds, the sometimes-complex braided, twisted straws, and the twin-centres so often seen – reason enough to demonstrate the impracticability and impossibility of artificial construction.

The scientists most excited by these discoveries are those with expertise in atmospheric vorticity because they perceive the innate potential for improving their understanding of the workings of the lower atmosphere. In truth, a whole new topic in boundary-layer meteorology is being opened up. (By the boundary layer meteorologists mean the lower 300 metres or so of the atmosphere). At the same time, the problem has such popular appeal that it has engaged the attentions of serious non-scientists, many of whom are excellent circle-spotters and contribute usefully to the basic data collection. Unfortunately, the subject has been invaded by comics and publicity-seekers as well, whose illogical and unsupported wild guesses regarding 'intelligent' or paranormal origins are providing a bizarre and irrelevant diversion to the matter, and whose antics are wholly anti-scientific and counterproductive.

FOLKLORE ACCOUNTS OF CIRCLES

If the circles problem is one which has always existed, it might be possible to find references to it in folklore contexts. Such a search is being undertaken and has revealed two useful stories as yet.

(1). The most remarkable one is the story of the 'Mowing Devil', an account dating from August 1678 in Hertfordshire. This came to Jenny Randles via a correspondent, and independently to R. Skinner. Since then, two other people have independently reported the same discovery to the author, one an agricultural scientist in Cambridge, England, who found a reference to the same tract in an old volume of the county's natural history proceedings, and the other a bibliophile in New York State who saw a copy of the original tract offered for sale in a book auction in Vernon, Connecticut, in fall 1989.

The mowing-devil story concerns a mower who wished to cut a field of oats for a farmer, but the latter preferred to deny the mower a fair wage. A dispute arose, so the men parted company, but that night a splendid circle (or more likely, perhaps, a ringed-circle) appeared in that very field of oats. Naturally for those times, the blame was apportioned to the devil. ". . . and if the Devil had a mind to shew his dexterity in the art of Husbandry, and scorn'd to mow them after the usual manner, he cut them in round circles, and plac't every straw with that exactness that it would have taken up above an Age for any Man to perform what he did that one night".

Besides this, amazing to relate, the previous night the "Field of Oats was publickly beheld by several Passengers to be all of a Flame, and so continued for some space, to the great consternation of those that beheld it". This is, it would appear, a reference of helpful antiquity to the luminescent effects that are now known to accompany some circle-making vortices, as we shall see shortly.

We reproduce this item in some fullness elsewhere in this book.

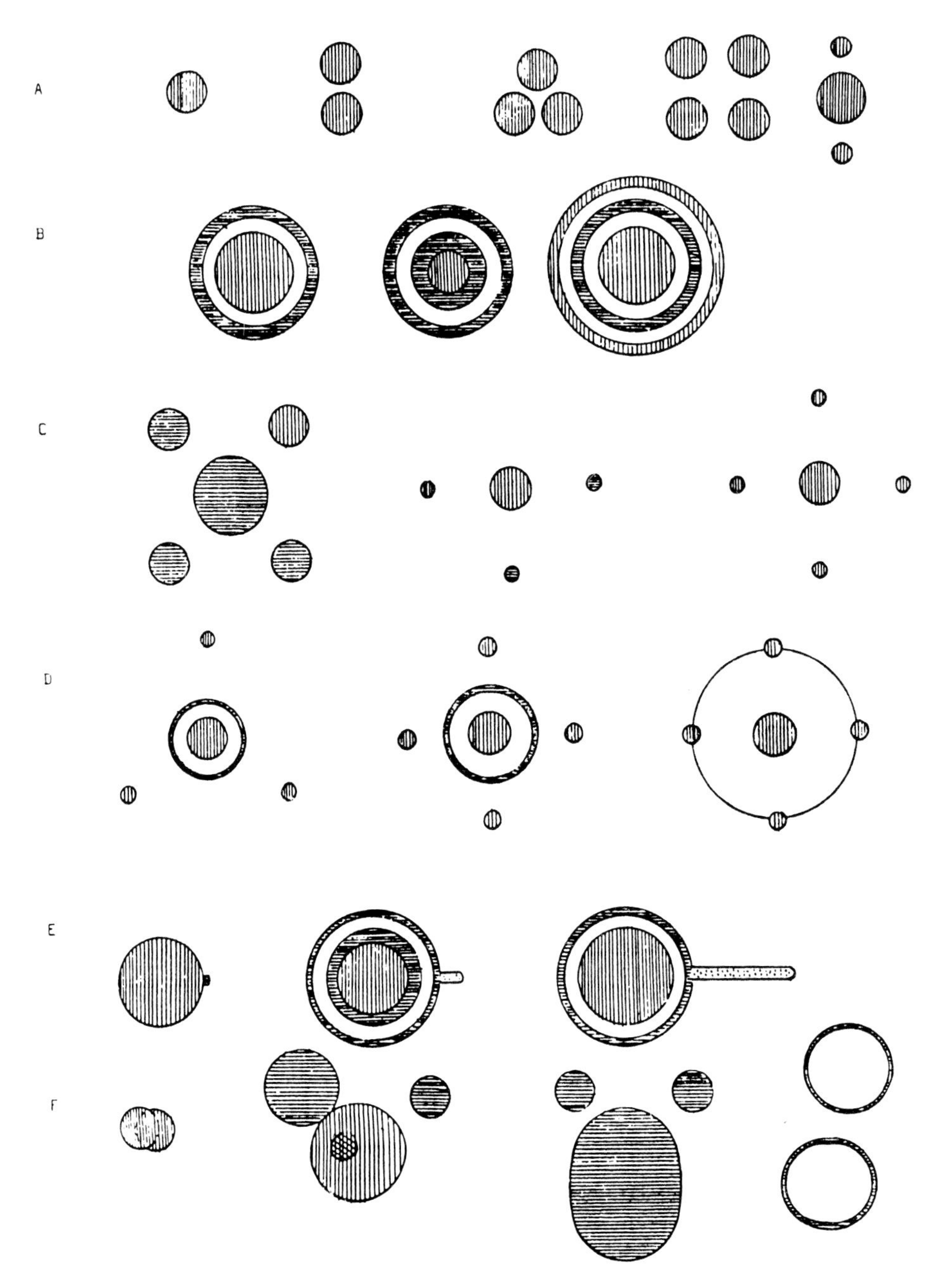

Fig.7: The basic circle-formation patterns known for the period 1980-1988. Some additional ones are illustrated further on. Clockwise and anticlockwise variants have not been allowed for in this simplified résumé. Row A: Plain singles, doubles, triplets and quadruplets. Row B: Ringed singles. Row C: Quintuplets, including a "defective" one with a satellite missing. Row D: Multiplets with rings. Row E: Circles and ringed circles with radially-directed spurs. Row F: Superimposed singles and doubles; an ellipse with two singles; circular and elliptical rings.

(2). Another folklore account, written in 1802, I found in March this year. In his *Minstrelsy of Scottish Border* Scott writes: "The fairies of Scotland . . . inhabit the interior of green hills, chiefly those of conical form . . . on which they lead their dances by moon-light; impressing upon the surface the mark of circles, which sometimes appear yellow and blasted, sometimes of a deep green hue; and within which it is dangerous to sleep, or to be found after sunset".

The blasted circles may well refer to the circles of 'the circles effect'; the green circles more likely indicate fungal rings found in green pasture. The other detail of intrinsic importance is the stated connection with hills. This is a principal characteristic of the circles-effect, for the parent vortices which spin out the circles are commonly produced by hills, as we shall see. *Indeed, the sites of almost all known circles,* and up to the start of the 1990 season we know of 850 for Britain, *lie close to or within range of hills, mostly quite low ones.*

TRIPLETS AND DOUBLETS

We now embark on a brief summary of some of the characteristic circle patterns with which we are familiar. Although single circles are by far the most commonly produced, some come in groups of such distinctive patterns as to indicate that their formation was mutually interdependent. Some basic patterns are illustrated in Figure 7.

As early as 1981 we knew of a circle triplet, namely three circles rectilinearly ordered, the outer ones of similar size but smaller and equidistant from the central one. This first occasion happened at Cheesefoot Bottom, a three-sided concavity in the hills south-east of Winchester just below Cheesefoot Head. The photograph in Figure 8 is by Steve Broom (Mryzyglod 1981; Meaden 1982).

Similar triplets have been seen many times in other areas since then, although not again yet at Cheesefoot. Equiangular triplets are known too, three circles of similar size nearly touching as if arranged at the corners of an equiangular triangle. Such triplet sets appeared at Cheesefoot and Corhampton (Hampshire) in 1987, having earlier been noted at Bratton (Wiltshire) in 1982. Doublets are, unsurprisingly, more common. Usually they are found as unequal pairs but near-identical twins are sometimes seen.

QUINTUPLETS

The first big bout of national publicity regarding circles arose in July 1983 when Bratton had its first five-circle set of the decade. This was the year of Stephen Spielberg's cinematograph masterpiece *E.T.* The symmetry offered by the size and dispositions of the four smaller satellite circles relative to the central one attracted newspaper attention. The London *Daily Express* gave enormous coverage. "E.T. phone the Express – have you come back to

Fig.8: Triplet of circles photographed by Steve Broome at Cheesefoot Bottom in 1981 *(Probe Magazine)*.

Earth?", urged the *Daily Express* (July 11th). "Why haven't you phoned, E.T.?", asked the paper next day. But to no avail. Quintuplet circles were the new wonder of nature. How could the 'erratic' wind achieve neatness like that?

Together with ringed circles, quintuplet circles (Figure 9) represent a great challenge for theoretical physicists to explain, but it should be solvable as a problem in fluid flow and vortex/boundary interactions, and I am confident the answer will be reached eventually. (A generalised explanation has been offered by George Bathurst – see his paper later in this book). Nothing has yet been found by unbiased investigators of the circles effect to suggest that there is anything in the effect that is likely to be beyond the reach of conventional science. All that is needed are the theoretical skills of the atmospheric and fluid-flow physicist, applied in a novel situation.

PLAIN RINGED CIRCLES

We now discuss some of the principal discoveries relating to circles which are more complex than the more straightforward singles, doubles and triples. The ring variation comes first.

In 1986 at Cheesefoot (Hampshire) and Bratton (Wiltshire), we surveyed our first ringed circles. In 1987 these same sites, and others as well, yielded double-ringed circles (Figure 10). Last summer the first triple-ringed circle was found. In 1989 of the 305 known genuine circles there were five with a

Fig.9: A regular quintuplet circle set, Beckhampton 1988.

Fig.10: Double-ringed circle on Longwood Estate, Hampshire June 1987, photographed using camera on a pole.

single ring, one with a double ring, and one with a triple. This May (1990) three triples have been found, one of them in majestic combination with a quintuplet, and most magnificent of all a four-ringed circle combined with a sextuplet on the downs near Bishop's Cannings in Wiltshire.

Some commentators query the increasing complexity of these formations. But are they becoming *more* complicated? Are plain circles being embellished by pranksters? Such facile questions belie the intricate matter which is the circles effect.

No-one has been beautifying the systems, nor are they hoaxes. The phenomenon is genuine, and did in any case occur before the start of our research in 1980. Retrospective research of the literature has shown that a double-ringed circle was found and surveyed in 1977 at Evenlode in Gloucestershire and this was pre-dated by a double ring at Twywell, Gloucestershire in 1960 (for which we have been supplied with a photograph). And the Hertfordshire 'mowing devil' case of 1678 was probably a ringed circle too.

The same applies to quintuplets. In Hampshire a Corhampton farmer found and photographed a quintuplet set of circles in 1978, five years before our discovery of the Bratton quintuplet. Later, in August 1986, an even more intricate quintuplet pattern appeared in Hampshire: a new combination based on quintuplet circles with a single ring around the bigger centre circle. In 1988 the satellites of a quintuplet lay on a concentric ring. In 1990 three rings surround a main circle there being four satellites on the middle ring.

The chief mystery about these ringed circles is not so much the presence of the rings but the *sharpness* of the rings. How can the walls be so steep, the rings so narrow, if moving air (albeit ionized air, i.e. ionized wind) is at work? (Figure 11). But there is a reason, and it is well within the capabilities of conventional science.

THE 'HARDNESS' OF THE CIRCLE BEDS – FAST-DESCENDING AND SLOW-DESCENDING VORTICES

Another matter is the variation in intensity that has been noted in the way in which the corn gets flattened. Sometimes the corn is more than just pushed down. It has been veritably 'blasted' flat, the pressure so intense as to drive the corn into the earth if the latter is moist enough to receive it. By contrast, the corn inside a circle is sometimes 'brushed' quite gently; indeed, it is not struck down at all, properly speaking. It is as if something has glided down from above, continually rotating but not descending completely, and then either dying out *in situ* or taking off again.

Whatever the origin of the vortex, the evidence is unequivocal in demonstrating that axi-symmetric vortices (such as breakdown ring-vortices possessing a swirl component) descend from above to strike whatever lies beneath. When a crop is present, a spiral-centred circle is swept out. In the

Fig.11: The steep walls of a single-ringed circle. Longwood, June 1989.

absence of a crop, it may be a car, a house, or cattle, or people, which are hit. Some examples are given in another section below.

SOME VARIATIONS ON THE PRINCIPAL QUINTUPLET PATTERN

We gather these into groups to indicate the range of data which is accruing.

(1). *Quadri-symmetrical Quintuplets*

Over the years diameter ratios of main-to-satellite circles have ranged from about 10-to-1 to 2-to-1. Among the earlier quintuplets investigated satellites were generally quite small and at a distance of several satellite-diameters from the main central one. More recently, quintuplet examples with bigger satellites located quite close to the main circle have come under scrutiny. This rather suggests a 'mechanical' origin for the subsidiary vortices, as could arise during boundary interaction of the air of a descending vortex with the surface material. Mixed directions of airflow are noted in some of these systems, i.e. both clockwise and anticlockwise flows are seen. We return to this later.

Some quintuplet circle systems include ring effects. A ring round the main circle was mentioned above (1986 Longwood Estate, Hampshire). On several occasions a ring has been seen interlinking the four satellites (notably in 1983, 1985, 1988 and 1990). The inference, together with certain instrumental evidence, is that ionized air has been flowing in such narrow rings, in the manner of an 'ion race'. However, as we shall indicate below, the probability is

Fig.12: A regular quintuplet, North Wiltshire, June 1989, in which the fourth satellite never achieved its full potential owing to its position exactly on the tractorlines.

Fig.13: A bi-symmetrical quintuplet, photographed by Mrs. M. B. Radcliffe over Dorset.

that the forcing element is initially 'mechanical' (non-electrical) in origin and that the apparent electrical effects caused by circulating ions are either consequential, i.e. a secondary effect, or maybe interdependent.

(2). *Incomplete Quintuplets*

Sometimes the quintuplet pattern is incomplete. One of the satellites may be missing. At other times it is there but ill-formed because it grew in the presence of the zones of weakness created by tramlines (tractor lanes), the subsidiary vortex not reaching its full potential but spinning instead on the smaller diameter suggested by the tramline width (Figure 12).

(3). *Bisymmetrical Quintuplets*

In 1989 bisymmetrical, as distinct from the common quadri-symmetrical quintuplet sets were spotted for the first time. Two English examples were noted, the one shown coming from Dorsetshire (Figure 13).

This symmetry seems to be part of a still more elaborate circle set which, if complete, might involve as many as eight satellites arranged about the centre circle. Indeed, close inspection of the photograph reveals several abortive mini-circles whose diameters are half-a-metre or less.

(4). *Sextuplets and Septuplets of the 'Cruciform Type'*

Sometimes additional circles along a diagonal axis of a quadri-symmetrical quintuplet turn these into six-circle or seven-circle sets (Figure 14). The undoubted relationship between these circles, although imperfect, demonstrates an interdependency of one upon the other. Note in particular that along the main axis of the Cherhill septuplet the centre-satellite spacing is reduced by virtue of the existence of the additional, more distant satellites along this line. This same effect is visible in the plain quintuplet shown in Figure 15.

The interspacing has been upset by a satellite vortex that did not produce a visible circle at crop-surface level but whose presence nevertheless made itself felt. The sequence is clarified in the sketch of Figure 16. This is another piece of evidence, newly acquired, in support of a surface/boundary interaction as the prime origin of the subsidiary circles which, doubtless we think, are scored out by fast-spinning currents of ionized air.

(5). *The Septuplet and Nonuplet Patterns in North Wiltshire in 1989*

Adjoining one another in the same barley field there were two circle systems in May 1989 such as we had never seen before. In the septuplet were six satellites of near-equal size. Their simultaneity of creation is unknown although their dispositions imply a contemporaneity of development (Figure 17).

The nonuplet included two pairs of mini-circles so positioned as to suggest that their formation was secondary to the principal four satellites, i.e. tertiary to the primary centre circle (Figure 17b). They may have appeared at points of

Fig.14: A deviant on the quintuplet theme but composed of seven circles in which the extra circles lie approximately along a main cross-axis. The seventh satellite was about 1½ metres diameter, and is not visible on this photograph (cf Figure 16). Shading downwards to the right indicates clockwise circles. The others are anticlockwise.

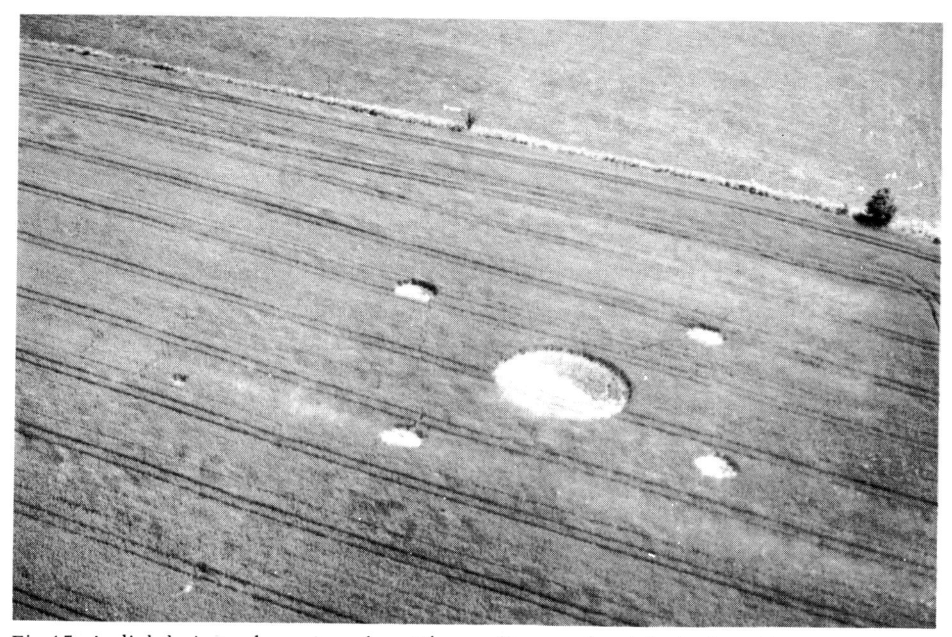

Fig.15: A slightly irregular quintuplet. The satellite on the right is the odd one as it is not equidistant from the central circle like the others. It is as though its position was influenced by a sixth vortex which never came to maturity (see next figure).

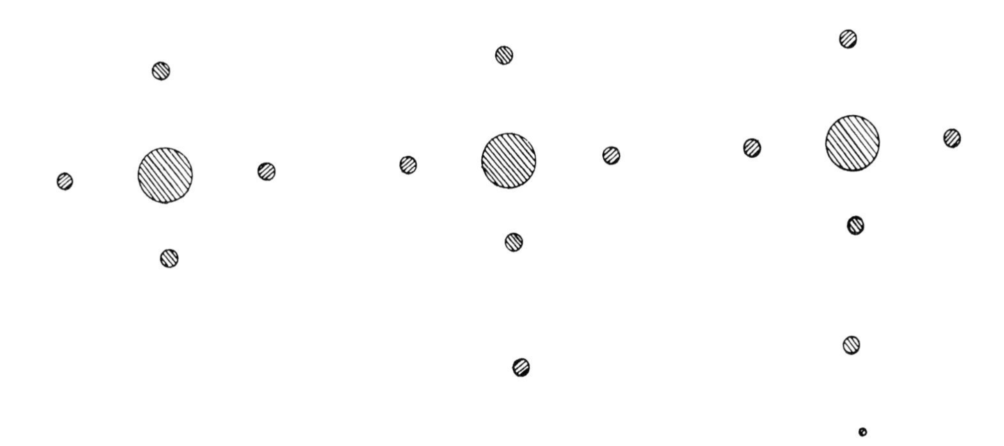

Fig.16: Comparison of three Wiltshire circle formations in 1989. Left, the quintuplet of Figure 15; centre, the sextuplet of Norton Bavant; right, the septuplet of Cherhill (Figure 15). In each case the fourth satellite is at a reduced distance from the centre compared with satellites 1 – 3.

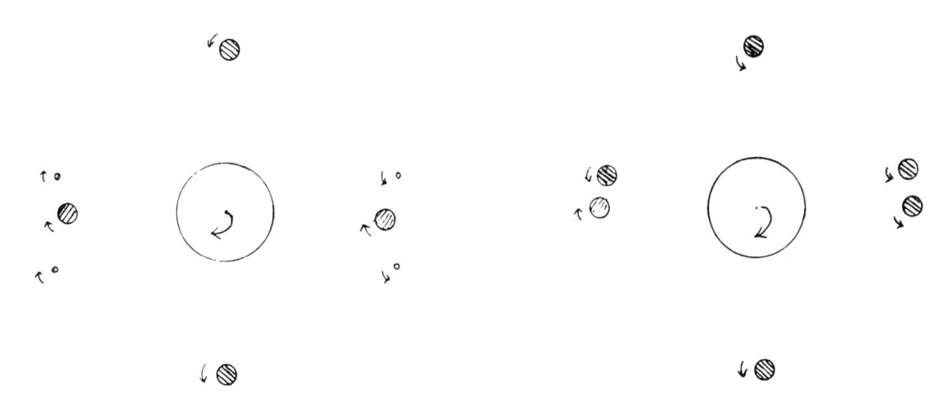

Fig.17: Sketch of septuplet and nonuplet formations from North Wiltshire, May 1989 (not drawn to scale).

intersection of a (non-visible) circle surrounding the primary and (non-visible) secondary circles surrounding the satellites. Again the implication is that a surface/boundary interaction of some sort has taken place.

Understanding the origin of these multi-circle systems is a complex task for the theoretical physicist, but we are confident that it will be achieved eventually. So little is known about vortex stability and instability in fluid flows that it is clear that one good procedure for advancing the work would be by direct laboratory simulation. Our lack of knowledge about this field is demonstrated by an announcement of a simple Dutch experiment in *Nature* as recently as April 1989.

Consider the rectilinear triplet (three circles in a straight line). In a recent paper van Heijst and Kloosterziel (1989) showed how a single vortex in a rapidly-rotating fluid can break down and reform into tri-polar in-line vortices. Although the parallel is not exact, it is surprising that something seemingly so simple as this was previously unknown. That this takes place in laboratory conditions suggests that triple-vortex stability is a natural tendency for vortex phenomena in sheared atmospheric environments as well. Hence we infer that our own circle observations are witness that this happens in the atmosphere as it does in the laboratory. We are amazed that such a simple result was not previously known. It confirms just how little is known about even fundamental processes in rotational fluid flow.

ORIGIN OF THE VORTICES

Let us turn to the general question as to where the vortices originate.

The author has shown on numerous occasions that the cause of the circle-making vortices is irregularities of landscape features which deviate the airflow and re-organize it into upflowing vortices of an eddy-vortex type (Meaden 1989b). Under the right stimuli these up-spinning vortices become possessed of a descending component, usually short-lived. The few scientists who have contested this conclusion display their ignorance of the phenomenon of vortex breakdown. The subject has recently been reviewed in some detail by Lugt (1989) who showed that vortex breakdown is known for all the natural atmospheric vortices (tornadoes, waterspouts, land-devils) as well as for the better-analyzed rotating fluids studied in spinning containers under laboratory conditions.

Dates and times of formation are known for many circles, and in a few cases eye-witnesses have seen vortices making circles. Eyewitness descriptions may be found in *J. Meteorology, Weather* and *The Circles Effect and its Mysteries.*

The first cornfield circles to appear in Britain each season are found in the spring. The dates of the earliest circles known for 1987-1990 are respectively May 8th (Hampshire), May 27th (Wiltshire), May 9th (Wiltshire), and April 20th-24th (Wiltshire).

The collation of years of painstaking effort studying the circles effect has resulted in a useful number of circles being accurately dated and timed. This means that for a range of well-studied cases the accompanying weather conditions are known. I must stress that knowing the weather conditions well and understanding the effects is the province of trained scientists. The feeble efforts alluded to by some non-scientific opportunists are trivial irrelevancies.

It seems that a common and sometimes essential prerequisite for vortex formation which ultimately leads to circular traces on the ground is stably-stratified air within the lower layers of the atmosphere. This region known to meteorologists as the boundary layer is the bottom-most few hundred metres. Another factor is an undulating landscape which often, but not always, features a prominent escarpment or isolated hill whose height is low enough that it can be immersed beneath the stable air of a temperature-inversion. The hills of central southern England whose heights lie chiefly between 30 and 200 metres above the surrounding countryside may be of optimum size for the effect.

Indeed, we have found that the majority of circles form close to hills or escarpments, usually within a few hundred metres. We have learnt that circle sites can appear at distances of even six kilometres *downwind* of major topographical obstacles. What seems to happen is that a species of eddy vortex or trailing vortex develops which is inherently unstable because it is governed by the *arrival and passage* of a gust-front, as for instance with an advancing microfront, weak cold front, or more rarely thunderstorm gust-front. Also, there is accumulating evidence to suggest that the high frequency of cool sea-breeze fronts over central southern England, in conjunction with the wavy nature of the terrain, goes part way towards explaining the high density of circles in this extensive cereal-growing area.

TWO SITE-EXAMPLES OF LONG-THROW VORTICES

Figure 18 shows the disposition of the eight circles which straddled the Westbury-Bratton parish boundaries in 1989. These formed on the night of 18th-19th July. Mr. Geoffrey Cooper, farmer, had left the farmhouse windows open because the night was calm, clear and warm. In the early hours

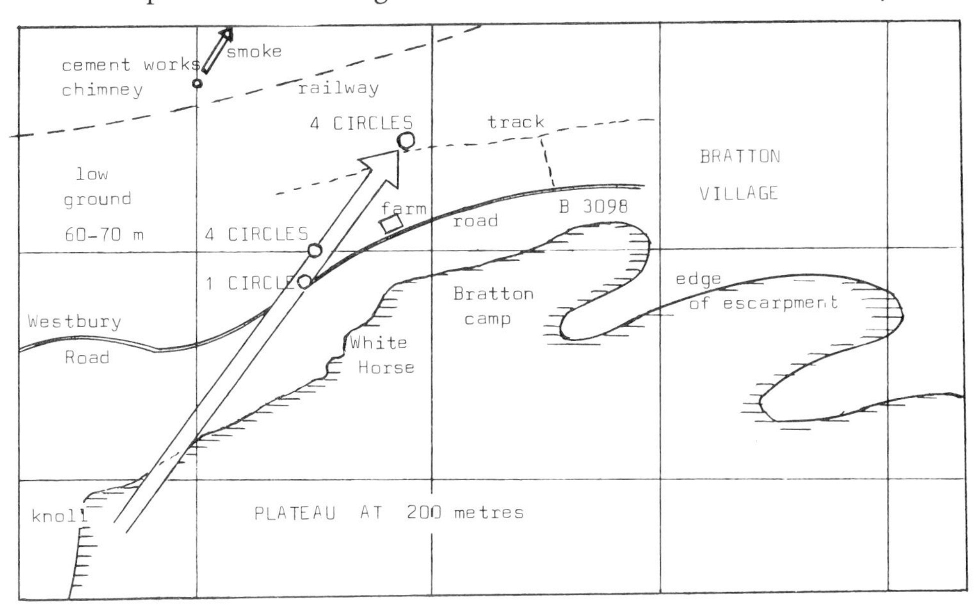

Fig.18: The Westbury-Bratton area showing the three sites where eight circles formed on the night of 19th July 1989.

of 19th while it was dark he was awakened by a sudden gust of wind which banged the windows so strongly that he was obliged to get up and close them. He reported seeing the hot smoke which ceaselessly issues from a tall chimney at the nearby cement works then streaming away in a north-easterly direction. Reference to the map shows that the circles found nearby next morning were aligned south-west/north-east. The inference is that the circles were made by vortices created within an incipient vortex sheet which developed in connection with the hill-spur on the escarpment south of Westbury. The circle furthest from the hill was an anticlockwise one 26 metres across, about two kilometres from the hill. The double-ringed circle was around half-a-kilometre from Mr. Cooper's farmhouse.

At Aylesbury in Buckinghamshire a quintuplet set was found on 22nd July. It was believed formed during the preceding three days throughout which period the wind lay between south and east-south-east. The distance of the circles from the Chiltern escarpment is six kilometres. Again, the inference is stong that the circles formed downwind of this escarpment.

CIRCLE-VORTICES ON MICROFRONTS

The Woolstone circles in Gloucestershire provide an association with a microfrontal passage. These four circles appeared overnight in a field opposite the house of Mr. Michael Rawlinson. At 5 a.m. G.M.T. on 21st July 1989 his barograph displayed a jump characteristic of a weak weather front (Figure 19). Overhead, there was some increase in the amount of altocumulus about this time; the gradient or geostrophic wind was from the south-east. Barograms were obtained from two other meteorological stations in Gloucestershire (Prestbury (nearby) and Churchdown, Gloucester) which confirmed the pressure-change details.

Other examples of circles formed on fronts and in the lee of hills will be given on another occasion. We may however summarize *some* of the 'frontal' situations as follows:

(1). Stable air, nocturnal as a rule (late evening, hours of darkness, after dawn) when thermals are absent, but in which the stability undergoes disruption *by the arrival of a microfront* including sea-breezes which in Sussex, Hampshire, Wiltshire and Dorset arrive from the south and tend to create vortices on the northern side of hillslopes. Note that even if the pre-existing wind is northerly, the sea-breeze can still progress northwards against it, although quite slowly, and cause an unexpected wind-reversal in the evening or night. A careless observer would be unaware of such local wind-changes. The passage of a shower cloud during an otherwise stable night can have similar effects, as can other forms of local microfront.

(2). Stable air in the daytime due to stagnant anticyclonic conditions stifling thermals, but in which a weak cold front is being pushed through by larger-scale geophysical motions. Example: the south-moving cold front of 9th May 1989 which terminated an early anticyclonic heatwave around

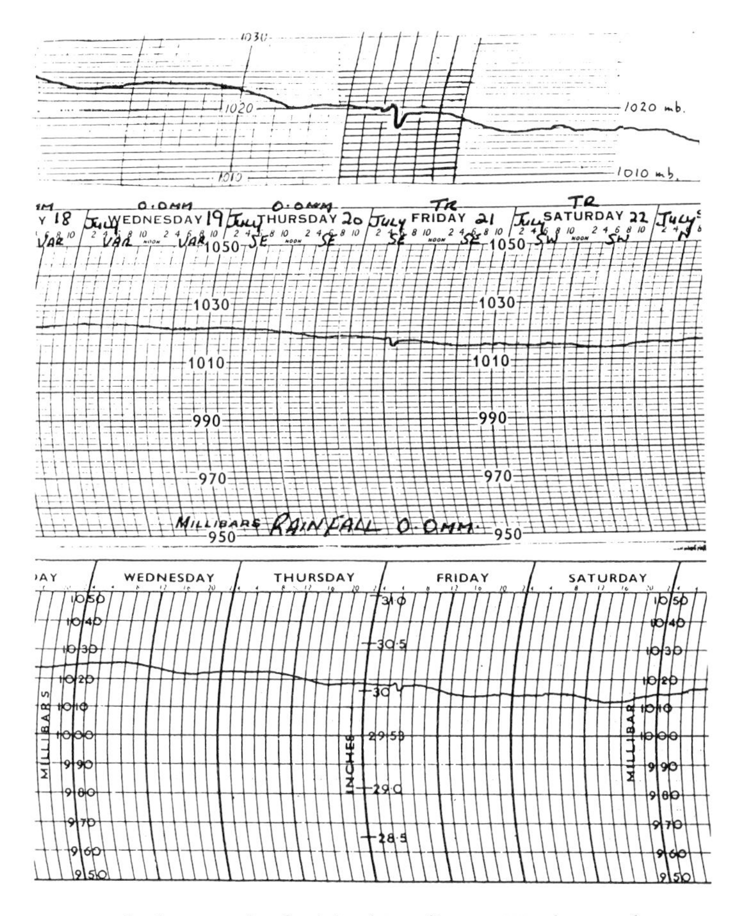

Fig.19: The barograph of Michael Rawlinson, Woolstone, shows an early-morning jump at what may have been the time of circle formation nearby. The other barographs from nearby Prestbury (lower) and more distant Churchdown (Gloucester) show similar effects, indicating a weak frontal passage.

midday in southern England and seemed responsible for the great circle outbreak (some 60 known circles) in North and West Wiltshire that day.

(3). Microfronts associated with slow-moving cumulonimbus clouds. Example: 2nd July 1982 when a circle was witnessed while it was forming on a hillslope south of Westbury, Wiltshire.

VORTEX BREAKDOWN

Physical meteorologists Prof. John T. Snow (Purdue University) and Dr. Tokio Kikuchi (Kochi University) have considered the development of instability in an eddy vortex and the consequences of a resulting breakdown of the core leading to the sudden descent of a swirling ring-vortex. On aerodynamical considerations George Bathurst independently reached a similar conclusion and has prepared his paper from the point of view of spherical ring-vortices. The component of the vortex which acquires a descending mode is a ring-vortex. It swirls in the manner treated theoretically by Prof. H. Keith Moffat of the University of Cambridge (Moffat 1988).

Upon reaching the crop a ring of damage is manifest which upon expanding is thought to induce a separation that creates a counter-rotating secondary vortex. This would prevent the primary ring from flattening more corn and help to generate the sharp edge around the circumference. These matters are the subject of papers given in this conference, but we will briefly quote an idea from Dr. Tokio Kikuchi which conforms with the laboratory results of smoke-ring experiments conducted by Yamada, Kohaka, Yamabe and Matsui (1982). The latter studied the flowfield in the vicinity of vortex rings as they approached a plane wall. Sometimes the main ring 'rebounded' and then reapproached the surface (a situation which was indeed witnessed in a wheatfield near Silbury Hill in 1989 when a large circle-making vortex-light was seen descending into a field upon which it rebounded immediately – cf Meaden 1990). This reaction would induce a second separation and lead to a tertiary vortex, so it could be the trigger needed for annular-ring development on account of the intrinsic swirl of the primary ring.

CIRCLE CENTRES

As mentioned before, some circles are found with pyramids of corn upright at the circle-centres – good evidence for ring-vortex descent. In others a former standing centre has been removed by vortex drift or oscillation. By contrast, there are occasions where the centre has been struck exceptionally hard, with no evidence for a one-time ring-vortex. Everything is simply swept clear and hard in a radial direction.

Furthermore, and perhaps rather too often for it to be due entirely to chance, the centre is sometimes a patch of pre-existing bare earth. This could suggest that the vortex, in the final part of its descent, 'aimed' for it – much as lightning follows the low-resistance path leading from or to pointed objects.

At the other extreme we know that a low percentage of vortices must descend gently, for only this can explain 'brushed circles', ones in which the crop has been skimmed rather than 'punched'. Indeed we have a good, unequivocal example in which all the evidence points to a vortex descending and then 'taking off' again (Meaden 1988).

So, overall, it seems that more than one vortex mechanism may be involved. With regard to the complex circle sets the intra-circle interactions, whatever their origin, must be quite powerful because of the great distances over which they evidently operate. Diameters of unified patterns involving giant quintuplets are now known to exceed 80 metres (260 feet). The biggest annular ring so far measured had a diameter of 92 metres (Wiltshire, 1 June 1990).

EYEWITNESS DESCRIPTIONS OF CIRCLES FORMED IN DAYLIGHT

Four independent sightings are on record of true crop-circles being created in front of observant witnesses in broad daylight – three of them in cornfields, the other in long grass. In addition, accounts are to hand of witnesses reporting circles being made by summer-whirlwind type vortices (these include Ross-on-Wye 1981, Pucklechurch 1989, and Roundway Hill, Devizes 1989). There are nocturnal reports as well in which eyewitnesses were present at the time that circles were thought being formed by self-luminous vortices.

The Shuttlewood and Bell accounts, both from West Wiltshire, have been cited on previous occasions. We should stress again here that Melvyn Bell had an excellent view into the field while the true cropfield circle formed because of his elevated position on horseback (Figure 20). His observation one evening in late July or early August 1983 took place only a few days after the Bratton quintuplet had appeared. The site was several kilometres to the east of Bratton on Littleton Down below Great Cheverell Hill, Wiltshire, in a hill-valley situation. Because Mr. Bell had seen the Bratton quintuplet that summer he was able to state categorically that the 10-12 metre diameter circle which he watched being formed was of the same species – a circular flattened area with sharp vertical sides. He added, that he could see dust, dirt and other debris being spun upwards only to fall back again, chiefly around the edge of the circle. Evidence in support of this type of perimeter observation is often found in dry conditions when the corn is ripe and brittle. Straws can be found lying on top of the surrounding, undamaged canopy. Like the third and fourth eyewitness sightings which follow, this observation was of the highest quality, his testimony unsolicited and the witness accurately recalling the original

Fig.20: Melvyn Bell, the observant witness who watched a crop-circle being flattened in Wiltshire in 1983.

details without prompting from any interviewer at any time.

The third known eyewitness to cropfield-circle formation also watched it happen in daylight in the early evening. This was at Westbury, Wiltshire, on 3rd July 1982 and took place as a shower of rain was ending. The circle was very big, its diameter reckoned to be '100-150 feet' by the observer Mr. Ray Barnes (in the first letter to the author a diameter of 150 feet was suggested). The corn went down in a matter of four seconds (Meaden 1989c). (This Mr. Ray Barnes is not to be confused with Mr. Frank Barnes who lives 80km away in Winchester and who has been cited by other authors for quite different reasons (the sighting of something luminous descending into Cheesefoot Bottom in 1980) in another publication).

The fourth eyewitness sighting is of considerable interest too, not least because it is a Scottish one far away from southern England. The observer was no more than 15 metres distant when a stationary atmospheric vortex made its presence known by the emission of a curious noise together with a violent rustling of the barley. The time of day was after dawn in daylight in late August 1989. After half a minute or more the barley suddenly went flat over a circle of approximate diameter 15-18 metres forming a typical cropfield circle with sharp circular perimeter. Until this happened the night had been fine and windless, characteristic of the calm conditions of a nocturnal temperature inversion. Further details and analysis have been given elsewhere (Meaden 1990b – see also special article in this volume p.122).

These four independent observations are fundamentally significant. They prove that circle-making vortices form by day as well as by night. The reason for a relatively high frequency of late evening, nocturnal and dawn circle-formations is that the criteria producing the apparently necessary atmospheric stability conditions more readily develop then.

Delgado and Andrews have consistently avoided recognizing this unimpeachable evidence although the first two cases were known to them when they prepared their paranormal-flavoured overview of the circle subject *Circular Evidence* (1989). There they categorically state that "after extensive enquiry, and prolonged personal observation, we have no evidence that these circles are created except at night". Their biassed viewpoint is emphasized by a further statement that "the evidence is overwhelming that circle creations only occur at night". Going further, they misguidedly claim that "with the exception of two possible cases . . . there have never been reports of sounds associated with the appearance of circles. It must have no lights or illumination associated with it". This entirely erroneous statement is quite definitely not to be believed, as we stress in what follows.

SOUND AND LIGHT: THE ELECTRIFIED VORTICES

Many eyewitnesses have reported circle-making vortices *and other hovering vortices* as emitting a humming noise remindful of the electric hum from high-tension wires. Land-devil whirlwinds make a similar noise which is related to axi-symmetric electrostatic fields resulting from triboelectric charge separation (the violent frictional forces, as the devil scrapes and raises dust from the ground, separate the charges, much as a low-hovering helicopter quickly becomes dust-covered due to its attraction for charged dust particles).

We reason that the circle-vortices are electrically-charged too, by some means dependent on their intense spin regime. The density of airborne particles serving as charge carriers, like pollen, dust and marine salt, may play a role in this, as also the water droplets of saturated air. (Many circle-vortices form in the saturated air of a nocturnal inversion which may additionally be loaded with 'dirt', i.e. dust, salt or pollen particles). Other factors may operate too, as they undoubtedly do in the ill-understood precesses which give rise to ball-lightning type volumes of ionized air or plasma-filled air. In our work we use the word plasma in one of its accepted scientific senses to describe air in a partially-ionized state, there being sufficient ions or electrons present that the physical properties of the air are noticeably affected (Meaden 1990e). Professor H. Kikuchi and Y. H. Ohtsuki similarly use the word plasma in this sense (cf their papers later).

Unlike fair-weather whirlwinds whose formation by rising air currents is restricted to daylight hours, circle-vortices happen at night too, so accompanying lights may sometimes be expected. Indeed they have been seen, as in Kent and Wiltshire last summer (see next paragraph but one), at the time of nocturnal circle-making.

It is well-known to American researchers of atmospheric physics that the common whirlwind generates its own electric field. The field is electrostatic, and arises from the electrification of dust particles which have been scoured by friction from the surface of the ground by the energy of the spinning winds (Freier 1960, Crozier 1964, 1970). Electric-field values exceeding $-450\ V\ m^{-1}$ at a distance of 30 metres have been measured as compared with a pre-existing fair-weather field of $+49\ V\ m^{-1}$. The illustration shown in Figure 21 is drawn after Freier. It shows how the local electric field varied as a land-devil approached and receded during the course of several minutes.

The electric field of tornadoes is known to generate acoustic and luminous effects (Vonnegut 1960). It could be similar with our circles-effect vortices. Light and noise imply the existence of electrical discharges. Moreover, there is a circle case from France many years ago (St. Souplet, Nord) in which circle formation in a large patch of spinach was coincident with a red ball of light and acoustic noise (Anon. 1976, Nord Matin, October 1954). Similar cases involving huge balls of light and their resultant cropfield circles were witnessed in England last year (29th June in Wiltshire and 10th August 1989 in Kent). These have been fully recounted elsewhere (Harris 1990, Meaden 1990). Briefly, around midnight on 28th-29th June 1989 a big orange ball of light was seen descending into a Wiltshire wheatfield. The witness saw the bottom 'go flat' as crop-and-ground contact was made, before disappearing after a single bounce *in situ* a few seconds later. Next morning a 15m *singly-ringed circle* was found at that spot. We may emphasize that the light was seen

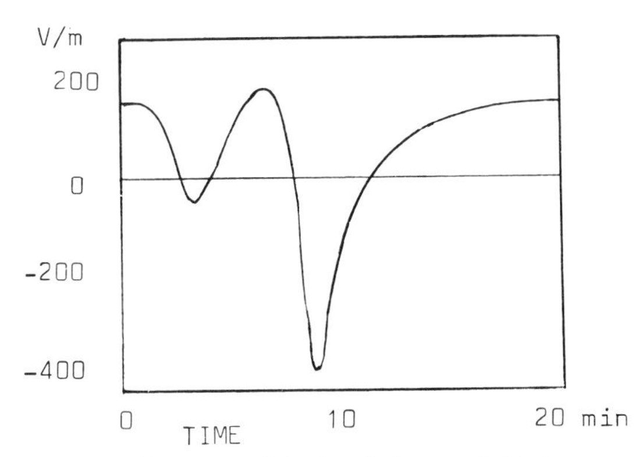

Fig.21: Behaviour of the local electric field during the approach and departure of a land-devil (after Freier 1960). The change of field from the normal positive to the abnormal negative values is due to the intense field generated by the land-devil.

against a background of sloping ground, and was of such a size that the observer fairly well estimated its diameter aided by his detailed knowledge of the local landscape.

The Kentish observation was much the same. Late on 10th August a 'vortex of light' was spotted in a wheatfield south of Margate. It dissipated before the witness got to the site, but immediate investigation by moonlight revealed a circle 18-metres in diameter.

These circle/light combinations have antecedents from countries other than Britain, among them France, Japan, Australia and the U.S.A. Taken together they support the case for the development of balls of light of exceptional dimensions which upon striking a crop create the circles. Some, like the Japanese incident of 1986 in Tamagata Prefecture, were accompanied by television interference indicative of r.f. emissions in the radio-communication bands. There is every reason to expect that the naturally-occurring wind vortices which form the circles are also electrical generators.

It is here pertinent to insert some remarks regarding the laboratory work of Professor Ohtsuki who has been successful in creating in his laboratory a self-luminous vortex composed of a 'dirty' plasma (i.e. ionized air with impurities). Moreover, by the method of microwave interference, he has created a self-luminous plasma out of ordinary air at normal temperature and pressure (see his paper, this volume). Thus, he has come nearer than anyone has done before at creating the atmospheric plasma about which I have written anteriorly in connection with the circles effect (Meaden 1989b).

In contrast to our conclusions about the physical and electromagnetic properties of the circle-making vortices it is only fair to record that an opposite viewpoint was stated by Delgado and Andrews concerning this. Their unequivocal opinion is plainly to the effect that electromagnetic phenomena are *not* involved. 1½ pages of discussion include the remarkable statement:

"Imagine the amount of (electrical generating) equipment that would have to be carried into a remote field in order to create a 20-metre diameter circle" (Delgado and Andrews, p.161). So knowing nothing about spinning plasmas and how they can be a source of electromagnetism, these authors could do no better than conclude: "This would seem to support the theory that the circles are created by an unknown force field manipulated by an unknown intelligence" (Delgado and Andrews, p.169).

TUBULAR COLUMNS

In his paper to this conference Professor Hiroshi Kikuchi extends his electrohydrodynamical-vortex approach to include tubular vortices in the presence of an external electric field and geomagnetic field. We therefore insert some remarks about sightings of luminescent tubes or pipes which appear absolutely authentic.

Firstly, at Silbury Hill, Wiltshire at 11 p.m. B.S.T. on 13th July 1988, a lady was eyewitness to a hollow pencil-shaped tube (not a beam) of light which reached from cloud to ground for an observed period of a couple of minutes. A huge volume of the cloud, which was at 4000 feet, appeared electrified. Details are given elsewhere (Meaden 1989b).

Next, following a lecture given in February this year I was approached b Wiltshireman who wanted to tell me of the only extraordinary nocturnal lig he had ever seen. This turned out, unexpectedly, to be another self-lumino tubular occurrence. He did not know of my existing interest in this ra phenomenon. So, secondly, we can put on record his similarly-luminescent tube case which happened near the White Horse, Bratton, Wiltshire, also in 1988. The occurrence was at about 3 a.m. one fine summer's morning when he was driving from Westbury eastwards along the main road. On passing the wood adjoining Mr. Scull's house he spotted a long *tube* (not a beam) of light which was reaching down into an empty field between the road and the escarpment, but within two to three seconds of sighting the light pipe it extinguished itself.

We also know of a Japanese tubular case on Hokkaido at Tomakomai dated July 1973 (Meaden 1989b) to which we can add a possible French case involving a 'luminous bar', at Laval, the night of 8th May 1768 (sent to us by Christopher Chatfield), and a multiple Scottish case of 'semi-transparent tubular shapes' each described as four times the width of a telegraph pole and which gave rise to a violent local wind (private communication from David R. Cowan).

ARE THE VORTICES TARGETTED TOWARDS CERTAIN PLACES ON THE GROUND?

We mentioned before that bare-earth centres for some circles are surprisingly common. It is as though the vortex aimed for the bare patch, just as lightning aims for the lightning conductor. This intimates a liaison with the earth's local electric field and by suggesting that the electron flow was there higher it helps confirm that the vortex has a field too. Following a suggestion by Prof. Hiroshi Kikuchi this leads one to think that simultaneous cyclotron-resonance effects may develop in which ions and electrons circulate more efficiently if their Larmor radii correspond to the wind-vortex radii. This might lead to a possibly distinguishable clumping of circle diameters around particular values.

WHAT HAPPENS TO A DESCENDING VORTEX IN THE ABSENCE OF A CROP?

Because we view the crop-damaging agent as a spinning volume of ionized air, we may consider the likely effects that would ensue if such a vortex, instead of striking a field, descends on people or animals or a motor-car or a house. The resulting effects of blasting wind are not hard to imagine, but we can quote from real case-histories.

We commence with Mr. Sharp, a retired farmworker at Norton Bavant who continued his habits of a lifetime by rising at dawn in midsummer. In July 1988 just after dawn on an otherwise calm, clear windfree morning he heard the *noise* of what he called a whirlwind suddenly battering the *roof* of the garage next to his house. It arrived suddenly as though it had dropped from above. It did not approach gradually, as did the common 'afternoon' whirlwinds, from across the fields. A couple of hours later the farmer's wife discovered that a pair of circles had arrived 'overnight' in the adjacent field.

What is it like for people to be hit by descending vortices or vortex rings? The cases of two Westbury ladies on 24th October 1986 (at 1615 G.M.T.) and a Bishopstrow man in March 1965 are recounted in *The Circles Effect and its Mysteries.* These witnesses reported calm conditions preceding the wind and then a veritable blast which was *downwards* and highly localized. Under grey skies, rain having just ended, the ladies were crossing a harvested unploughed field where the remains of two cropfield circles were still present. Conditions were wholly inappropriate for heat whirlwinds to form. In a letter to the author the witnesses said: "When we reached the spot where the circles had been, we were suddenly caught up in a terrific whirlwind. It came without warning, no gradual build-up. We could hardly stand up against it and it was difficult to get one's breath. It was all spinning, with the noise of the wind. Bing (the dog) went wild. Altogether quite frightening, but when we finally got past this spot the atmosphere was calm again and there was no wind at all. We concluded it must be whirlwinds which cause these circles".

Physiological effects have been reported on several occasions, especially in relation to animals but sometimes seriously affecting humans too. These independent descriptions conform with the several eyewitness observations now known of cornfield-circle formation. Examples were provided in *The Circles Effect and its Mysteries.* A useful start on exploring the physiological aspects of the problem has been made by J. Randles and C. P. Fuller in their new book *Crop circles: a mystery solved* (see also their paper in this present book). It seems likely that some individuals may be sufficiently sensitive that they could go so far as to hallucinate if they encounter the extraordinary conditions postulated for some of the violent electrified vortices of the circles effect.

ELECTROMAGNETIC EFFECTS ON ELECTRICAL APPARATUS

Numerous examples can be given of humming spinning light-forms which affect electrical apparatus in their vicinity. Some are recounted in *The Circles Effect and its Mysteries.* Many cases involving motor car performance can be found in compilations like *The Vehicle Interference Project* (Falla 1979,) where there are 400. Professor Ohtsuki recounts the case of a plasma vortex independently sighted and monitored by the radar of two Japanese ships in the Pacific Ocean (see his paper, this book). I commence with a simple story, which has recently come to my attention, involving the sounding of a burglar alarm where there was a possible circle link.

At Great Cheverell, south of Devizes, Wiltshire, a quintuplet set of circles appeared one Monday night in July 1987. The time of occurrence is not known but a singular event happened at the house nearest to it in the darkness of that night. This was an instance of a 'false' alarm to the occupants's burglar alarm (the only time it has ever happened there), the house being 150 metres north of the circle site, itself at the foot of the chalk escarpment of Salisbury Plain. It is thought that the alarm might have been triggered by drifting ionized air from the electrified vortex which had just formed the circles (or from a second vortex even closer to the house).

The accumulated evidence of the ongoing circles research is that electrical phenomena accompany the descent of circle-making vortices, and that weak electromagnetic effects persist in the vicinity (in particular in the earth and perhaps straw) for some time afterwards. For example, last summer when wishing to photograph the bare-earth centre of the double-ringed circle at Bratton by holding the camera pointing vertically downwards, the shutter would not function. The camera was a fully automatic Minolta 7000 being used in the self-focussing programmed mode with a 50mm lens. It was held about 1½ metres above the ground. I knew that the batteries were weak so I first thought that the non-functioning of the shutter was the inbuilt signal to discard the batteries. However, before proceeding to do this I pointed the camera elsewhere and was surprised to find that it worked without problem. This led me to try various experiments, as a result of which I could say that the camera worked in every direction that I tried, and in every place to which I moved, until I returned to that same central spot at which the camera would not function in a vertical position. Later in the day the batteries did fail completely, and had to be replaced.

Finally I give one example from the compilation by Falla (1979) because the observations were made by independent groups of scientists and the description seems to fit some of the deduced characteristics of the electrified or plasma vortex under present study. This is an observation of a large grey-blue sphere which was sighted by Dr. Francisco Padron and Francisco Esteves as their car rounded a curve near Galdar on the Canary Islands (Falla 1979, p.77). It was stated that the 'object was transparent with stars visible through it', and that it was suspended a metre or two above the ground. The car radio suddenly went dead and the witnesses felt very cold (because of descending cool air brought down by the vortex?). The object started to rise and seemed to grow larger as it rose higher. The men went to a nearby farmhouse where the farmer told them that his television set had suddenly gone dead. The object was also seen by several other witnesses near Galdar and by three astronomers at the Monte Izane Astrophysical Observatory. The astronomers described the object as a brilliant sphere with a swirling centre and were unable to account for the origin of the object.

Among the points worthy of note in this story is the transparency of the spinning coloured object: 'The stars were visible through it'. Many similar accounts can be found of luminous objects which betrayed their transparency by passing through barbed wire fences or closed gates. In one case, although a humming pulsating object was seen to be in a field 10 metres beyond a metal gate, the gate became sufficiently electrified to give an electric shock to the observer who touched it.

SOME CONNECTIONS FOR THE UFO PROBLEM

Our deduction that descending vortices at night which are able to create circles on the ground in the presence of a suitable tracer may on some occasions be well-illuminated have considerable interest for what has become known as the U.F.O. problem. In their own paper C. P. Fuller and J. Randles explain the excitement that this has engendered among serious U.F.O. researchers. For amidst the hard core of *unexplained* but highly believable accounts of low-level hovering or descending, spinning or pulsating nocturnal lights that have been observed or filmed in recent years (these total no more than 5-10% of all reported observations of mystery light sightings) there is a good fraction which appear explicable in terms of the circle-making vortex phenomena that I am discussing. Sometimes the spinning lightform reached the ground and resulted in cropfield or grassland circles. In others the light did not reach the ground or did not interact with an impressionable surface capable of leaving a trace but provided instead other kinds of evidence like effects of wind or electricity on people, animals, motor-cars, etc.

Consider for instance the car with two occupants which was crossing Salisbury Plain in Wiltshire on 24th September 1966 between Tilshead and Shrewton when the car engine, lights and radio died. It was dark, the time 2020 G.M.T. The occupants then noticed a red haze or mist which had descended a short way behind the car and landed on the roadway. They heard a faint humming noise as the mist shifted up and down. The red haze or mist then vanished, at which moment the car lights and radio came on again and the engine fired normally. This is the sort of story, seriously reported by credible witnesses, which for want of a home has found itself securely housed, but scientifically 'lost', in a U.F.O. collection of inexplicable reports of patently atmospheric sightings, and yet which would with the hindsight of plasma-vortex knowledge be potentially reclassifiable as a spinning volume of ionized air of the type under present discussion.

I will cite another case which happened at Chapelle-Taillefer around 0230 on Sunday 19th March 1967 (Anon 1967; Campbell 1983; Meaden 1990d).

Three witnesses saw a big red-orange light, diameter estimated as 10 metres, descending from the sky at about 45 degrees near them. It crossed the first barn of the village and terminated its downward path in a field only a few metres away from them. The shape was egg-shaped with the more pointed end at the top, and was surrounded by a halo of white sparks 5 metres long which were brighter than the orange-red ball. The sparks were likened to those of a Catherine Wheel, as was the sound it emitted. The sound was also described as 'a loud purring noise, the sound of a car's starter, the sound of the old windmill wheels'. The ball seemed to be engulfed by the ground as it sank into it in a burst of sparks. It had been visible for a total of 15 seconds. A fourth witness, a motorcyclist, also saw the ball pass overhead. Next day *a circular patch* 7 metres in diameter was found in the grass, some of which was said to be slightly yellow. The night was cold, several degrees below zero, and slightly overcast but not in any way stormy, and there was no wind. The investigator R. Dupire, wondered whether it might be ball lightning. Mr. Steuart Campbell (Campbell 1983) agreed, but in a later article (Campbell 1986) attributed the event to a misidentification of the magnitude 0.92 star Antares rising in the south-east (the object was seen to the south-west)!

In fact the great size of the object makes it an unlikely candidate for conventional ball lightning (still less an astral event), but we can see how well the details of the story fit with the requirements that I have spelled out for the new plasma-vortex (Meaden 1990d). This description is just one of many thousands in the literature of U.F.O.'s and ball lightning held in the specialized collections of GEPAN, TORRO, CUFOS, BUFORA and other research bodies in Europe, America and the rest of the world. Even two of the cases studied in the U.S. government-backed Condon Report (cases 10 and 38) are explicable in terms of the new plasma vortex (Meaden 1989). For instance, case 10 refers to an observation made by a nuclear physicist at Haynesville, Louisiana, on 30th December 1966, which was a dark rainy night. "A pulsating reddish light seen below treetop level from a highway at night became brilliant white briefly, then resumed its earlier character" (Condon 1969). It pulsated regularly, ranging from dull red to bright orange with a period of about two seconds.

P. Fuller and J. Randles go into this general problem of reinterpreting U.F.O. sightings in some depth. This includes not only circle-making events but also ones which involve electrical failures to cars, unexplained effects on animals and humans, etc, in connection with proximal light forms of unknown origin. It does indeed appear that the responsible research side of the U.F.O. movement has been monitoring a genuine physical effect all the time – one of which the scientific community has been unaware, and one which is sure to be of considerable importance to the physical sciences in the future.

REMARKS ON SOME UNUSUAL CLAIMS REGARDING CIRCLE PHENOMENA

From time to time amazing things have been said – although on no firm evidence – about peculiar happenings or discoveries claimed to be linked to cropfield-circle events. Most of these have emanated from the indefatigable Delgado and Andrews and few have yet been acceptably substantiated either by them or anyone else.

To begin with, consider the tragic case of the Harrier pilot who ejected without his parachute when it was crossing the region of Winterbourne Stoke, South Wiltshire, in October 1987. Two months earlier a couple of kilometres away four splendid cropfield circles had been discovered and investigated by F. C. Taylor, Nigel Taylor, Isabelle Meaden and myself. Delgado and Andrews, in attempting to find a newsworthy link between these unrelated events, failed to mention that the Harrier had been flying four miles high, at an altitude of 20,000 feet or more. As these authors believe in paranormal and poltergeist occurrences, they have admitted the likelihood that extraterrestrial forces may be involved (they have also intimated the contrary possibility that earth-sourced forces may operate instead, causing the corn to heel over from beneath!). Our reasoning is that although the circles can be said to arrive 'from the sky' they do not descend from tropospherical heights. The vortex-making circles arrive from the 'lower part of the sky', the boundary layer of the atmosphere which chiefly means the lower 300 metres or 1000 feet.

Or again there is the Goodworth Clatford quintuplet circle set of August 1985, the first circles investigated by C. Andrews and F. C. Taylor. Not only was Mr. Taylor the discoverer of these circles by aerial observation but he was the first to spot the 'luminous white, jelly-like substance' which was sent by Omar Fowler to a laboratory for analysis but never fully identified. This sort of deposit, including those of the pwdr ser type, turn up from time to time in the countryside. Possible origins are numerous, and include casual losses by humans (e.g. confectionery) and animals. For instance some years ago I found a superficially similar-looking, white, jelly-like substance on my own lawn, the only time that I have done so in 30 years of lawn-cutting. This specimen was certainly the vomit from an overflying bird. A similar-looking sample which had been sent to me for examination by a *J. Meteorology* reader (Philip Buller, Building Research Establishment, Garston) was analysed by a biologist (T. J. Turvey, 1980). One suggestion was that an aquatic bird, possible a heron, had regurgitated it. We emphasize that it is unscientific to associate finds of this kind with cropfield circles in a manner intended to sensationalize the subject unnecessarily.

Another chestnut, often repeated in the 1989 season, was that the flattened corn was subject to unstated 'molecular changes' that might render the grain unfit for human consumption. This irresponsible 'one-liner' seems to have had its origin in a belief that cereal-stalks which have been knocked down continue to grow sideways. "They do not turn up afterwards", it is said.

But of course, if the stems of a crop have fully matured (i.e. lignified) they cannot possibly respond as stated, because when the stem has set there cannot be any further geotropic response anyway. The nodes *cannot* move. Indeed, it is only while the main shoot is immature that any possibility for nodal bending exists. This limits us to no later than stage 39 on the Zadoks-Chang-Konzak decimal scale of cereal-growth. For southern England in spring-summer 1989 growth-stage 39 corresponded approximately to winter-sown cereal crops struck down by vortices in mid-May or earlier. In the 1989 circle season the first known English circles developed on 9th May in Wiltshire. In these circles I was able to find many examples in ensuing weeks where the geotropic response had acted in the classical manner which allowed the youngest nodes from the flattened stalks to respond in the usual fashion by turning upwards.

In view of the considerable public interest in this phenomenon I am again paying strict attention to this effect in this and future seasons. For a start, in early May 1990 several circles on the Beckhampton Downs, Wiltshire, together with the early circle in barley south-west of Windmill Hill, displayed the normal effect expected of the geotropic response. Fresh growth was sufficiently advanced by the date of discovery to indicate a vortex-descent date some two weeks earlier, possibly corresponding with the date of formation (?20th-24th April) of the rapeseed circle in the same district which had been found on 28th April. Again, the normal geotropic response was found happening to the fallen corn inside the 13th May 1990 triple-ringed quintuplet when I checked the site two weeks after the vortex incident which had occurred when the corn was around 50cm high at growth stage 33 on the ZCK scale.

MORE CURIOUS CIRCLES FROM 1989

At Winterbourne Stoke in August 1989 Busty Taylor was responsible for finding a circle type which was wholly new to our inquiry (Figure 22a) and then a few days later only a kilometre away a still more complex variation on this unusual species (Figure 22b). Both have a small centre with double rings around them, and both have a clockwise ring around the circumference, but the second has a most curious offset quadranted structure which by close comparison with Figure 22b can be seen in Figure 23. George Bathurst makes a reference to this in his paper.

In a separate paper David Reynolds recounts the peculiar tooth-like damage

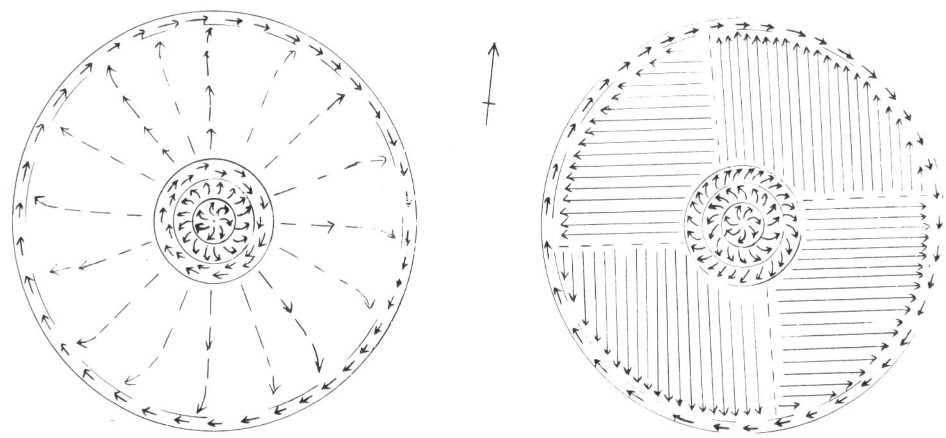

Fig.22a,22b: Diagrams (not to scale) to show the complex patterns left by two vortices at Winterbourne Stoke, South Wiltshire, in August 1989. Circle diameters were 21 metres.

patterns based on radial-ring symmetry discovered in Staffordshire in June 1989 by aerial archaeologist James Pickering. Two similar structures had been reported to us a year earlier by a correspondent from Deal in Kent who had found such patterns in 1980 on the sands at low tide. The nature of these rings suggests ring-vortex symmetry possibly coupled with explosive decay.

In Hampshire on Longwood Estate near Cheesefoot Head in July there was formed a clockwise circle with a long incurving hook-spur meeting the circle

Fig.23: A photograph of part of the circle sketched in Figure 22b. Notice, by comparison with the sketch, the positions of the offset quadrants.

Fig.24: Clockwise circle with a 20-metre long incurving path laid flat in the same clockwise direction as the main circle. The point of intersection is shown. Cheesefoot Head, July 1989.

at its perimeter. The length of the curved hook was 20 metres and its width 1.05m. The bed was monotonically flat (Figure 24). Varieties of this species of hooked circle have been noted before on a different scale. Fuller details will appear on another occasion.

It is not anticipated that comprehension of these unusual and rare varieties of circle formation can be beyond the reach of conventional science and mathematics. But as Professor Snow says in his paper the theoreticians must apply themselves to the basic tasks of understanding the simpler circles before embarking on the complex ones. Meanwhile the study goes on, for data collection is fundamental to the inquiry, and the proper assembly and co-ordination of data provide an ever-rising number of clues about the processes at work in the vortices that form the circles.

RECENT CIRCLES FROM THE REST OF THE WORLD

We have said much about British circles in this paper, but circles happen in other parts of the world too and some recent cases require mentioning. Several circles from Manitoba were reported in the Winnipeg *Chronicle-Herald* of 4th November 1989. They included a 6-metre circle in long grass on one farm and a 24-metre circle in a cereal-field on another.

Again in November 'a circular depression of spiralled grass located in South Shoreline Park, Florida, was reported on Wednesday November 15th, 1989' by the *Gulf Breeze Sentinel.* Investigations revealed a 2½ metre clockwise circle with a very tightly-spiralled centre. Additional but unverified reports for 1989 mention a corn circle (i.e. a maize circle) in Texas, a grass ring 14 metres in diameter in Iowa, and other possible sites in Pennsylvania, Ohio and Kentucky.

The last circles of 1989 were announced from Speed, Victoria, Australia. Twelve were found, spread across two groups, and investigated by a Melbourne study group. John Pinkney of the *Weekend Truth* (16th December 1989) reported a farmer as saying: 'Obviously something exerting colossal force has set down there. Outside the circles you can scratch dirt up with your fingers. But inside, the ground is incredibly compressed, like cement. The wheat appears to be woven, almost like a straw basket. The stalks are quite amazingly undamaged, with the grain fully matured in the heads'. Further details, together with what appears to be an earlier plasma-vortex observation, have been given elsewhere (Meaden 1990c).

Many older cases of circles from beyond Britain are known. Besides plain circles and multiples of various sizes they include ringed circles (Delroy, Ohio, 1965; Bowden, Alberta, 1967) and a quintuplet set (Australia). Some of them were associated with descending lights, often accompanied by electric-type hums, electrical forces and wind effects. Randles and Fuller (1990) give details in their new book.

FREQUENCY OF CIRCLES IN SOUTHERN ENGLAND

Why are circles so common in Southern England? Many dates for *circle-formation* are now known, which allows us to determine what the weather was doing at the time. In several cases circles were associated with weak weather fronts crossing the region, and these fronts have been of different kinds. A map of circle-frequencies across England, Wales and Scotland is given in Figure 25.

It is certainly due to the frequent passage of weak cold fronts (and this includes occasional sea-breeze fronts) that hilly Southern England, with its numerous cereal fields, owes its reputation as the home of the circles-effect problem. In the summer months sea-breezes penetrate deep inland, sometimes reaching a hundred kilometres from the coast by late evening or after dark when conditions have otherwise fallen calm. This means that a wind can unexpectedly rise again, sometimes from a reversed direction! There are even occasions when it can later reverse again and become a retrograding front repulsed by the rising of a 'pressure-gradient wind'. However, sea-breeze fronts are likely to be only part of the answer. Other types of weak cold front are known to sweep across the hills of Britain too, not forgetting katabatic winds. They will all need close scrutiny as the occasion demands.

It takes much experience to monitor and understand such changes. In every way the circles effect is an arduous research topic fraught with pitfalls for the careless amateur. When it comes to determining wind strengths and directions on a continuous basis throughout the night and day, either a qualified person must be present or excellent instrumentation must be left in place.

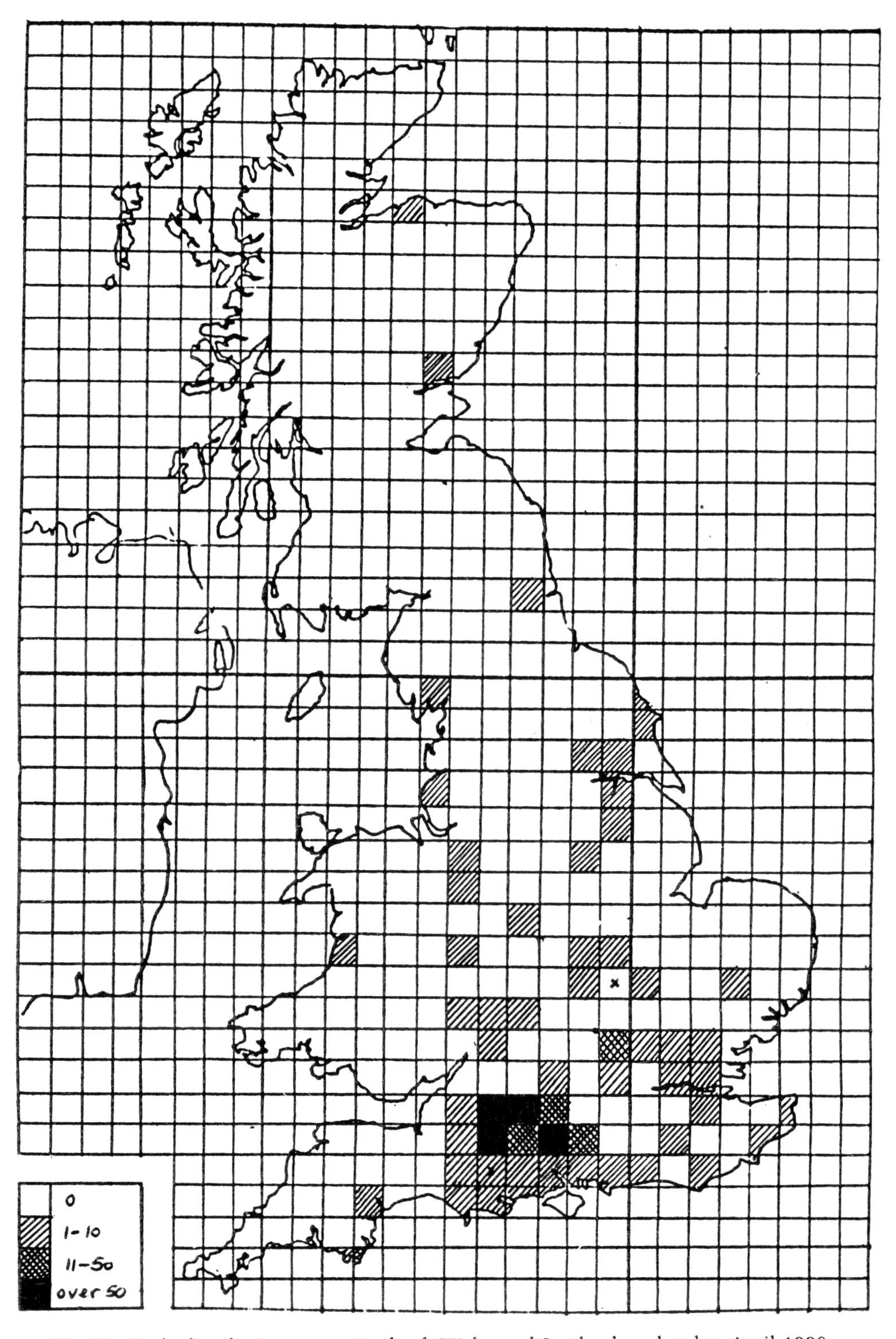

Fig.25: Circle distribution across England, Wales and Scotland, updated to April 1990.

It would appear that the hills of southern England are of the right height relative to temperature-inversion depths, sea-breeze depths and other local front depths to permit a comparatively high frequency of downwind vortices to form. The densities and nature of the aerosols and the character of the crops may well be significant, the former in contributing to the plasma effects, the latter in ensuring good circle-formation and retention. Over thirty years ago R. Mulheisen (1959) carried out pertinent measurements of the electrical properties of North Sea and coastal aerosols by determining the atmospheric electric field and the space charge density. He showed how the space charges, which were found to be positive, probably arose in the surf, and are transported inland on a sea breeze and thereby considerably influence the pre-existing fine-weather electric field. We may add that pollen and dust are other likely charge carriers easily levitated by advancing winds and then highly concentrated at the time of development of fast-spinning vortices, especially the breakdown-vortex version. These particulate impurities, especially in water-saturated air, could be the impurity basis of the 'dirty' plasmas known to plasma physicists. The high concentration of electric charges within vortices, together with a return of excited atoms and molecules to ground states, can account for the reported effects of electromagnetism and luminosity.

In short, we emphasize that there is nothing in the whole of circles research about which we have heard, as yet at least, which does not appear capable of being explained scientifically – and this includes the initially-surprising dowsing-rod reactions (which we can all detect when we try) currently being investigated by Richard Andrews. Fundamentally, it seems that the metal-rod movement of the dowser may be related to a reaction to minor changes in the local magnetic field of the soil induced by the plasma vortices and their fast-spinning fields. For their part the hand-held rods may be magnifying many times tiny muscular responses to these field changes.

CONCLUDING REMARKS

The circles effect is one of the most thrilling new phenomena to come to the attention of physicists and meteorologists in recent years. It is a genuinely great mystery of considerable interest for science. There is every reason to hope that a full explanation in terms of conventional physics and meteorology will be forthcoming as more and more scientists apply their skills to the many facets of the problem. Indeed, we can see the circles serving as a powerful research tool whereby the cropfield impressions bring us new possibilities for studying the behaviour of the lower atmosphere and the electrical effects that develop there. At the same time, it is an area of research to which good amateur investigators are able to contribute usefully to the general fund of knowledge.

I urge everyone to adopt a cautious, scientific approach to the matter. We will find that major observational and theoretical discoveries will continue to appear for many years yet. Indeed there is more that I have discovered and not yet divulged, but these announcements must await another day. The circles which are so common in southern England in spring and summer undoubtedly occur in many other countries too but at a lesser frequency, so do keep looking wherever you may be. By being prepared your chances of discovering circles are raised considerably.

REFERENCES

ANON (1967): S'Agissait-il de foudre globulaire? Phenomenes Spatiaux 12, pp.17-23, 1967. (Groupment d'Etude de Phenomenes Aeriens et d'Objets Spatiaux Insolites (GEPA, Paris).

ANON (1976): Quasi-atterrissage a Saint-Souplet (Nord). *Lumieres dans la nuit.* p.22, mars 1976. (See also *Nord-Matin,* Lille, October 1954).

BARRY, J. D. (1980): *Ball lightning and bead lightning.* Plenum Press, New York; London.

CAMPBELL, S. (1983): Ball lightning at Chapelle-Taillefert in Central France. *J. Meteorology.* Vol. 8, 103-105.

CAMPBELL, S. (1986): A ball lightning report objectively reconsidered. *J. Meteorology.* Vol. 11, 204.

CONDON, E. U. (1969): *Scientific study of Unidentified Flying Objects.* Bantam Books, New York.

CROZIER, W. D. (1964): The electric field of a New Mexico dust devil. *J. Geophys. Research.* 69, 5427-5429.

– – – (1970): Dust devil properties. *ibid.* 75, 4583-4585.

FALLA, G. (Ed.) (1979): *Vehicle interference project.* BUFORA, Burgess Hill, Sussex.

FREIER, G. D. (1960): The electric field of a large dust devil. *J. Geophys. Res.* Vol. 65, 3504.

FULLER, C. P. and RANDLES J.: *The controversy of the circles.* BUFORA, 1989.

HARRIS, P. (1990): Nocturnal eye witness observation of circles in the making. Part 1: East Kent, 10th August 1989. *J. Meteorology.* Vol. 15, 3-5.

JONES, H. L. (1955): The tornado pulse generator. *Weatherwise.* Vol. 18, 78-79.

LUGT, H. J. (1989): Vortex breakdown in atmospheric columnar vortices. *Bull. Amer. Met. Soc.* Vol. 70, 1526-27.

MEADEN, G. T. (1981): Mystery spirals in a Wiltshire cereal-field. *J. Meteorology.* Vol. 6, 76-80.

MEADEN, G. T. (1982): Mystery spirals in a Hampshire cornfield. *ibid.* Vol. 7, 45-49.

MEADEN, G. T. (1988): An anticlockwise spiral-circle in a cereal crop. *ibid.* Vol. 12, 44-49.

MEADEN, G. T. (1989a): A study of the effect of aircraft trailing vortices upon a cereal-field near an airport. *ibid.* Vol. 14, 9-17.

MEADEN, G. T. (1989b): *The circles effect and its mysteries* 1989. Artetech Publishing, 54 Frome Road, Bradford-on-Avon, Wiltshire, BA15 1LD, England.

MEADEN, G. T. (1989c): Eye-witness account of a spiral-circle at Westbury, Wiltshire. *ibid.* Vol. 14.

MEADEN, G. T. (1990a): *The circles effect and its mysteries.* Second edition (£11.95) 1990.

MEADEN, G. T. (1990b): Eye-witness account of a cropfield circle. *Weather.* Vol. 45, (to be published).

MEADEN, G. T. Editor (1990c): *Ball lightning studies.* Artetech Publishing Company, 54 Frome Road, Bradford-on-Avon, BA15 1LD, England. (£8.00).

MEADEN, G. T. (1990d): Quelques consequences pour la recherche ufologique de la découverte d'un nouveau phenomène electromagnétique dans l'atmosphère; le vortex plasmatique et ses traces circulaires visibles au sol. *Actes des quatriemes rencontres de l'AESV. Lyon.* April 28th-30th, 1990.

MEADEN, G. T. (1990e): Discovery of a new phenomenon in the atmosphere; an electrified vortex and its physical properties as revealed by patterned ground traces and electromagnetic, acoustic and luminous effects. In H. Kikuchi. *Proc. U.R.S.I. Conference, Tokyo, Sept. 1989.* Springer Verlag, Germany,

MEADEN G. T. (1990f): Nocturnal eye-witness observation of circles in the making. Part 2: North Wiltshire, 29th June 1989. *J. Meteorology.* Vol. 15, 5-7.

MOFFAT, H. K. (1988): Generalized vortex rings with and without swirl. *Fluid Dynamics*

Research. 3, 22-30.
MRZYGLOD, I. (1980, 1981): Articles in Probe Magazine.
MULHEISEN, R. (1959): The atmospheric electrical relationships of the coastal aerosol. *Arch. f. Meteorol. Geophysik U. Bioklimatol. Serie A.* 11, 93-108.
RANDALLS, J., SKINNER, R. (1989): The mowing devil or strange news out of Hartfordshire 1678. *J. Meteorology.* Vol. 14, 381-389.
RANDALLS, J. and FULLER, C. P. (1990): *Crop circles: a mystery solved* Robert Hale.
SIMPSON, J. E. (1977): Inland penetration of sea-breeze fronts. *Quart. J. Roy. Met. Soc.* Vol. 103, 47-76.
TURVEY, T. J. (1980): Analysis of the Pwdr Ser sample of 3rd February 1980. *J. Meteorology.* Vol. 5, 117-120.
VAN HEIJST, G. J. F. and R. C. KLOOSTERZIEL (1989): Tripolar vortices in a rotating fluid. *Nature.* 338, 569-571.
VONNEGUT, B. (1960): Electrical theory of tornadoes. *J. Geophys.* Vol. 65, 203-212.
YAMADA, H., KOHSAKA T., YAMABE, H. and MATSUI, T. (1982): Flowfield produced by a vortex ring near a plane wall. *J. Phys. Soc. Japan* 51, 1663-1670.

(Note: All photographs in this paper are by the author except for Figures 1, 5, 8 and 13).

THE ROLE OF AERIAL RECONNAISSANCE IN CROP-CIRCLES RESEARCH

By F. C. TAYLOR

Since discovering the Goodworth Clatford quintuplet from the air in August 1985 the author has discovered hundreds of circles by means of systematic aerial reconnaissance over Wiltshire and Hampshire. This presentation of slides and a 15-minute video film shows some of the most interesting discoveries of the period. The work includes photography from high poles in addition to aerial photography. Among the more recent unusual formations are the hooked circle of Cheesefoot Head (July 1989), various quintuplets, sextuplets and septuplets, the Winterbourne Stoke quadranted circle (August 1989) and the triple-ringed quintuplet of Beckhampton Down (May 1990).

Fig. 1: The Cheesefoot Head clockwise circle with incurving hook, photographed by F. C. Taylor using the high-pole technique. © F. C. Taylor.

POSSIBLE MECHANISMS FOR THE PRODUCTION OF CROP CIRCLES

By JOHN T. SNOW
and
TOKIO KIKUCHI

INTRODUCTION

Meaden (1981, 1989a,b) describes an atmospheric phenomenon he terms the "circles effect" since it most frequently manifests itself as circular damage patterns in fields of cereal crops. Usually the damaged areas are circular regions in which, at first sight, all plants are laid down in an outwardly-radiating spiral pattern. Diameters range from 1 meter to over 60 meters. The phenomenon has appeared both as single, isolated circles and as several circles apparently distributed at random across a field. Figure 1 is an example of such a circle. Particularly striking features are the near-perfect circularity[1] of the damaged area and the sharpness of the boundary between damaged and undamaged plants.

In addition to simple circles, a variety of more complex forms have been observed – twins (two circles of equal size) or unequal doublets, triplets (most commonly a large central circle with two small satellites, all along a straight line), quadruplets (a central circle with three satellites, the latter all at the same radial distance and spaced 120° apart), etc. . . . In some cases, narrow rings of crop damage concentric with a central circle have been observed. In such patterns, the damaged plants indicate that the direction of rotation alternates from ring to ring, with that of the innermost ring being opposite to that of the central circle, and so on.

Field work to date has focused largely on documenting both the occurrence of circles and internal details of the damage patterns. The former has resulted in the beginnings of a "climatology" for the occurrence of these events in the United Kingdom, while the latter has provided a wealth of data but only limited information concerning causative mechanisms. The literature does contain a few reports of observations of some steps in the formative process (e.g., Meaden, 1990: Meaden, 1989b – see especially his Chapter 2), but these are more tantalizing than conclusive. Additional observations of circle occurrences are needed, especially ones documenting formation on film or videotape.

A few occurrences of this effect have been reported outside the United Kingdom. Besides one 1986 observation quoted in Meaden (1989b), fourother occurrences have been reported in Japan; one in 1979 in Ibaragi prefecture was carefully studied by Takanashi (1980). There have also been reports from Canada and from Australia.

1. Sensationalized accounts have made much of the "perfection" of the patterns. However, while the degree of circularity is remarkable, neither the individual circles nor the complex patterns exhibit "perfect" circularity.

Fig.1: A typical crop circle. This one is 8.2 meters in diameter in wheat about a meter tall. It was discovered in a field in Norton Bavant, Wiltshire on 8th August 1987 by G. T. Meaden and F. C. Taylor and photographed same day by G. T. Meaden.

2. OBJECTIVE

Our present purpose is to describe conceptual models for possible formative mechanisms of the basic circular pattern. We emphasize that any model put forth at this time is highly speculative since it must be based largely on circumstantial evidence. There is no intent to be complete or definitive.

If formulated on a consistent physical basis and kept Spartan in details, speculative models have great utility. For example, they can provide guidance in formulating hypotheses and planning field programs. They can also serve to better expose the hierarchy of questions that must be addressed to develop a complete explanation of a phenomenon.

3. PRELIMINARY CONSIDERATIONS

As a prelude to stating our conceptual models, we summarize and comment briefly on points gleaned from published descriptions of circles. Some of these may be obvious, but are included for completeness.

First impressions of the manner in which plants are laid over within the circles indicate a spiraling flow. In many cases, a more detailed examination shows the plant damage to contain a layering that, in some sense, reflects a time-sequence of the formative process.

Few if any of the damaged plants are uprooted or stripped of branches. This places bounds on wind speeds, suggesting that they are not exceptionally great.

The time scale involved appears to be between 1 and 10 seconds.

The phenomenon appears to be related to topographic features, occurring most frequently in the lee of hills or escarpments. A good example of this relationship are the series of occurrences apparently associated with Cley Hill (see Figure 9 in Meaden, 1989). Some areas appear to be favored, with circles appearing in the same or nearby fields on several occasions over several years.

Most events are observed in June, July and August. While undoubtedly the concentration of observations in these months has much to do with the state of the crops resulting in their being good "tracers", it may also reflect the general synoptic conditions prevailing during this period of time. While we are not familiar with the synoptic climatology of the United Kingdom, we suspect that the June-August period is a synoptically quiet time of year, so that the surface-layer temperature structure is largely controlled by solar forcing during the day and long-wave radiative cooling at night.

The phenomenon appears to occur most frequently from late afternoon through early morning. During this same time period, under fair skies and quiet synoptic conditions, a surface inversion usually is present. This develops from the bottom up, beginning in late afternoon.

There are some indications that the phenomenon is related to the passage of mesoscale shear lines, such as the advance or retreat of the sea-breeze front. This suggests a transient mechanism.

The available "tracers" – low field crops such as rape, soy beans, or cereals of various types – play a key role in what is seen. In most of the fields where circles have been found, the crops are planted fairly densely. While visually the plant canopy might appear to be nearly solid, in fact it is largely open so that the role of the flow within the canopy must be considered. Leaves are concentrated in the upper one-half of the crop stand.

Most field crops "streamline" when subjected to strong wind. However, the stems of the plants fail when the flow exceeds a critical speed. For a given field, factors such as degree of maturation, moisture content, availability of certain nutrients, density of planting, etc. . . . combine to produce a set of "critical windspeeds" required to flex the crop, to bend it down without permanent lodging, to break stems and leaves, etc. . . . As an additional complexity, these values vary through the life of the crop. Luckily for present purposes agricultural science has produced plants that are almost uniform.

4. CONCEPTUAL MODELS

We focus on models for events leading to formation of single circles. We begin by suggesting that the mechanism producing the circles is embedded in a one-scale-larger circulation aloft. This parent circulation can take several forms; however, in our view *all are produced by environmental flow around or over local topography.*

We first discuss the possibility that the circles are produced by a previously-unrecognized member of the family of geophysical columnar vortices[2]. In this model, each circle documents the interaction of a columnar vortex with the crop canopy. We then describe an alternative model, one in which a circle is produced by a descending swirling vortex ring. This is viewed as a microscale analog to the downbursts that occur with some thunderstorms. Finally, we combine features from both the columnar vortex model and the vortex-ring model, suggesting that a phenomenon termed vortex breakdown is the producing mechanism.

5. DISCUSSION 1 – THE "MISOCYCLONE"

In our view, the mechanism giving rise to the circles has its genesis in the family of one-scale-larger eddies and vortices that occur in flow of air around and over topographic features. Field and laboratory studies have shown that over a wide range of surface layer conditions, when steady wind is intercepted by an isolated hill[3] or by a steep escarpment, separation at the boundary leads to a bewildering variety of swirling flows at several scales. This includes both a pattern of large eddies in the flow around an obstacle and small transient vortices that form in the strong shear of the separation zone – see Figure 5.18 xiv in Scorer (1978) for an illustration of these last. Eddies that seem particularly relevant to the present situation are large, vertically-oriented two-dimensional ones, and horizontally-oriented "horseshoe" and "rotor" vortices as they can have effects far downstream of the generating obstacle.

Following Fujita (1981), we will use the term "misocyclone" to denote a large vertically-oriented eddy; depending on topography, atmospheric

2. This family includes tornadoes, waterspouts, fire whirls, dust devils, steam devils, and many other small vortices.

3. There have been a number of studies of flow over isolated hills, much of it in the United Kingdom. Taylor et al. (1987) provide a review. Most of the studies they list have had as an objective the development of techniques for assessing the potential of hill-top sites for wind-energy conversion systems. Consequently the focus of many of the studies has been on the flow at the top of the hill and so the findings are not directly relevant to present purposes. However, a few have looked at the full three-dimensional flow field surrounding the hill. It would useful to examine the listing of hills investigated in the United Kingdom in the last 15 years to see if any of them have associated "circles".

stability and the wind field, this may either be a standing eddy locked to terrain, or one of a series of shed eddies. Figure 4 in Baines and Manins (1989) provides a graphic illustration of this type of eddy; laboratory work reported by these authors also provides clues as to conditions[4] under which such eddies might be expected.

The horseshoe vortices bound the wake that extends downstream of the obstacle, while the rotor vortices form in the wake as air flows over the obstacle. The horseshoe vortices can extend round the front of an obstacle. Rotors are often part of a larger standing wave pattern produced in the flow over the obstacle (Scorer, 1978).

Figures 14, 15, and 16 and the accompanying discussion in Hunt et al. (1978) illustrate the complex, eddy-rich flow around bluff obstacles. In particular, their Figure 15 shows the complex arrangement of vortices that occurs around a simple cube from flow normal to a face. It illustrates both the horizontal horseshoe vortex trailing downstream behind the obstacle, and a smaller vertical horseshoe vortex on the lee face of the cube. Their Figures 14 and 16 show similar but simplified flow patterns for flow over an axisymmetric "hump", which is perhaps a better model for an isolated hill. Tamai et al. (1987) provide other examples of the complex array of vortices that can form downstream of a model hill.

The results of the study by Jenkins et al (1981) show that trailing vortex structures similar to those observed in the laboratory do occur in nature. Key to the interpretation of their particular observations is the asymmetry of the hill, which gives rise to "wing-like" behavior. This produces a very strong trailing vortex analogous to the vortex shed from an airplane wingtip. Their report of strong flow along the axis of the induced trailing vortex should also be noted.

The apparent tendency for the phenomena to occur in late afternoon and early evening suggests a limited direct roll for buoyancy, so that the formative mechanism is not a form of dust devil embedded in a slowly rotating thermal plume. However, buoyancy may play an important indirect role as flow around a hill under neutral or stable conditions is quite different from that under unstable conditions. This is particularly true is the hill extends up through the stable layer[5]. On the other hand if the atmosphere becomes too stable, it becomes more difficult to induce significant vertical motion. This suggests the existence of a critical range of stability.

Efforts to correlate occurrences with the meteorological situation have been made difficult by uncertainties about when circles were formed. In a few

4. Many of the different eddy forms occur only in a stably stratified atmosphere (one where the potential temperature increases with height). This suggests that future field investigations should pay particularly close attention to clues indicating the stability of the atmosphere. If circles are discovered to occur under conditions when the near-surface layer could reasonably be expected to be neutrally stratified (no change in potential temperature with height), then our hypothesis that lee eddies play a key role would be weakened.

5. On the mesoscale, such an effect plays an important role in the process giving rise to the "Von Karman vortex streets" observed in satellite imagery downwind of some islands.

cases where the interval of time in which formation must have occurred is narrow, there is a suggestion that the occurrence was associated with the passage of mesoscale boundary, such as the retreat of the sea breeze front in early evening. The passage of such a boundary by a terrain feature results in a reorganization of the eddy pattern around the feature. Experience in the laboratory suggests that during this transient phase many of the vortices may be at their most intense level.

6. DISCUSSION II – THE CONCENTRATED VORTEX

The spiral pattern in which the plants are laid down suggest that the producing agency is a swirling flow. The overall circular geometry also argues for this. However, it is not immediately clear whether this swirling flow is convergent or divergent. The small tuft left at the center of several circles (see Figure 2) is suggestive of a surface inflow turning to form a small updraft. In this discussion we consider the likely effects of a convergent flow, such as would be present at the base of a columnar vortex.

Aspects of the formation of columnar vortices are discussed in the appendix. We suggest that here the necessary source of rotation is provided by one of the various eddies resulting from flow around nearby topography. While in the present case the origin of the flow force is not clear, we suggest that it could be a local mechanical response to lower dynamic pressure aloft in the core of one of the horizontal vortices that trail off downstream from the hill.

Beneath a columnar vortex that extends to surface, strong radial inflow occurs in response to an unbalanced pressure gradient force. The surface pressure field is established by the quasi-cyclostrophic flow aloft. Cyclostropic balance is upset in the surface layer due to the retarding effects of friction acting on the tangential component of velocity. Angular momentum tends to be conserved and thus the converging inflow produces extremely high speeds very near the surface, especially where the radial flow "overshoots" its equilibrium due to inertia (Snow and Lund, 1989).

In this case, the producing mechanism can be considered a mesoscale vortex core pendant from a small misocyclone. A circle would mark the radius at which the speed of the inflowing air exceeds the critical value for laying down the plants. Since tangential motions vanish at the axis, one might imagine that the initial appearance would resemble a small ring with a tuft in the middle; a slight wobbling of the vortex center line probably assures the quick removal of this central tuft in most cases. As a vortex intensifies further, its radius of critical wind speed expands, and the hole enlarges. The descent of the vortex breakdown to surface (see remarks below) might produce an abrupt enlargement of the hole. Still further spin up would continue to gradually enlarge the diameter of the hole.

While this mechanism provides a possible explanation for the appearance of circles of different sizes, it does not account for the outward lie of the plants in at least the top layer of damaged plants.

Fig.2: A typical tuft of crop stems. Approximate dimensions of this tuft are a ground diameter of 80 centimeters and a height of 50 centimeters. This particular tuft was found near the center of a circle that was meters in diameter. This circle was discovered in a field in Beckhampton, Wiltshire, on 5th August 1989 by pilot Mr. F. C. Taylor. The tuft was photographed by G. T. Meaden next day.

If direct interaction of a columnar vortex with the crop is to be advocated as the producing mechanism, then we must adopt as a corollary that either the vortex is nearly stationary or else that the damage is done very quickly. Any significant motion of the vortex during the time the circle was being formed would elongate it into an ellipse and remove the central tuft. However, a stationary vortex is inconsistent with many observations that show small vortices (e.g. dust devils and snow whirls) generally to travel at moderate speed (typically, a few meters per second)[6]. On the other hand, the complexity of the internal patterns recorded by the laid-over crop *argues for a quasi-stationary mechanism.*

Another perplexing feature is the high degree of larger-scale circular symmetry present in the complex forms, particularly of those with satellite circles. Experiences with tornadoes and dust devils suggest that satellite circles might be the result of the occurrence of some form of "multiple vortex phenomenon" within the core of a large parent vortex. However, all observations of such secondary vortices show them rotating around the center of the parent vortex. Thus the occurrence of satellite circles also implies that

6. An important exception are the previously-noted horseshoe vortices that form in the immediate lee of a blutt body. These are generally "locked in place" relative to the obstacle. They may exhibit rapid local wander and under some circumstances they may break loose and be carried downstream but usually only for short distances.

either the "secondary flows" producing the satellites must be nearly stationary with respect to the earth, or else the patterns are produced in very short periods of time.

7. DISCUSSION III – THE SWIRLING VORTEX RING

In a microburst (Fujita, 1985), a negatively-buoyant current of air strikes the earth and spreads out rapidly. The leading portion of the current consists of a horizontal vortex ring in which the flow is meridional, with all circulation about a horizontal axis. As the descending current approaches the ground and begins to diverge, the ring's diameter expands and its core vortex is stretched. Flow around the core is strengthened so that beneath the expanding ring the near-surface wind speed can reach more than $50ms^{-1}$.

Although the length scales are different, microbursts and crop circles are similar in that in both the damage spreads radially outward from a center. Therefore, as an alternative to formation by a columnar vortex, we can consider the production of a crop circle by a descending current whose leading edge rolls up into a vortex ring. However, in a crop circle the damaged plants are laid down in a spiral pattern indicating the generating flow is in rotation about the vertical. The descending current is taken to be swirling[7] so that the vortex ring has significant internal swirl (that is, circulation about the central axis of the ring). A theoretical discussion of a vortex ring with swirl has been given by Moffatt (1988).

In this view, a circle is produced by the strong winds immediately beneath a descending, expanding swirling vortex ring. As the swirling vortex ring approaches the ground, it expands and its core vortex is stretched in the same way as in the microburst. This is illustrated in Figure 3. The size of the circle would then represent the extent to which the outward travelling ring was able to maintain, in the face of surface friction, wind speeds in excess of those required to damage plants. While this model would seem unlikely to give the exceptionally sharp cutoff in damage observed at the perimeter of a circle, an important clue may be found in the experimental study by Yamada et al. (1982) of vortex rings near a plane wall. They found that the front of an expanding ring can induce a separation that produces a secondary vortex ring rotating counter to the first; this prevents the primary ring from expanding further. Sometimes the primary ring rebounds, then approaches the surface again and induces a second separation leading to a tertiary vortex.

To summarize, in this model the circle-producing mechanism is the rapid downward penetration of a vortex ring through the stable air of the near-surface boundary layer. The penetrating downflow, can be considered a mososcale microburst that descends from a small misocyclone.

Since a descending vortex ring would be influenced by the mean wind in the surface layer, it is hard to see how a "perfect" circle would be formed.

7. Significant swirl has been observed also in some thunderstorm-related microbursts (Fujita, 1985).

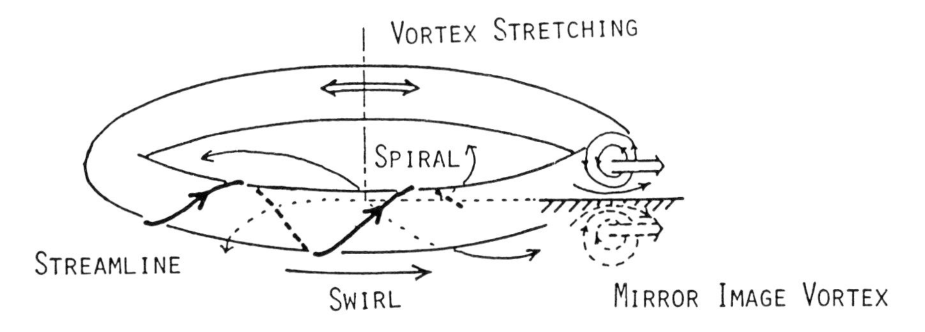

Fig.3: Schematic of a vortex ring with swirl near the ground. If the sense of the meridional rotation is such that the flow at the center of the vortex ring is directed downward, then by the Biot-Savart law the ring travels downward. As the swirling ring approaches the ground, it expands and its vortex core is stretched. The highest air speeds occur in the space between the core and the ground. The motion of the ring can be modeled by assuming a mirror-image ring below the plane of the earth's surface.

Another difficulty with this model is identifying a mechanism by which the vortex ring is formed. The required rotation could be provided by convergence within the misocyclone, but the mechanism by which convergence and sinking is initiated is not clear. It seems unlikely that high values of negative buoyancy could be produced on the scales required.

The formation of the tuft at the center of the circle is not easily incorporated in this model. An explanation of the formation of patterns of satellite circles is also not apparent.

8. DISCUSSION IV - VORTEX BREAKDOWN

It is noteworthy that vortex rings have been studied in relation to what is termed vortex breakdown. In this phenomenon, the core of a concentrated vortex undergoes an abrupt increase in diameter. Upstream of the breakdown, the core flow is super-critical (that is, all waves are swept downstream); the core is of relatively small diameter and generally smooth in appearance. Downstream of the breakdown, the core flow is subcritical (so that waves can propagate upstream); the core is larger, usually turbulent, and often contains an inner region of reversed flow. While the flow structure immediately downstream of the point of breakdown is complex and poorly understood, some of its forms resemble a vortex ring.

Vortex breakdown can be viewed both as a transient feature during spin-up of a vortex core to a high-swirl configuration and as a steady-state feature of a moderate-swirl core. In either case, the point of breakdown first appears aloft, then descends through the core as the vortex spins up. Whether it remains at some height or descends all the way to surface and is lost in the transition to a large-vortex structure depends on the background conditions forcing the vortex.

An example of a quasi-steady breakdown located some distance above the

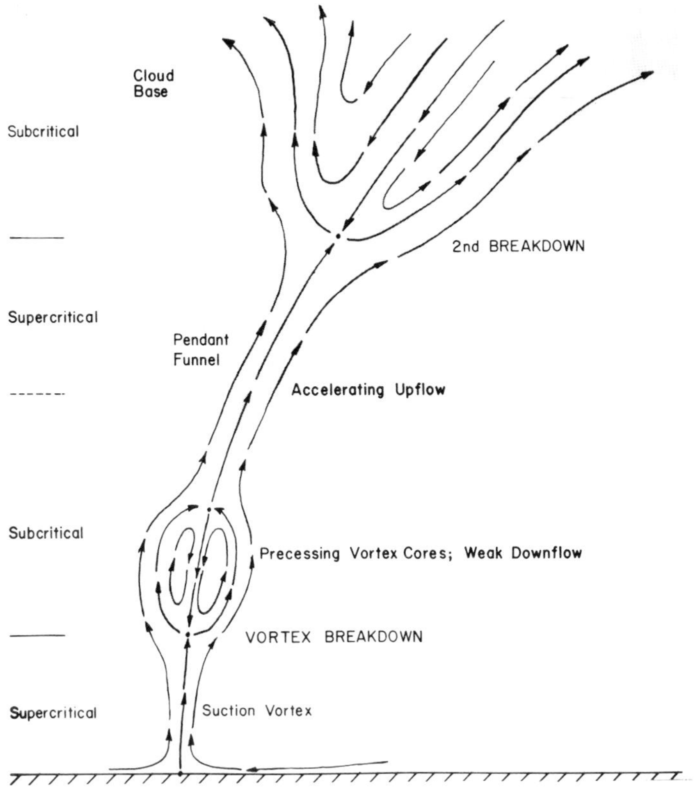

Fig.4: A cross-sectional sketch (not to scale) showing the inferred meridional structure of the 18th July 1986 Minneapolis, Minnesota tornado. In this case the point of vortex breakdown appeared to remain aloft. This is a composite depiction and does not necessarily represent the tornado at any single instant. Taken from Figure 8 in Pauley and Snow (1988).

ground is illustrated in Figure 4. In this case the super-critical core between the surface and the point of breakdown, though small in size, was exceptionally violent.

Perhaps of greatest relevance here is the flow configuration wherein the super-critical flow is confined to a very small depth, perhaps only a meter or so. The breakdown occurs immediately after the flow erupts from the surface. Again, this can be either a quasi-steady situation or a transient stage in the spin-up of a large vortex core. This configuration has been termed the drowned vortex jump by Maxworthy (1972); see also Maxworthy (1973) for an illustration of this flow structure in dust devils. Exploratory studies of the flow in a drowned vortex jump suggest that the highest near-surface wind speeds that can occur do so here, since the inflow penetrates to its smallest radius. (Once the vortex has evolved to a high-swirl configuration wherein the vortex breakdown has been driven all the way to surface, the core expands and near-surface air speeds are reduced).

In the drowned vortex jump configuration, the inflow is progressively squeezed into an ever thinner layer as it approaches the centerline. In the case of the crop circles, given the probable scale of the parent vortex core (taken to be roughly equal to the observed circle radius) and based on experiences with dust devils, this inflow layer may be only 10 or so centimeters thick. This is less than half the height of many of the plants so the inflow is largely below the leafy canopy. However, it is likely a few plants would fall, producing an inward spiral.

The inflow passes into a super-cyclostrophic region and then erupts to form a short section of supercritical core. This almost immediately breaks down in a vortex jump (perhaps at an elevation of 0.5 meter) and the flow moves outward. Finally, at a distance of a few meters from the centerline, the flow turns downstream in an annular region; downflow may occupy the center of the vortex core. The outflow in the breakdown spirals outward and interacts with the leafy portion of the canopy; many plants fall, producing an outward spiral.

As with the simpler vortex model, if a steady drowned vortex jump is the mechanism by which the observed circles are produced, then the vortex must be nearly stationary. On the other hand, if the drowned vortex jump is a transient stage in the evolution of the parent vortex (and the only time wind speeds in the near-surface layer exceed the "critical value"), then a circle might form in one or two seconds. Translation of the vortex would only slightly distort the circle.

9. CLOSING REMARKS

The majority of reports of occurrence have come from the southern portion of the United Kingdom. Of course, this is where the most concerted effort has been made to document events. However, it is of concern that few similar events have been reported elsewhere. This suggests that either there is some meteorological aspect of this portion of the United Kingdom that is unique or the phenomenon remains unrecognized elsewhere.

There appear to be no ready explanations for many of the exotic details (such as the sometimes-multiple circumscribing rings) that have been documented. In fact, it is probably premature to attempt to formulate even speculative explanations for these. While interesting and visually appealing, exploration of these details will have to wait until the life cycle of the process producing the basic circular patterns is more fully documented.

An explanation of the circles provides a new research topic in boundary-layer meteorology. While on one hand micrometeorological disturbances are generally thought to be a matter of probability (i.e. turbulence), on the other hand, coherent flow structures on this small scale do occur frequently (e.g. dust devils).

Serious scientific research regarding the circles must by necessity be a multidisciplinary effort. For example, involvement of an agronomist could provide estimates of the wind speeds required to produce the observed effects.

Finally, we must recognize that a significant fraction of the scientific community, particularly in the United States, still views this phenomenon with skepticism. In part, this is due to a lack of hard scientific evidence concerning the phenomenon. It also is a natural reaction of many scientists to the sensationalism that has surrounded some events. However, such skepticism should also be viewed as a part of the scientific process that creates an impetus for providing clear, convincing proof on a discoverer. History tells us that establishing the existence of new phenomena on the basis of circumstantial evidence can be a long and frustrating task. As encouragement, we should recall that there are recent precedents for recognition of a "new" meteorological phenomenon[8]. With continued careful documentation of circles as they occur, groundwork will be laid for appropriate field programs. It is likely that the majority of the skeptics will be convinced of the reality of this phenomenon only when the formation of a circle is clearly documented on film or videotape. Furthermore, understanding of the formative mechanism will probably not come until the necessary measurements are made on the miso and mososcales.

8. As an example, in 1970 Fujita proposed that "suction spots" occurred within some strong and violent tornadoes. He based his concept on characteristics of damage patterns within tornado tracks. Following a fortuitous observation of a giant dust devil, Fujita was soon able to identify his "suction spots" with "suction vortices", rapidly spinning secondary vortices circling the periphery of a parent vortex core. However, these "multiple vortices" were discussed for 10 years before being accepted as a fundamental part of the structure of some tornadoes.

APPENDIX

Notes on The Formation of Columnar Vortices Through Convergence

In considering any columnar vortex, two quantities must be discussed:

The source of the rotation. Initially, vertical vorticity must be converged and stretched to produce a concentrated core. Once the vortex is established, angular momentum must be continually supplied to the air flowing through the vortex to maintain the rotation.

The "flow force" that produces the necessary convergence and stretching of the vorticity. This is most clearly seen in dust devils where buoyancy in the core drives the swirling flow.

Observations of the formation of columnar vortices in the field and in the laboratory suggest that some form of (perhaps loosely organized) sink flow is present first. This may be driven directly (e.g., by buoyancy in the case of the dust devil), or indirectly by forcing from aloft (e.g., by buoyancy in the case of the tornado). This sink flow leads to both convergence and stretching of vorticity to produce the concentrated core. Due to the frictional drag of the surface slowing the air flow in the lowest layers, the swirling core appears aloft, where the vorticity first becomes concentrated.

Once a segment of core has formed aloft, it locally reorganizes the sink flow via a "dynamic pipe effect" in which cyclostrophic balance retards radial motions. A developing concentrated core draws in air mostly through its tip (in a sense, it is trying to "fill"). This inflow in turn draws in more vorticity so that the core builds downward progressively until it interacts with the surface, which then limits filling from the lower end. At this point, all inflow is squeezed into a thin surface layer which erupts to form the core. Because of the strong convergence and approach to small radius that occurs there, very high swirling velocities and great pressure falls can occur at the base of the core.

If the balance of vorticity and flow force is favorable, the vortex continues to spin-up, but in so doing changes its configuration. The most important feature to appear is vortex breakdown. This appears first aloft where the dynamic pressure induced at the center of the vortex by swirl overcomes (locally) the upward motion driven by the flow force. In a sense of the vortex begins to fill from aloft. As the vortex continues to spin up, this feature moves further upstream until the surface is reached. The highest swirling velocities and greatest surface pressure falls occur just before the vortex breakdown reaches the surface. Maxworthy (1972) calls this particular flow configuration the "drowned vortex jump".

Still further spin-up results in weakly swirling downflow extending to the lower surface and the core increasing in diameter. All strong swirling motions are confined to annular region that forms the periphery of the core. Strong secondary vortices (sometimes termed suction vortices) may appear in this annulus. These give rise to a complex multiple-vortex configuration. Additional details on the spin-up of a columnar vortex can be found in Snow (1982).

Acknowledgements: We wish to thank Dr. G. T. Meaden for providing photographs reproduced in Figures 1 and 2, for considerable correspondence and for the opportunity to participate in the international conference on the circles effect. The travel support received from Purdue University is also gratefully acknowledged.

REFERENCES

BAINES, P. G. and P. C. MANINS, (1989): The principles of laboratory modeling of stratified atmospheric flows over complex terrain. *J. Applied Meteor, 28,* 1213-1225.

FUJITA, T. T. (1981): Tornadoes and downbursts in the context of generalized planetary scales. *J. Atmos. Sci., 38,* 1511-1534.

FUJITA, T. T. (1985): *The Downburst, Microburst, and Macroburst,* The University of Chicago, Chicago, Il, 122pp.

HUNT, J. C. R, C. J. Abell, J. A. Peterka, and H. Woo, (1978): Kinematical studies of the flows around free or surface-mounted obstacles; applying topology to flow visualization. *J. Fluid Mech., 86(1),* 179-200.

JENKINS, G. J., P. J. MASON, W. H. MOORES, and R. I. SYKES (1981): Measurements of the flow structure around Ailsa Craig. *Quart. J. Roy. Meteor. Soc., 107,* 833-851.

MAXWORTHY, T. (1973): A vorticity source for large scale dust devils and other comments on naturally occurring columnar vortices. *J. Atmos. Sci., 30,* 1717-1722.

MAXWORHTY, T. (1972): On the structure of concentrated, columnar vortices. *Astronaut. Acta., 17,* 363-374.

MEADEN, G. T. (1981): Mystery spirals in a Wiltshire cereal-field. *J. Meteor. (UK), 6,*76-80.

MEADEN, G. T. (1989a): The formation of the circular-symmetric crop-damage patterns by atmospheric vortices. *Weather, 44,* 2-10.

MEADEN, G. T. (1989b): *The circles effect and its mysteries.* Artetech Publishing Co., Bradford-on-Avon, England. 114pp.

MEADEN, G. T. (1990): Eye-witness account of a crop-circle in the process of formation – Scotland, late-August 1989. Accepted for publication in *Weather, 45.*

MOFFATT, H. K. (1988): Generalized vortex rings with and without swirl. *Fluid Dynamics Research, 3,* 22-30.

PAULEY, R. L., and J. T. SNOW (1988): On the kinematics and dynamics of the 18th July 1986 Minneapolis tornado, *Mon. Weat. Rev., 116,* 2731-2736.

SCORER, R. S. (1978): *Environmental Aerodynamics,* Ellis Horwood Ltd. 488pp.

SNOW, J. T. and D. E. LUND, (1989): Inertial motions in analytical vortex models. *J. Atmos. Sci., 46,* 3605-3610.

SNOW, J. T. (1982): A review of recent advances in tornado vortex dynamics. *Rev. Geophys. Space Phys., 20(4),* 953-964.

TAKANASHI, J. (1980): Mysterious "doughnut-shaped" site in Ibaragi rice field. *Japan Flying Saucer Investigation, 84,* 1-26 (in Japanese).

TAMAI, N., T. ASAEDA and N. TANAKA, (1987): Vortex structures around a hemispheric hump. *Boundary-Layer Meteorol, 39,* 301-314.

TAYLOR, P. A., P. J. MASON and E. F. BRADLEY, (1987): Boundary-layer flow over low hills. *Boundary-Layer Meteor., 39,* 107-132.

YAMADA, H., T. KOHSAKA, H. YAMABE, and T. MATSUI (1982): Flowfield produced by a vortex ring near a plane wall, *J. Phys. Soc. of Japan, 51(5),* 1663-1670.

IS THE CAUSE OF THE CIRCLES EFFECT INDEPENDENT DESCENT BY A SPHERICAL VORTEX?

By GEORGE BATHURST

Abstract: There are several provisional explanations for the circles effect related to atmospheric vorticity (Meaden 1989, Kikuchi and Snow (1990)), and this suggestion of descent of a vortex-ring by gravity, acquiring swirl in either sense from topography, and then sinking further on more humid surface air may sound like yet another, but it has the merits of simplicity, aerodynamic logic, and the required variability of forms.

I am aware that J. T. Snow and T. Kikuchi have written a paper for presentation at this conference on descending vortex-rings as the likely cause of the circles effect, whether of micro-burst or vortex-breakdown origin. This is not far from what I am attempting to portray, but there seems no reason to doubt that a special kind of vortex-ring, namely a Hill's spherical vortex, could be involved on some or most occasions. This has the advantage that it could form independently making use of the milder forces over southern England and elsewhere. For example, the vortex could be formed at relatively low levels with the assistance of a component of swirl, or else it could continue to fall from aloft through or near a charged cloud and then acquire luminescence leaving swirl to be acquired in the final stages.

The main advantage of a Hill's spherical vortex (Scorer 1958), as hopefully apparent from Figure 1a, is that it would not have to require or store much energy for even a prolonged descent from aloft, and it would sink from cool, less visible air just as a bubble rises in water. It should be able to do so because energy lost through internal friction is continuously restored by displacement of the surrounding air. A pressure drop near the x – x' axis should accompany flow convergence and thus oppose indefinitely the tendency of vortex-rings to expand.

Another advantage is that in its possible tear-drop configuration, as in the diagram, it would not only combine less drag and more stability, important when nearing the surface even when a light wind is blowing across it, but it would have a preference for certain types of locality as seems to be the case. Spherical vortices are by no means a mathematical abstraction, nor an admitted limitation to aircraft wakes made more visible by vapour trails, because they accept a given proportion of the radius inside a furnace burner or gas turbine combustion chamber when known as recirculation bubbles (Stambuleanu 1976). The role then is to return heat from a flame near the axis towards surfaces and a spray of incoming fuel, no doubt reducing the swirl component as concentrated in the course of vaporisation, which then allows it to be restored around the outside or axially-flowing leg. The much larger and cooler spherical vortex of descent would be geometrically similar but adopting a lower swirl number and velocity, except at the eventual impact.

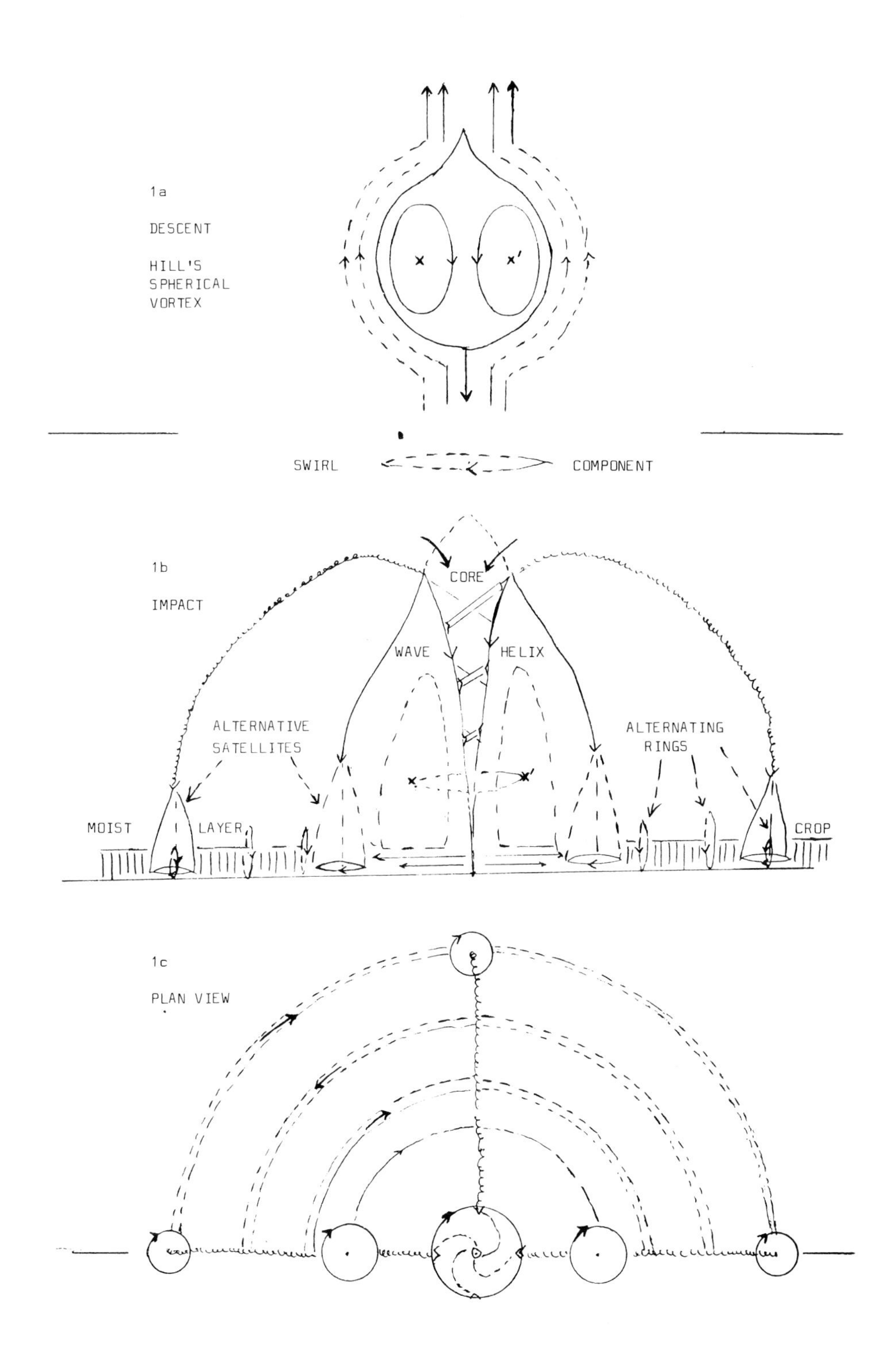

Fig. 1(a): Diagrammatic representation of a Hill's spherical vortex, and its postulated behaviour when impacting the crop (b). Some alternative consequences for circle and ring formation are shown in (c).

This is seen as something of a converse of a sighting by the present author relating to a vertical array of vortex-rings above the Yorkshire moors in July 1962, an observation which I did not offer for publication until last year (Bathurst 1989).

What might be expected from a low velocity impact following first the acquisition of swirl and then an ensuing displacement of moister surface air? The answers seem to be that swirl is first concentrated towards the X/X' axis as suggested in Figures 1b and 1c, and then leads to the formation of a vortex core of varying strength and width indicating a change from free to solid rotation as in a Rankine vortex. A helix of waves could be drawn in from above and be circulated with an even distribution usually in opposite pairs around the core walls. Even the mild shock of an impact would serve to convert these waves into vortices, much as the far larger and slower atmospheric waves become cyclonic. Two routes seem to be available for these potentially *satellite vortices,* one close-in and relatively large in radius and tending to draw rotational energy from the substance of the parent vortex causing triplets. The other path would be further away, often smaller and more numerous, and probably owing a reluctance to reverse its axis and sense of rotation to a combination of gyroscopic and magnetic forces. It seems that an outer ring of narrow width occasionally passes through the exact diameters of three or four satellites, itself rotating in the same anti-cyclonic or cyclonic sense. This might represent traces of the vortex core wall ejected at the same time as the satellites and subject to similar, as it were, separation and parachuting descent. This outer ring seems to be different from that, or those, of intermediate radius that exhibit contra-rotation.

But why are there narrow concentric rings or paths of contra-rotation with the resultant rings numbering between one and four, given the intervening intervals of varying width of still-standing straw? The most likely answer is the (third) law of motion about action and reaction needing to be equal and opposite, with the motion here confined to a limited volume and horizontal planes. The limitation of volume is partly due to the pressure drop and partly to the outer barrier or second position of the core wall. There may well be rings of contra-rotation beyond this barrier ring but seemingly incapable of levelling straw. Another such possible explanation is that in some cases, especially when a spherical vortex has landed with a net electrical charge, magnetic forces begin to intervene, but acting more like an axle differential gear than a brake. Traces of contra-rotation appear in whirlwinds of the upflow type but they are not easily seen. For example, a Texas airport meteorologist once saw a tornado not only overhaul its cloud and "blow" a fresh one to 35,000 feet in one minute, but eject enough hail for its shadows to be visible on the cloud surface wall exemplifying in this instance the anticyclonic sense of rotation (Wobus 1940). The author once made an experimental fire-whirl generator standing in a tray of water for cooling light materials (Bathurst 1962), and on one subsequent occasion demonstrated that the outer tower or duct could be supported by an annular float if made even lighter. This duct was of course free to move, and it proved to rotate in the opposite sense to the contained whirl.

Other, but not all puzzling, features of the circles effect ought to be mentioned if only to seek to justify my notion. One of these is the *radial outflow spur,* and also the apparently unique *quadrants of levelled straw* lying at right angles to those of the next quadrant around the circle. The former seems to confirm the existence of a radial outflow boundary layer, perhaps not accepting the addition of swirl on this occasion because aligned with one or both tractor-tyre tram-lines through the crop in a presumably similar direction along an approximate diameter. The latter (i.e. the quadrants of levelled straw) probably confirms the upper radial divergence of a helix of four evenly-spaced waves, on this occasion flattened by an exceptional impact against the ground, without time being given for satellite or ring formation. The occasional lack of symmetry of a pattern might be attributed to re-bound of a spherical vortex, and hence an imperfect contact with the surface below.

Eye-witness daylight accounts of circle formation or physical encounter seem to number at present as few as four, but two of these received an impression of progressive levelling of the straw rather than simultaneously, as might be implied by a spherical vortex descent. On the other hand, these latter accounts appear to concern sloping ground as might make a difference in that the boundary layer could radiate progressively, starting where the sloping ground happened to be nearer and then clockwise or anticlockwise. For example, the 1982 sighting near Westbury, Wiltshire, not only suggests sloping ground but also records a preliminary radial-length wave advancing across the heads of the crop at about 50mph. Naturally enough, to explain both the wave and a progressive levelling tendency when anchored, a horizontal-axis vortex thesis has been put forward (Meaden 1989). But an alternative is possible, and this is that a landfall was initiated faster than the wind by a spherical vortex which then acquired swirl possibly by wheeling against the sloping ground to attain the clockwise sense. There would then not have been much time for the concentration of vorticity or displacement of a boundary layer, but enough to level straw along a radial front of some 20 metres, beginning where the sloping ground was nearer. Straw length or resistance is clearly critical, and it so happens that about 1981 a shorter and stiffer variety began to be introduced in the U.K. soon followed by growth-limiting sprays. The purpose was to resist levelling by wind and rain whilst providing larger heads, but this could have made the circles effect more perceptible.

Finally, it is worth mentioning in support of any vortex-ring hypothesis that relatively simple models can be contrived to project smoke-rings over ranges of at least 30 diameters by means of weak aerodynamic forces rather than buoyancy effect. For example, a drum-like aimed tube with a tappable membrane across its upstream end and a hole piercing the opposite centre, projects a vortex-ring with enough stored energy to extinguish a target candle flame at the opposite end of the room. This is without the addition of swirl that might cause the ordinary vortex-ring to expand even more diametrically when on its own, but the same situation might not apply to spherical vortices which are less easily projected from ducts. Also, in support of a low-energy displacement theory, there is the Inverted Gas-Turbine Cycle that seems appropriate to depressurised vortex cores and the use of latent heat as the low-temperature equivalent of fuel (Hodge 1955).

REFERENCES

BATHURST, G. B. (1962): *Bull. de l'Observatoire du Puy de Dome,* no. 4, October 1962.
BATHURST, G. B. (1989): *J. Meteorology,* Vol. 14, no. 138, 123-125.
HODGE, J. (1955): *Cycles and performance estimation,* Butterworth Press.
KIKUCHI, T. and SNOW, J. T. (1990): Speculations on the origin of crop damage. Paper presented at A.G.U. West Pacific Coast Meeting, Japan, 1990.
MEADEN, G. T. (1989): *The circles effect and its mysteries,* Artetech, 1989 and 1990.
MEADEN, G. T. (1989): Eye-witness observation of a circle being formed at Westbury, Wiltshire. *J. Meteorology,* Vol. 14, no. 140, 265-270 (July/August 1989).
SCORER, R. S. (1958): *Natural aerodynamics,* p.69. Pergamon Press.
STAMBULEANU, A. (1976): *Flame combustion processes in industry,* p.213. Abacus Press.
WOBUS, H. B. (1940): Tornado from a cumulonimbus. *Bull. Amer. Met. Soc.* November 1940.

SWATHED CIRCLES-EFFECT DAMAGE IN STAFFORDSHIRE: A TOTALLY NEW FORM OF CROP DAMAGE

By DAVID J. REYNOLDS

Abstract: This paper describes and discusses a totally new form of circles-effect damage, first reported by James Pickering from the air and subsequently investigated by the writer, in a field of oats in Staffordshire, England. The damage is composed of many flattened swathes of crops which form a circle and also approximately parallel swathes elsewhere in the field. Among the parallel swathing, two poorly formed swathed circles can be identified, as well as two arcuate swathe features. It is suggested that each swathed circle has resulted from the explosion of a toroidal vortex (shaped like a 'smoke ring') which would have otherwise gone on to form a 'traditional' circle.

LOCATION

The damage in a field of oats was first noticed on 24th June 1989 from the air by James Pickering close to the village of King's Bromley, near Rugeley, Staffordshire (the grid reference of the prominent circle is SK 111 164). The site is located in the flat Trent Valley at 62m above ordnance datum, with the flood plain being about 4km wide at this point. The river itself is 0.5km to the north of the field containing the damage. The land rises gently to about 150m some 10km to the north, while to the south-west is the 200m high plateau heathland and coniferous forest of Cannock Chase (highest peak 242m, 7.6km to the south-west of the circle). There is no laterally continuous slope of a great extent because the plateau is well dissected by valleys, but there are nevertheless steep slopes around the periphery, the nearest edge to the damage being about 6km to the south-west (i.e. close to the highest point of Cannock Chase).

THE PROMINENT SWATHED CIRCLE

It was not possible to recognise the circular formation of the swathes as such, shown in Figure 1, during the site visit because the circle was so large. The diameter (from end of swathe to end of opposite swathe) is estimated as 70m from air photography, which is bigger than the largest known 'traditional' circle of 61m at Bishop's Cannings in Wiltshire (found May 1990) although smaller than the biggest known annular ring at 85m. Most of the swathes were 3-5m in length, but some were so small it was only just possible to stand in them. The width of 0.3-0.4m was far more constant, both along the length of a swathe and when several widths were compared. In a few places, the swathes fanned out a little so that standing crops separating neighbouring swathes eventually became flattened, resulting in a 3m width of continuously-flattened crop in one measured example at the north-eastern side of the circle. All crops in the swathes were flattened away from the centre of the circle.

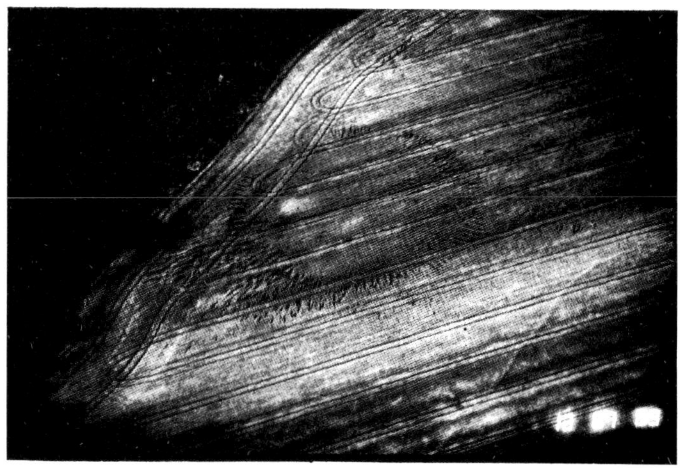

Fig. 1: The prominent swathed circle photographed by James Pickering on 13th July 1989. Parallel swathes are also in evidence. The tram lines are aligned SE (left) – NW (right).

Where a swathe crossed or ended at a tram line, the crop would suddenly bend round and follow the tram line (which were aligned 135° – 315° (magnetic)) towards the north-west – a turn through over 90° since this was observed only on the eastern side of the circle (see Figure 2a). At the south-east quadrant of the circle the swathes merged into neighbouring swathes width-ways, and the damage continued away from the circle. In this area, some swathes crossed one-another, as shown in Figures 2b and 3. (Note that one of these swathes could not have possibly been confused with a tram line,

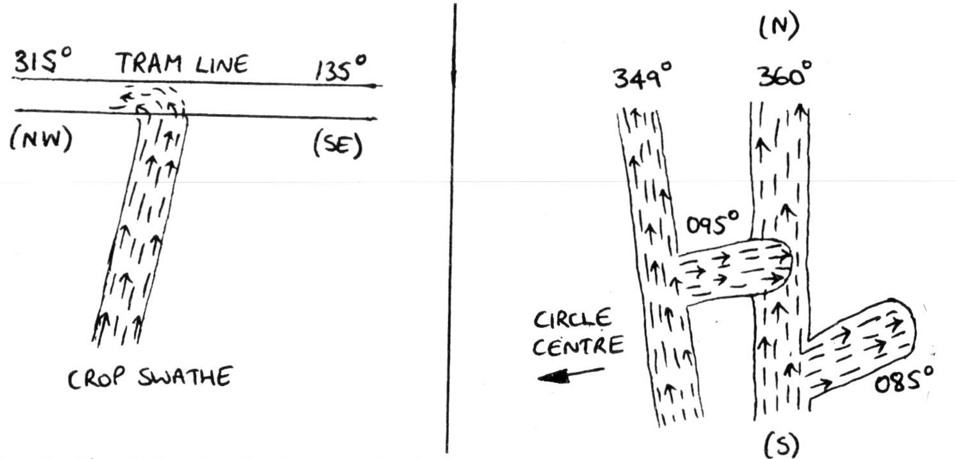

Fig. 2a: Sketch showing the change in the direction of lying crop upon terminating at a tram line (plan view).

Fig. 2b: Sketch showing crossing swathes.

Fig.3: Photograph of crossing swathes by the writer. The swathe entering to the left is associated with the circle; the swathe down which the photograph was taken terminates at the top of the picture.

because tram lines are devoid of crop or contain very little). Aerial photography reveals a few swathes in the otherwise undamaged circle centre; these were missed during the site investigation. Another feature recorded by these photographs is the decrease in the depression of the crops when the swathes come close to or cross the tram lines; this was also noticed at ground level. The decrease in depression is quite marked at the south-south-west side, which suggests some other factor was at work since part of this arc is away from tram lines.

PARALLEL SWATHES

Elsewhere, other parts of the whole field were affected to some degree by crop swathes, this time forming mostly in 'swarms' approximately parallel with neighbouring swathes (Figure 4). The extent of this swathing was not realised at ground level; as a result only a few isolated swathes were studied in a relatively undamaged area in the centre of the field, and also close to the farm buildings. Those which were visited had dimensions comparable with the circle swathes, and again a few were barely large enough to stand in, whilst from aerial photography some appear to be about 10m long. However, close to the farm buildings, one swathe was measured at 0.1m wide

Fig.4: View of the parallel swathing by James Pickering. The two arcuate features may be seen on the right, one opposite the road junction and the other at the extreme bottom right of the picture. The bottom half of the 80m diameter central circle is at the bottom left.

yet 1m long; this was only noticed because of its close proximity to a tram line. This damage could not have been caused by a small animal since the damage characteristics were identical with other swathes, and there were no entry or exit tracks. In common with the circle swathes, there was a reluctance for the parallel swathes to cross tram lines.

From the aerial photography, it would appear that neighbouring fields do not show any such damage. However, it is likely that the field adjacent to the wood and the circle field would have displayed damage if it had not been permanent pasture.

SWATHE CHARACTERISTICS

Some characteristics were displayed by all of the swathes that were inspected without exception. All had vertical walls of standing, undamaged oats, with the flattened oats laid down parallel to the walls. No plants were pushed into either wall, except into the undamaged crop at the end of the swathe. At the start of a swathe, the transition from standing to flattened crop occurred within 2cm (approximately the spacing between each plant – see Figure 5).

The swathe beds were composed of flattened oats whose stems were bent within 10cm of ground level; in a few cases (principally close to the start of a swathe) the stems were bent at ground level. No cases were observed where the crop had been powerfully flattened to the ground. The damaging force appears to have weakened towards the end of a swathe, since crops were bent over at an ever-decreasing angle from the vertical until they eventually attained their normal upright position, as can be seen in Figure 6. A typical longitudinal section is shown in Figure 7.

Fig.5: View of the start of a swathe by the writer. © D. J. Reynolds/CERES/TORRO.

Fig.6: View of the end of a swathe by the writer. © D. J. Reynolds/ CERES-TORRO.

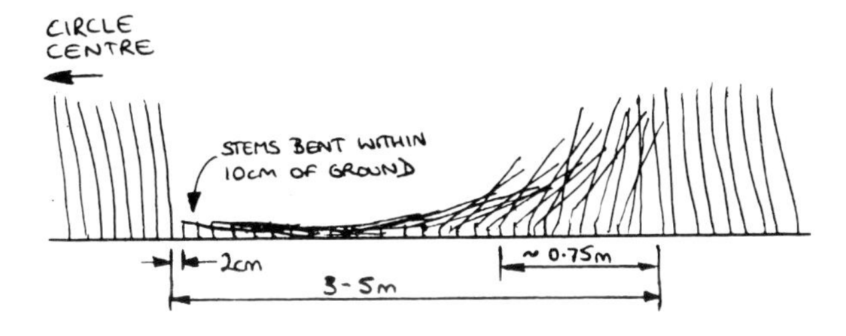

Fig.7: Sketch of a longitudinal section of a typical swathe.

PRIMARY VORTEX ORIGIN

Because the date of formation is not known, wind directions can not be used to identify the hill from which the vortex developed. The nearest hills which might be capable of generating a circles-effect vortex are those of Cannock Chase, peaking 7.6km away to the south-west, as described previously. It is also relevant to note that a traditional circle, 9-12m in diameter, appeared in roughly the same position as the swathed circle the summer before (1988). Previous to this, no other circles have been known on the farm, nor are any known from neighbouring farms – although there is a considerable amount of permanent pasture in the area. These circles are the farthest known of any from a hill from which the vortices originated, assuming that the vortices did form over Cannock Chase.

A passing note should be made about an airfield which was to have to been built on the farm just before or during the second world war. Instead it was built 5km to the south-east at Fradley (near Lichfield) because it was considered that there was too much turbulence above the farm. The decision to change the site may have been made quite quickly, since the hedgerows had already been taken out leaving large fields, one of which contained the circles-effect damage.

A probable circles-effect vortex event is known 11.5km further up the Trent Valley at Severn Springs, Colwich, near Rugeley where in August 1988 a pulsating red light was observed on top of a hedge which was slightly damaged (see Meaden (1989b) p.54 for more details; surveyed by the writer). This site lies right at the bottom of the plateau slope.

Circle formation sites are rare in the West Midlands region; in fact only one other site aside from this is known (at Ditton Priors, Bridgnorth, Shropshire, in 1989). The primary circles-effect vortices appear to form during the passage of weak fronts, such as sea-breeze fronts as occasionally in Wessex. Because the West Midlands region is totally land-locked and is a considerable distance from the open sea, sea-breezes never occur so the frequency of weather conditions which may lead to circle formation are much less frequent than regions which do experience sea-breezes.

DAMAGE INTERPRETATIONS

Much of the damage is at the moment difficult to explain; it is telling us far more about the nature of the circles-effect vortex than we can understand at the present time. As a result, some of the following discussion is rather speculative.

During breakdown of a vertical vortex a toroidal vortex develops which then moves downwards (see Lugt (1989) for breakdown in major whirlwinds, and Kikuchi, Snow and Meaden (to be published, 1990) for vortex breakdown leading to crop circle formation), expanding upon reaching the ground and thus forming a traditional circle. If the toroid ever reached the surface in this case, then it was of insufficient strength to permanently bend the crop over.

It is suggested that the plasma or electrified air in the breakdown vortex became unstable and exploded outwards creating the swathes; this agrees with all the circle swathes because the crop was pushed away from the circle centre. However, one might ask as to why there are no swathes converging towards the inside of the circle; indeed why the damage should be swathed at all. The swathing might have resulted from the explosion of plasma which had been concentrated by the "pinch effect" in regular, discrete antinodal (?) positions in the centre of the toroidal vortex, akin to bead lightning. (Bead lightning and the pinch effect are considered in detail by Barry (1980)). It is possible that the observed swathing may be related in some way to circles and ringed circles with spurs, tangential ejections into circle walls (Meaden 1987), the skipping nature of the damaging agent which formed the ring at Westbury, Wiltshire in August 1987, and the banding and arcs of standing crop observed in circle beds (see Meaden 1989b pp.68-73). Rather than the fanning out of the flattened crop at the end of the swathe, the damage actually narrows (Figure 6). This may suggest a progressive neutralisation of the presumed electrical charges at the swathe end.

The reason why the crop at the end of a swathe which enters a tram line should suddenly swing round and follow that tram line is unclear. Only a very few swathes which terminated at a tram line were observed, all of which were at the eastern side of the circle with a crop following the tram lines to the north-west. This would seem to indicate the channelling of wind by the tram lines. Had more swathes terminated at tram lines, would the resultant pattern of bending crops have indicated an anticlockwise rotation, which might have been the dying rotational wind from the toroidal vortex just after the plasma exploded? (or even the decaying primary vortex?).

The decrease in crop depression around tram lines may be the result of a slower fertiliser uptake by the crop, as suggested by David Lowe to the writer at another circle site-investigation at Ditton Priors, Shropshire. Soil under and around the tram lines is compacted by the weight of the tractor, thus reducing the interconnected void volume (effective porosity) for water-containing nutrients, particularly nitrogen, to flow through. Coupled with a lower infiltration rate, this means that plants adjacent to tram lines have a slower fertiliser uptake, and consequently a higher cellulose content and less luxuriant growth. Such crops would require a greater force per unit area to displace them from the vertical. (A poorly developed satellite circle in tram lines is shown in Figure 2 of Meaden (1990)).

The parallel swathes are much more difficult to explain. The distribution of this damage has not been affected by an underground 415-volt cable running alongside the farm drive, nor a 90cm diameter cast iron pipe at the same end of the field, but only by the tram lines.

A closer inspection of the aerial photography of the parallel swathes reveals two nearly identical arcuate swathe features near to the farm drive, and also the outline of two other poorly swathed circles, in line with the prominent circle (see Figure 8). The central circle (SK 110 165) has an estimated

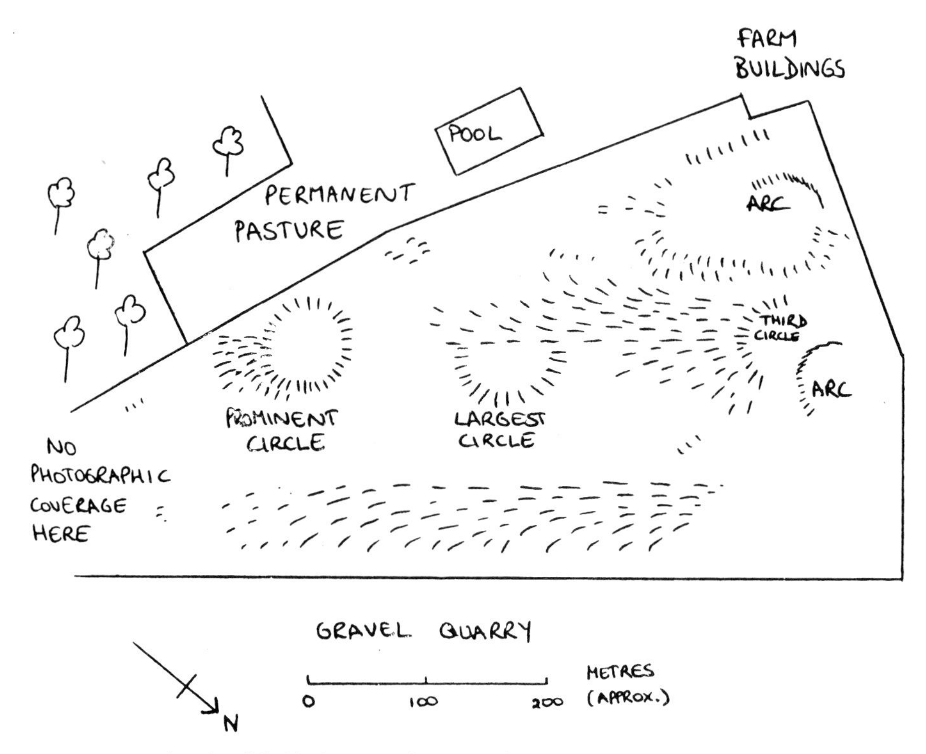

Fig.8: Sketch of field showing the main features discussed in this paper.

diameter of 80m. Was this the result of the explosive termination of an attempt to form an in-line triplet formation? The circles are approximately equidistant and of the same diameter – a rare characteristic of traditional in-line triplets, where the central circle is flanked by two noticeably smaller circles of equal size. Alternatively, the three circles may have been sequential events along a shear line.

The writer also suggests that there have been two (or more?) episodes of damage, i.e. the circle and the parallel swathes (plus the two arcs and other circles) were formed at different times. This would explain the existence of some swathes crossing others (Figures 2b and 3) and the swathes in the centre of the prominent circle. These two damage episodes were probably separated by only a few tens of seconds, maybe less.

CONCLUSIONS

The damage described and discussed here is of a previously-unknown damage signature of the circles-effect. The origin of each circle could have been caused by the explosion of discrete volumes of a multi-nodal toroidal vortex. The origin of the parallel swathes and the two arcuate features remains obscure, although it must be related in some way to the circles because all the swathes have similar characteristics.

Whatever their cause, one thing is certain: swathed damage is very rare – with nearly 1,000 circles known, this paper has considered the only known swathed circles anywhere, apart from a 1980 report of two at Broadstairs, Kent. (See addendum).

ADDENDUM: MORE SWATHED RINGS

A further instance of swathed rings or circles has been discovered retrospectively. Patricia Roger and Marilyn Beugg found two circles in the sandy beach between Louisa Gap and Dumpton Gap (TR 3966) at Broadstairs, Kent, one morning in spring or autumn (definitely not summer) 1980. The circles were on the higher part of the beach, which is bounded by a 10 – 20m high sheer cliff, and within 2km inland is a plateau 50m in altitude. Patricia Roger said that the higher part of the beach is covered by the tide only once a day, and the sand dries out quickly and becomes hard. She contacted Thanet District Council and R.A.F. Manston at the time, and neither could offer explanations. She added that the "surrounding sand was completely undisturbed, and there were no track marks".

In contrast to King's Bromley, these circles were an order of magnitude smaller and more in keeping with the size of traditional circles, being estimated at about 4.5 – 6m in diameter. An important feature of these circles which supports the explosion theory is that every swathe had a smaller counterpart on the inner side of the circle. The directions in which the sand was excavated are unfortunately unknown, but the writer predicts that the outer swathes were excavated outwards, and the inner swathes inwards towards the circle centre; this is consistent with what is known at King's Bromley and what would be expected from an explosion. Although the lengths and widths of the swathes are unknown, the excavations were to a depth of at least 0.6m with the outer swathes deeper than the inner, so the excavation was quite considerable in total. Undisturbed sand lay between the swathes, both laterally around the circle and between the inner and outer swathes. The two circles were next to each other, and from the sketch supplied by Patricia Roger they appear like two cogs with the outer swathes of each circle being engaged like teeth. As it is not known whether any of the swathes overlapped, it is not known which circle formed first. It is suggested that the Broadstairs event represents the explosive abortion of a traditional doublet formation.

An important difference from the King's Bromley damage is that at Broadstairs there was a total absence of any damage referred to as parallel-swathing earlier. However, the existence of an inner swathe band at Broadstairs helps to explain the absence of this feature at King's Bromley. The Broadstairs swathes were described as being excavated in hard sand to at least 0.6m, and the outer swathes were deeper than the inner swathes; at King's Bromley the oat stems were lightly brushed and only rarely bent over at ground level. From this it may be concluded that the King's Bromley circles were low energy-density events, whereas the Broadstairs circles were high energy-density, and that the explosion towards the centre of the circles at King's Bromley was of insufficient strength to create the mirror-image swathes in the oats. This answers the question of the lack of inner swathes in the earlier discussion, but asks another as to why apparently more energy goes into creating the outer swathes.

Although the Broadstairs event occurred near a cliff, it is more probable that the primary vortex formed from air flow across the hills inland. Nevertheless, there seems no reason why a cliff or cove of suitable dimensions may not readily create circles-effect vortices which, if the tide is out, leave their mark as a circle in the sand. Such a circle might quickly be washed away by the tide or trampled on by holiday-makers, although in contrast to crops, sand is capable of displaying a trace at any time of the year.

At both sites the swathed circles were not associated with traditional circles, so (on obviously limited data) it would appear that if one toroidal vortex explodes so might any others that are present at about the same time. Should any swathed circles be found with one or more traditional circles in the future, this may be because the events were separated by a period of a day or more, as if occurring in the same day/night the differing events may be due to two different weak fronts, or the same frontal system that returns due to wave formation, separated by a few hours perhaps.

More evidence that suggests that the toroidal vortex that explodes to create the swathed circles may be of a multi-nodal nature comes from the possible capture of ball lightning on video by Mr. R. Cahill at 0030Z on 10th September 1989 at Ashford, Kent. The possible ball lightning, considered by Meaden and by Stenhoff (in *J. Meteorology,* April 1990) and by Jennison, Lobeck and Cahill (in *Weather,* April 1990) appears in distinct toroidal form, with a weakly illuminated ring surrounding a non-luminous centre. The ring contains discernible nodes and antinodes, and, as discussed earlier, it is suggested that the explosion of a similarly-shaped multi-nodal structure in a toroidal vortex created the circular swathing observed at King's Bromley and Broadstairs.

D. J. R.

Acknowledgements: I would like to thank aerial archaeologist James Pickering (Hinckley) for bringing this important damage to the attention of CERES, and John Groves for help with the site investigation. Special thanks are offered to Stan Prince who farms the area for comments and for permission to inspect the damage, without which even less would be known about this bizarre manifestation of the circles-effect.

REFERENCES

BARRY, J. D. (1980): *Ball and bead lightning.* Plenum.

KIKUCHI, T., SNOW, J. T., and MEADEN, G. T. (1990) (to be published, on the creation of crop circles by vortex breakdown).

LUGT, H. J. (1989): Vortex breakdown in atmospheric columnar vortices. *Bull. American Meteorological Society,* 70, 1526-1537.
MEADEN, G. T. (1987): An anticlockwise spiral-circle in a cereal crop. *J. Meteorology,* 12, 44-49.
MEADEN, G. T. (1989a): Circle formation in a Wiltshire cereal-crop – an eye-witness account and analysis of a circles-effect event at Westbury. *J. Meteorology,* 14, 265-270.
MEADEN, G. T. (1989b): *The circles effect and its mysteries.* Artetech.
MEADEN, G. T. (1990): Nocturnal eye-witness observation of circles in the making. Part 2: North Wiltshire, 29th June 1989. *J. Meteorology,* 15, 5-7.

CREATION OF THE PLASMA VORTEX

By YOSHI-HIKO OHTSUKI

Abstract: This paper commences with an account of the remarkable detection of a plasma vortex by radar situated on two different ships in the Pacific Ocean on 21st December 1986. Observers saw large distinct radar images moving around the position of a boat although nothing was visible directly in the atmosphere. We can interpret this phenomenon as due to plasma-vortex creation. The second part of the paper reports on trial laboratory experiments for simulating the creation of plasma vortices under natural circumstances. These experiments began in 1988, firstly using electrostatic discharge and secondly using microwave interference. Some results reporting the success of plasma-vortex formation are presented.

INTRODUCTION

We can believe that the plasma vortex proposed by Meaden (1989) contributes to the formation of circles and circle-ring patterns in fields. So there are two possibilities to confirm this theory, one by computer simulation, the other by experimental means. Here we report on our experimental trials for creating plasma vortices by two different methods: (1) using electrostatic discharge, (2) using microwave interference.

Firstly we recount remarkable reports concerning the detection of plasma-vortices by ship's radar from a boat operated by Japanese scientists in the Pacific Ocean in 1986. We show that the reports are important to our research for several reasons.

RADAR IMAGES OF THE PLASMA VORTEX

The radar images were reported by Dr. M. Naganobu (1988) (Ocean Research Institute, University of Tokyo) and his four colleagues in the boat *Kaiyomaru,* a research boat of Marine Product, Ministry of Japan, which was in the Pacific Ocean near Hawaii (25° 50.6'N, 166° 10.7'E). The date was 21st December 1986, and the local time was 18.00. The weather was fair, the wind south, and the temperature 25.4°C.

Mr. Y. Sasaki observed at first images on radar (JMA-860 and JMA-850-12) of a huge object at a distance of five kilometres to the north when the object was moving away northwards. Mr. S. Shimojo, M. Takayanagi and M. Muratsuka also observed another image of the large object at 20.30 at 8 to 16km from the boat, and on the radar saw the object move around the boat. After circling the boat twice the object started to approach the boat. However no-one witnessed either an object or lights in that direction. The speed of approach was very high (5000km/h, Mach 4). The object, watched by radar, did a U-turn or V-turn when at a distance of 2.4km (1.5 miles) and disappeared at 22.40 (Figure 1). The next object appeared at 23.10 five kilometres to the west, and rapidly neared the boat. Three people heard a loud sound and saw a bright light.

These reports are important from a scientific standpoint for several reasons:

(1). Two independent radar machines traced the objects.

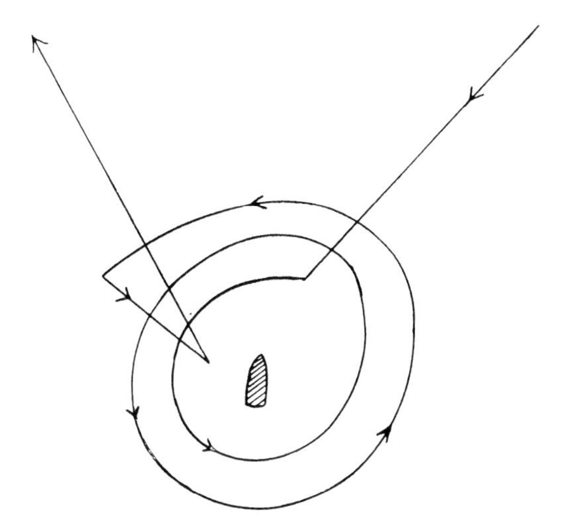

Fig.1: Trajectory followed by a plasma vortex as observed by ship's radar.

(2). The radars could easily identify and distinguish between aeroplanes and our object whose size was 402 metres and highest speed was 5000km/h (see Figure 2).

(3). The radar traced a strange trajectory (the U-turn or V-turn in particular was notable), and

(4). The two radars were checked by engineers at Nihonmusen Company confirming that there were no mechanical problems.

It is therefore my opinion that the radar images of the flying objects were formed by *a plasma vortex.* This is the first known detection of a plasma vortex by means of radar.

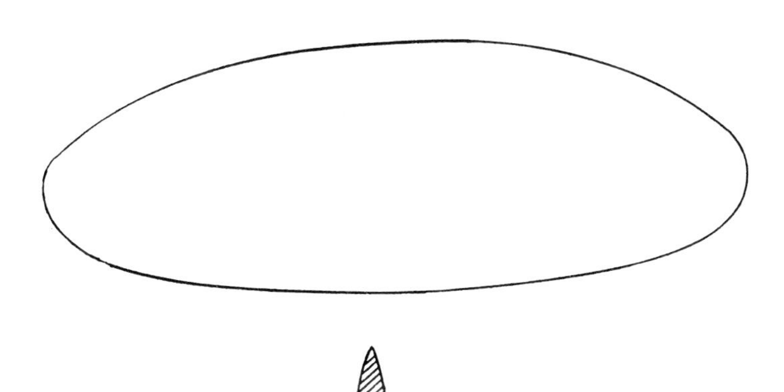

Fig.2: Plasma vortex seen in the Pacific.

EXPERIMENTAL FORMATION OF A PLASMA VORTEX

1. *Electrostatic discharge*

We began trials to produce plasma vortices under *natural circumstances* by means of electrostatic discharge in 1988 and microwave interference in 1989.

The electrostatic discharge experiment was conducted in a similar manner to Barry's experiments (Barry 1980) using different chamber sizes. We used power voltages of 1.3 to 1.7kV, capacitance of 2 to 20 micro F, and both an aerosol (namely, cotton fibres with a volume of about $100cm^3$) and dilute ethane gas.

Three types of fireball are formed in these experiments. The first is a floating-up fire ball (type A) which is created at the density of the gas just before combustion (Figure 3). The size was 10 – 15cm diameter and the lifetime about a second.

The second type of fire ball is created after combustion (type B) which is made of separated flames). This kind of fire ball is stable for many seconds (about 10 seconds) if there is moderate air flow (supplied by a small fan in our case) (see Figure 4).

These two types of fire ball are reproducible. However, the third type of fire ball (type C) is a very rare phenomenon. In 1989 we created this type of fire ball only twice. This C-type is small (about 2cm). It moves very rapidly up and down *and rotates.* Its lifetime was short, about 2.5 seconds, but it was very bright (see Figure 5). *We can attribute the C-type of fire ball to its being a plasma vortex.* However, it is very difficult to choose the parameters and exact conditions necessary for the creation of the C-type vortex at this moment.

Fig.3: Type A fire ball, diameter 10 – 15cm, created in the laboratory.

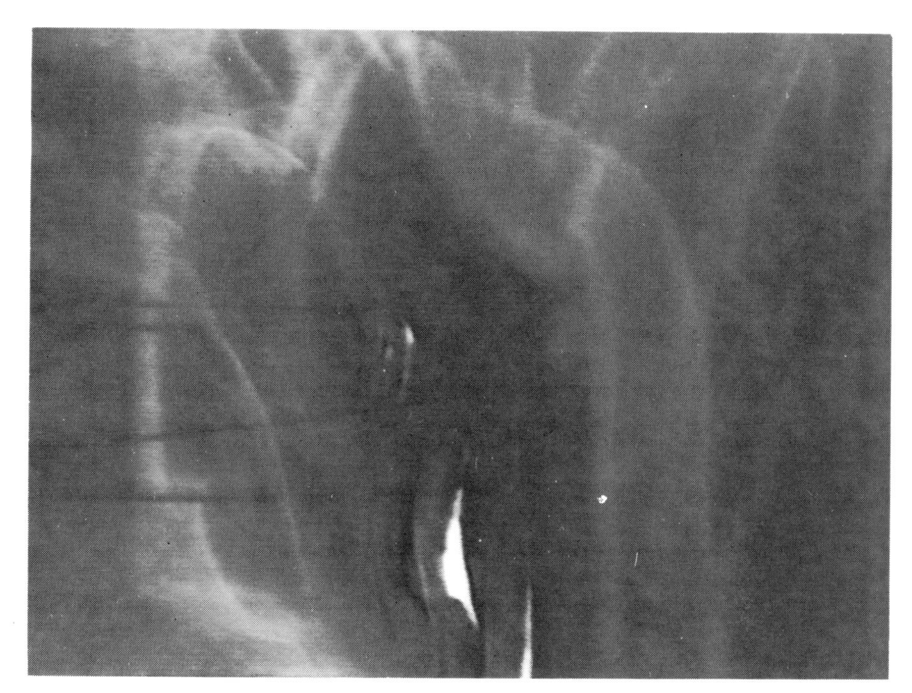

Fig.4: Type B fire ball, stable for 10 seconds or more when there is a moderate airflow.

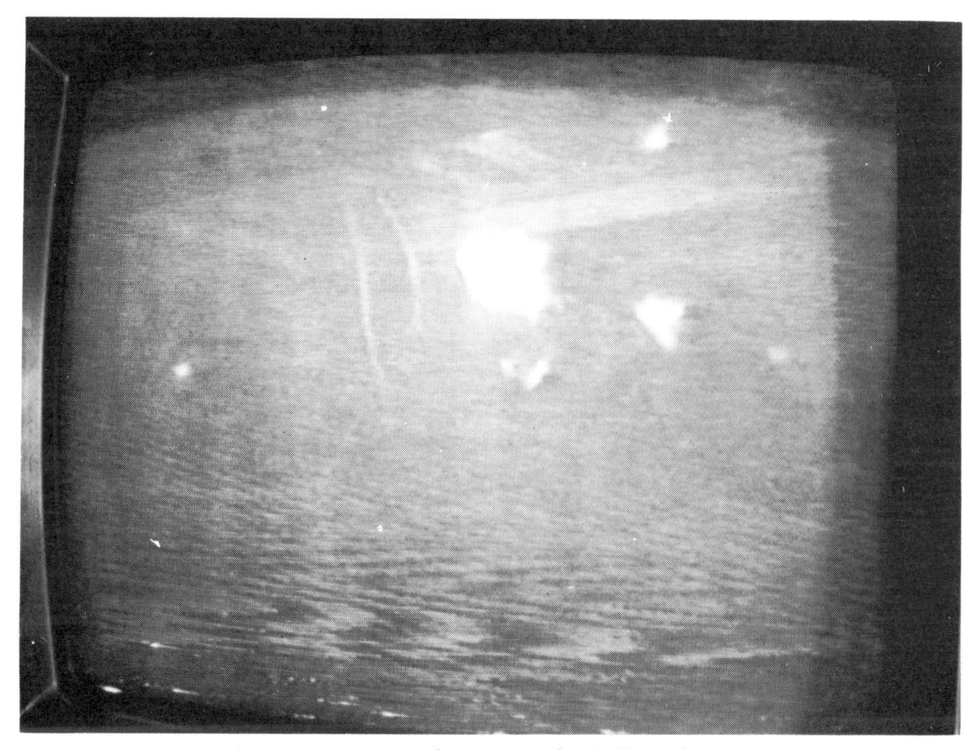

Fig.5: Laboratory creation of a rotating fire ball or plasma vortex.

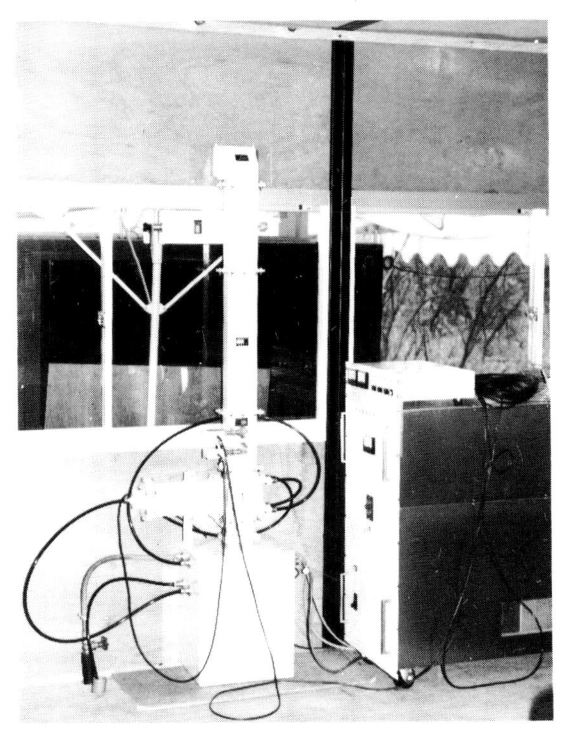

Fig.6a: Apparatus used for creating plasma in ordinary air by means of microwave interference.

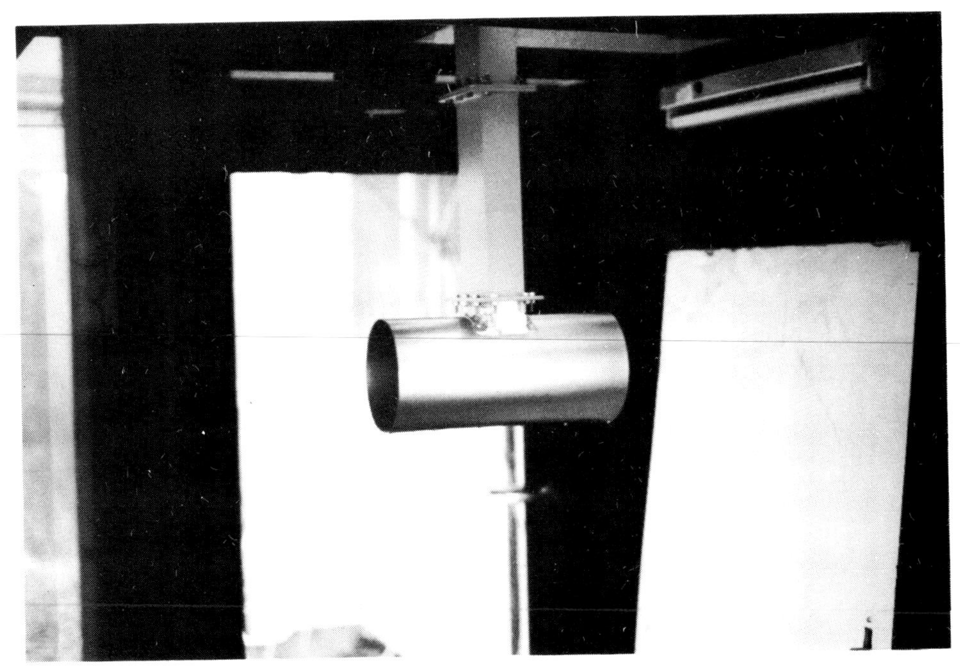

Fig.6b: Apparatus used for creating plasma in ordinary air by means of microwave interference.

2. *Micro-wave Interference*

The high-power micro-wave source ('Hinotama 89' MKN-503-3T) was constructed in 1989 in Tsukuba Science City near Tokyo and Narita. The magnetron YJ-1600 has a power of 5kW and a frequency of 2450 +/- 50MHz (12.2cm). The micro-wave was guided by the solid circuit for 2.7m by a linear wave-guide tube with two E corners.

Firstly, we set the semi-meshed cavity of the column-type made of copper (Figure 6). When increasing the power a small discharge was seen at about 1kW or more. At a power level of 2.2kW two types of flame of different colour appeared with a size of 5 – 10cm near the centre of the cavity. *This is important because we obtained the plasma in an atmosphere consisting of natural air.* By changing the interference conditions many possibilities exist for producing plasma fire balls.

REFERENCES

BARRY, J. D. (1980): *Ball lightning and bead lightning.* Plenum Press, New York.
MEADEN, G. T. (1989): *The circles effect and its mysteries.* Artetech.
NAGANOBU, M. (1988): *Science* (in Japanese). p.46, no. 9, 1988.

EHD VORTEX IN THE ATMOSPHERE WITH ELECTRIC AND SPACE-CHARGE FIELDS AND HELICAL TURBULENCE AND ITS RELEVANCE TO THE CIRCLES PHENOMENA

By HIROSHI KIKUCHI

SUMMARY

There are a number of atmospheric meteorological phenomena involving or accompanying electric discharge and ionization with electric and space-charge fields such as thunderstorms, cold and jet fronts, hurricanes and tornadoes including triggered and ball lightning or whirlwinds. For these phenomena, however, there have been few attempts to take this effect into account from the point of a unified clear view. This is because conventional hydrodynamatics (HD) breaks down for ionized gases, while even magnetohydrodynamics (MHD) is also not relevant for partially ionized, collisional or ionizing gases where the roles of electric and space-charge fields become significant, since conventional MHD does not take this into account.

To effect this, it seems that the following disciplines are required: (1) creation of a new theory of collision-dominant plasmas involving ionizations; (2) creation of a new theory of dusty or dirty plasmas containing charged dust grains or aerosols; (3) creation of a new electrohydrodynamics (EHD), or more generally, electro-magneto-hydrodynamics (EMHD) combining plasma physics and meteorology. Along this line, the author has introduced three novel concepts: (1) electric reconnection; (2) critical ionization velocity; (3) ponderomotive force that might play an essential role in treating *meteoro-electric phenomena* mentioned above and in establishing EHD or EMHD.

Electric (field) reconnection or merging occurs commonly when space charges are separated into a number of charge groups or clouds in the air like a system of miniature thunderclouds, accompanying tiny discharges between charge groups or parts of the clouds that may be triggered or facilitated by the EHD wind due to the ponderomotive force and its critical velocity, occasionally manifesting luminosity and noise, electro-magnetic and acoustic, as well as for the case of real thunderstorms. This is analogous to magnetic reconnection phenomena such as solar flares familiar to plasma physicists and geo-astro-physicists.

As is well known, the conventional neutral wind or flow is produced by the gradient of the mechanical gas pressure and the wind vortex by the rotation of flow, while the conducting or plasma flow and vortex are produced by the total of mechanical and magnetic forces, the latter being due to the gradient of the magnetic pressure. These HD and MHD vortices have been well investigated for large-scale structures and are presently the subject of active research for small-scale turbulence on the basis of the HD or MHD equations.

As mentioned above, meteoro-electric phenomena where electric and space-charge fields play a significant role must be treated in terms of a new EHD or EMHD, taking into consideration the electric or ponderomotive force that is the gradient of electric or radiation pressure. Along this line, the present paper first presents the fundamental equations of EHD and EMHD and considers on this basis meteoro-electric phenomena where the electric effect is large compared to the magnetic effect but for the initial state. Apart from specific models of atmospheric phenomena, we proceed to the essential and universal role of small-scale EHD helical turbulence in its energy transfer to coherent large-scale vortex structures in an EHD or EMHD regime with reference to *the circles-effect phenomena.*

In recent studies of self-organizational processes in nonequilibrium media, it has been shown that helical hydrodynamic or magnetohydrodynamic turbulence and/or some additional symmetry-breaking factors can lead to the generation of large-scale vortex structures and magnetic fields. Essentially all of the additional factors are of the nature of a release mechanism which makes it possible to pump some of the energy of helical turbulence into large-scale vortex structures and such a process has naturally been interpreted as a vortex dynamo.

In the present paper, we examine a small-scale helical turbulence with electrical and space-charge fields from the aspect of EHD rather than MHD. To effect this, fundamental equations of EHD proposed are employed in this context for the study of a new type of large-scale EHD vortex formation. A procedure similar to that for HD or MHD turbulence is applied to find the evolution of the instability, namely how it is accompanied by the transfer of energy from small-scale to large-scale sizes.

Special attention will be focussed on how initial EHD helical turbulence evolves into eventual *tubular vortex formation* in particular in the presence of an external axial electric field, for instance due to cloud-to-ground charges, and a geomagnetic field.

Some results obtained from the present and past studies, including triggered and ball lightning, will be applied to an attempt to indicate *the association of EHD vortices with circles-effect phenomena* as well as commenting on the electrical effects observed in some circles.

CROP CIRCLES: A SCIENTIFIC ANSWER TO THE UFO MYSTERY?

By PAUL FULLER and JENNY RANDLES

Abstract: This paper considers unusual atmospheric phenomena which, through lack of recognition and hence lack of understanding, have come to be classified as UFOs (unidentified flying objects), special attention being paid to the relationship that they bear upon the crop-circles problem within the wider UFO problem. The first part, Section A, introduces the subject of UFO research to the international community of meteorologists and physicists. We show that most UFO reports have relatively mundane explanations which leaves only a residue of cases, amounting to 5-10%, hitherto unexplained. Section B provides a brief summary of BUFORA's crop-circles research of the 1980's. Finally in Section C we demonstrate how Meaden's theory of natural atmospheric vortices with their accompanying electrical or plasma effects having provided a generalized solution to the crop-circle mystery seems also to explain many of the UFO reports which had until now not been understood. As a consequence we can say that UFO research in its own right is now dead and has become part of meteorology!

Section A: UFOs: A Modern Myth of Things Seen in the Sky

INTRODUCTION

"Nothing has come from the study of UFOs in the past twenty-one years that has added to scientific knowledge. Careful consideration of the record as it is available to us leads us to conclude that further study of UFOs probably cannot be justified in the expectation that science will be advanced thereby". (ref Condon report, p.1 – i.e the *very first page* of a 1000 page scientific report).

Thus read the opening gambit of the University of Colorado Report into Unidentified Flying Objects (UFOs), published in 1969 after an eighteen-month investigation funded to the tune of half-a-million dollars by the American public. The Condon Report, as it became known, posed a question that many millions of people all over the world have been asking themselves for more than four decades. 'Is man alone, or are there other life forms in the universe?'

In fact, we agree with one conclusion of the Colorado University Report. ET spaceships are not proven to be visiting us by the UFO evidence. However, we do contend that in choosing this approach the Condon Report asked the wrong question. We can demonstrate that with the following quotes from its pages:–

"This is one of the few reports in which all factors investigated, geometric, psychological, and physical appear to be consistent with the assertion that an extraordinary flying object . . . flew within sight of two witnesses". (Report on the McMinnville, Oregon, daylight photographs, 1950 . . . p.407).

"This unusual sighting should therefore be assigned to the category of some almost certainly natural phenomenon, which is so rare that it apparently has never been reported before or since". (Report on radar-visual from aircraft over Labrador, Canada, 1954 . . . p.140).

"In conclusion, although conventional or natural explanations certainly cannot be ruled out, the probability of such seems low in this case and the probability that at least one genuine UFO was involved appears to be fairly high". (Report on the Lakenheath, Suffolk, radar-visual case, 1956 . . . p.256).

"His superior officer declared that the trooper was dependable and truthful. His chief was convinced that this report of an UFO sighting was not the result of hallucination or dishonesty . . . With (the trooper's) approval a series of psychological assessment tests were administerd by project personnel and psychologists . . . In addition a test utilizing partial hypnotic techniques was conduced by Dr. Leo Sprinkle, Professor of Psychology, the University of Wyoming . . . Dr. Sprinkle expressed the opinion that the trooper believed in the reality of the events he described". (Report on Ashland, Nebraska, abduction of a police trooper, 1967 . . . p.390-1).

Unidentified Flying Objects (UFOs) are a subject that has provoked intense controversy for more than forty years in almost every developed nation on earth. From a scientific viewpoint, this fact is in itself a fascinating social phenomenon. Why do people report seeing UFOs? Why does the subject attract such massive media interest? And what are these people really seeing if they are not observing spaceships from another world?

The existence of such a belief-centred topic clearly fulfils a need for a large proportion of the population, whether or not they accept what is being reported. Every year, newspapers in Britain publicise thousands of UFO reports, almost invariably portraying them as sightings of "spaceships" or "craft". What is the truth behind these reports? And how can we – as people who study such reports – possibly justify our presence at an international conference debating unusual meteorological phenomena?

Let us start by looking at a case in point. It took place at 4am on 20th January 1988 on the coastal highway between Perth and Adelaide south of the Nullarbor Plain in Australia. The road was quiet but a couple of trucks and a car driven by the Knowles family from Perth were spread across several kilometres.

To cut short what was a protracted and quite frightening experience, here is a summary of what serious, dedicated investigators with the group UFO Research Australia found to have taken place.

The Knowles were on their way to pay a surprise visit to family in Adelaide during the country's Bi-Centennial celebrations. What they saw ahead of them on the road was little more than a funnel of light (described at closest approach as akin to an egg resting in a tapered egg-cup – or, in other words, something that looked suspiciously like a vortex funnel). This swayed about from side to side and was glowing but also disappeared from time to time.

During the most harrowing phase of the experience they felt the thing was actually on top of their car (although they saw nothing) and believed that the vehicle was literally sucked off the road for a time before being dropped down again. There were numerous peculiar effects, such as a strange smell (akin to bakelite) and a black powder which came into the car. Their voices also underwent a peculiar alteration in pitch as if responding to major pressure changes in the local atmosphere. In their panic to escape the UFO the car burst a tyre and careered off the road.

Some minutes later at the nearest town of Mundrabilla they met with local residents and the truck drivers (one of whom had seen the light in the distance as he passed the location). As daylight arrived these observers were able to attest to the fine dust, the smell and four small dents in the roof of the car. They could also tell that the family (mother and three adult sons) were evidently shaken by what had taken place.

The story was reported to police at the town of Ceduna that same morning and an investigation began. Unfortunately, a TV station heard about the matter and intercepted the family before they arrived in Adelaide. They were soon to find themselves tempted by the media interest.

Once they had given the TV station their exclusive story no time was wasted by the moguls in spreading this around the world. Britain was typical. BUFORA receives press cuttings via an agency and so we could monitor the reaction from all national and regional sources. This case generated almost 150 separate stories in such newspapers. Most British dailies carried it. This was the largest amount of publicity for any single UFO case yet on record within this country.

What were these stories like? The headlines all over the world followed a predictable trend. What the Knowles family had *simply reported* (quite honestly) *lights, smells and pressure forces,* these quickly escalated in some quarters into "craft" and "alien powers". The stories ranged across mildly presumptive yarns such as 'The pong from outer space' (a British tabloid) to another (German) source that reported (in somewhat of an exaggeration) how an 'alien beam' had 'destroyed' the Knowles car!

In other words, the case quickly became so far removed from the reality that even the witnesses might have struggled to recognise their own experience in some versions. The understandable reaction of most sensible folk, all serious media sources and virtually every scientist who heard this tale was to quickly forget about the hysterical nonsense and assume that it was reflective of what occurred and of no value whatsoever.

But the Mundrabilla case is worth re-examination in this light. The witnesses observed a glowing mass that is described as being like a vortex funnel. It moved like a tornado in its 'twisting' motion and there were signs of electrical ionization, upwards suction and downwards pressure, plus air pressure changes.

Indeed, one Adelaide university scientist, Professor Peter Schwerdtfergger, actually suggested at the time that a dry electrical storm might have caused the encounter. His views were widely dismissed by the media and more extremist UFO groups, but rational ufologists subsequently uncovered several reports from other motorists out on that same night which may well support the meteorological connection. Most notable was one driver on the same road close to the time of the UFO encounter who reported suddenly striking hurricane force winds that disappeared as quickly as they arrived. What if some sort of vortex were passing through the area and the Knowles family just happened to come into direct proximity whilst this was visible and at peak intensity? What would they have reported? We believe they would have described the UFO encounter they DID report; the one that came to imply aliens and spaceships in the minds of others and provoked media stories which grew like a fisherman's tale as they spread all over the world.

The outcome of this case shows in microcosm the problems that we face when trying to understand the UFO phenomenon. Careful investigation has offered numerous clues which suggest to rational investigators that a natural, atmospheric solution could be very feasible. But by the time it was possible to document the case it had already become so distorted by media representation that all hope of scientific interest had long since disappeared. Only ufologists were left to preserve data and, for perhaps understandable reasons, some ufologists frequently record cases with other motives in mind and so are not always the best judges of scientific reliability.

Yet amidst all the hyperbole there is a nugget of evidential truth to this case, just as there is with so many others. It can lead us into new research about the forces at work within our atmosphere. But to do so, many prejudices must be overcome and it remains a tragedy for modern science that the bizarre ideas and wild theories of a few ufological mavericks who may profess to be 'circle research scientists' can prevent mainstream analysts in atmospheric physics and meteorology from looking at the gold-dust within the UFO evidence that is waiting to be discovered.

THE EVIDENCE

The purpose of this paper is to introduce the international meteorological community to the UFO subject and to suggest areas of work where ufologists and meteorologists can collaborate. We believe that it is our scientific duty to acquaint meteorologists with the useful evidence that some ufologists collect and to disseminate to a wider audience the results of our years of endeavour. It is our belief that many cases exist in the UFO literature that deserve careful scientific scrutiny by specialists in the atmospheric sciences, but we reject through solid evidential grounds the popular belief that the reports represent encounters with an alien technology. The harsh truth is that ufologists normally deal with reports of phenomena that look much more like the piece of movie film here described.

This film was taken by building surveyor Peter Day at Cuddington, Buckinghamshire on 11th January 1973, at about 09.00 hrs, and is fairly typical. There is no alien spaceship with whirling antennas and bug-eyed aliens. The film merely depicts a pulsating orange ball of light that drifted across the sky and was observed for at least two minutes by Mr. Day before he was able to stop his car and film it. Fortuitously, the object was observed by two groups of independent witnesses at the same time that Peter Day was recording the object on film. Using triangulation we know that the object was at least three quarters of a mile from the cameraman and that it was probably less than two thousand feet above the ground. One of the independent witnesses, teacher Elizabeth Thompson, reported that the object was round like a ball on top, but flattened on the bottom. She reported that the object appeared to be spinning rapidly. (ref: – "Fire in the Sky, The Buckinghamshire UFO Movie Film", BUFORA 1989).

Unlike many UFO reports, there is no doubt in this case that something odd was definitely seen in the sky. The key question that remains is what was it?

A number of possibilities have been suggested, including a helicopter with an orange flashing light on top, a jet aircraft on 'after burn' and – almost inevitably – 'ball lightning'. BUFORA have spent seventeen years investigating this case, but have yet to provide a definitive solution. However, we can suggest some answers. The UFO may have been ignited jet fuel trapped by unusual meteorological conditions, but it seems far more likely to have been a rare atmospheric process. In 1978, Jenny and a colleague arranged for a behind-closed-doors showing of this film to a dozen atmospheric physicists from leading British research institutes (such as Harwell). This was at the Kodak Laboratories in north London. The consensus view of these experts was that ball lightning was *not* the object on the film. One scientist actually told Jenny – 'Why be frightened of calling it a UFO. That's what it is!' She had used the term UAP (Unidentified Atmospheric Phenomenon) to avoid the misleading spaceship imagery that UFO conjures up. However, every scientist refused her offer to take the film back for detailed analysis in their laboratories. One even said; 'I would be afraid for my next research grant if I had to justify the study of UFOs'.

Although the Peter Day film has never been satisfactorily explained, it is atypical because mere lights in the sky are nearly always explicable after proper scientific investigation and offer little in the way of evidence for the existence of novel new phenomenon. These UFOs quickly become IFOs – or Identified Flying Objects, and skeptical ufologists have learnt to treat them with only passing interest. Typical misperceptions range from aircraft lights seen under unusual circumstances, bright stars and planets and meteors, through to more unusual stimuli like satellite debris re-entering the atmosphere, gas clouds released by rockets as part of scientific experiments, and even owls that glow in the dark after consuming diseased fungi! (See some good examples in: *Spooklights,* David Clarke and Granville Oldroyd).

However, we do have some good cases that are slightly more tangible. A series of photographs taken by a research team setting up a meteorological station on the uninhabited Trindade Island in south Atlantic is a case in point. They were shot by the official photographer aboard this converted Brazilian Naval Vessel taking part in an International Geophysical Year project on 16th January 1958. Many of the crew saw the object also and there were reported electrical failures on board as it drifted by. The photographs clearly depict a

Saturn-shaped mass that seems to be comprised of fuzzy particles. There are grounds for suspicion that these were dust particles attracted into this particular shape by a strong electromagnetic field. In other words, this may well be a genuine unknown atmospheric process at work.

By seeking explanations for UFO reports, skeptical ufologists have established the following 'Facts of Life' about UFOs:

UFO Fact of Life Number 1:

As many as 90 – 95 percent of reported UFO sightings are not unidentified in any true sense of the word after careful investigation. They are merely *believed* to have been unexplained at the time of the event by someone unfamiliar with the manmade or natural phenomenon that was misperceived. This finding is universal, and is replicated by many official and civilian UFO statistics:–

(a) During 1976 the US Centre for UFO Studies paid a professional astronomer, Allan Hendry, to investigate UFO reports full time for a year. Hendry's job was to try and find explanations for the 1,307 UFO sightings reported via the centre's toll-free telephone line by contacting airports, the police, military bases, meteorological organisations and employing simple common sense. Hendry found that almost 90 per cent of reported UFOs were simply nocturnal lights, and of these 90 per cent were immediately explicable. Of his entire sample of 1,307 cases, only 113 reports (8.6%) remained unexplained after investigation, and even some of these suggested evaluations that could not be proven. The number of unexplained cases in this sample continues to fall as new data become available.

(b) Between 1975 and 1979, the Northern UFO Network received 1,051 reports of UFOs, which were investigated and evaluated by several groups of responsible ufologists located in the north of England. Only 155 (14.8 per cent) of these reports were judged to be unknowns (i.e. no identification could be suggested). It should be stressed that these groups did *not* have the resources available to Hendry to search for all resolutions . The remainder break down as in Table 1:–

Table 1:

Aircraft	312	Electric Sparks	3
Insufficient Data	111	Airship	2
Meteors	84	Insect Swarm	2
Stars	57	Aurora	1
Balloons	53	Dog	1
Satellites	48	Film Fault	1
Helicopters	38	Frost	1
Optical Phenomena	20	Fungi	1
Venus	20	Jupiter	1

Continued on next page

Birds	20	Lens Flare	1
The Moon	18	Mist	1
Hoaxes	17	Model Aircraft	
Flares	14	Sunspot	1
Ball Lightning	12		
Clouds	11	TOTAL EXPLAINED	896
Psychological	10		
Ground Lights	9	TOTAL (SO FAR) UNEXPLAINED	155
Vapour Trails	9		
Fires	4	TOTAL	1,051
Kites	4		
Fireworks	4	Ref:–	
Space Debris	4	UFO Reality, Jenny Randles, Robert Hale 1983 page 26	

* 'Insufficient Data' was only adopted if the original investigators and a subsequent evaluator could not agree on an evaluation.

UFO Fact of Life Number 2:–

Our first 'fact of life' tells us that up to 95% of the *millions* of people now known to have claimed UFO sightings from every civilised nation on earth are reporting 'evidence' of craft and intelligences (usually aliens in spaceships) that simply do not exist. This indicates that there is a subconscious model common to 20th century society which dictates what UFOs must look like, what they can do and what they represent. This cultural stereotype is the result of one-thousand-and-one science fiction films, books, newspaper stories and TV features that promote the myth that UFOs represent alien intelligences.

Let us examine a few examples of this process in operation.

(a) Allan Hendry found that many UFO witnesses were being fooled by Advertising Planes. These are small light aircraft which display a bank of multi-coloured lights on the underside of their fuselages which flash in sequence (they are much less known in Britain). When seen at dusk, and down wind, these displays appear very peculiar and are almost always described by witnesses as a silent and rotating disk rather than a row of flashing lights. A high proportion of these witnesses reported that they could actually *see* the saucer shape of the UFO, which they believed to be rotating, even though all they were really seeing was an aeroplane with some fancy lights. This proves that in general, witnesses "read in" a model of what they believe UFOs are (alien spaceships) and what they think UFOs look like (circular craft). Figure 1 (opposite) shows a typical selection of sketches made by these witnesses of what they saw. Remember, in *every case* Hendry proved conclusively that all that was really seen was a small light aircraft with a display of flashing lights.

(b) In December 1987, hundreds of witnesses in the English Midlands were fooled into reporting UFOs by a United States Air Force in-flight refuelling exercise involving a giant tanker aircraft surrounded by numerous small jets.

This procedure is now occurring with increasing frequency and requires a large array of dazzling lights to reduce the risk of mid-air collision. At ground level, the exercise takes on the appearance of a single very low and immense object (rather than several relatively smaller objects flying together at great height), yet many observers falsely 'saw' this as a circular UFO. Both the Ministry of Defence and BUFORA noted that a refuelling exercise overflew the area at the precise time that these witnesses were reporting UFOs, but our solution for the sightings was met with disbelief by the media. Many witnesses were stimulated by the media view that if you see a UFO you are 'normal' but if you mistake a mundane phenomenon then your intelligence must be called into question. So they preferred to believe that they had seen

Fig. 1: How the eye can be deceived. Typical sketches drawn by witnesses who believed they were observing UFOs. Note how these (American) witnesses believe UFOs to be circular-shaped 'craft' with a row of 'portholes'. *Every single one* of these witnesses was in fact observing *small light aircraft* with a row of sequentially flashing lights displayed on the fuselages, seen downwind and under poor lighting conditions.

something unusual, rather than face up to the fact that they had simply been deceived by their senses, as indeed we all are from time to time.

(c) On New Years Eve, 1978, hundreds of people all across northern Europe were fooled by the spectacular re-entry of a Soviet satellite – COSMOS 1068 – which plummetted to earth and burnt up above northern Europe at about 19.05 hrs GMT. The British UFO Research Association subsequently collected almost 200 reports from witnesses spread across Britain. Jenny Randles analysed a hundred of the best reports and found that although the majority of witnesses correctly reported parameters like the time of the event, the direction that the object followed (from north-west to south-east), and the reported duration, on the other hand the witness *descriptions* of what had seen differed considerably, e.g.

'a railway carriage blazing with light from its windows',
'a ball surrounded by a glowing trail of light',
'a solid, metallic object with a row of windows',
'a Russian spaceship with ionic propulsion steamers'.

Again the tendency for witnesses to 'read in' a structured object behind what was simply a trail of blazing debris is obvious. These examples (and there are many more) conclusively demonstrate that many people *want* to believe in UFOs (often as spaceships) and that they already *know* what they are supposed to be reporting (i.e. circular-shaped 'craft') because the stereotype is engrained within society. We suggest that the need to believe in something utterly fantastic is a basic human requirement which *masks and distorts* what UFO witnesses are really seeing. This need to report sightings of 'alien craft' in turn feeds all the major media outlets, which greatly reinforces the cultural stereotype that UFOs are spaceships. The whole thing becomes a vicious circle that self-generates a modern mythology. We suggest that this belief system (which is all it really is) is directly responsible for the understandable dismissal of the serious side of the subject and the hard evidence which *does* exist by the Scientific Community.

UFO Fact of Life Number 3:–

The UFO Myth (that UFOs are 'spaceships') began in 1947 when a private pilot (Kenneth Arnold) observed a formation of crescent-shaped objects over the Cascade Mountains of Washington States, USA. A journalist reported on this account (where Arnold termed what he saw as *flying* 'like saucers when skipped across water' – or – perhaps more familiar to most of us – skipping a flat stone across the surface of a lake). The reporter used the term 'flying saucer' referring to this motion but almost everyone who subsequently heard the tale assumed that 'flying saucer' described the objects *shape.* Artist reconstructions, science-fiction movies and (much more importantly) thousands of witnesses started to literally *depict* UFOs *as* saucer shaped. In other words we know for certain that a key tennet of the UFO myth (the reputed saucer shape) is not a real feature of the phenomenon at all, but an accidental consequence of a chance phrase used to describe something else altogether. This effect of social trends moulding and, to a large extent, *controlling the form* of the phenomenon can be seen repeatedly within the evidence.

UFO Fact of Life Number 4:–

UFO reports are not a new phenomenon. Reports of unexplained aerial phenomena have been made throughout history, and can be found by any historian searching through the archives. Here are some examples:

(a) In 329 BC, as Alexander the Great attempted to cross the river Jaxartes into India, two large "shining silver shields" suddenly appeared, repeatedly shooting across the sky and causing elephants and horses to panic.

(b) At Basel, Switzerland, at sunrise on 7th August 1566, numerous large black, red and orange fiery globes appeared in the sky, dancing around in irregular motion and eventually fading away.

(c) In 1897, thousands of people in the United States reported seeing giant 'airships', with blinding lights, cavorting across the skies. This was repeated in 1913 in Britain and Winston Churchill even debated the 'UFOs' in parliament on the premise that they were German blimps on pre-war spy-missions. History subsequently proved this was impossible and some of the sightings at least are now known to have been hoaxes and triggered responses to mundane stimuli (e.g. Venus).

In other words, the exact same observational and social principles were turning natural lights in the sky into other more structured phenomena long before the terms flying saucer and UFO were invented.

People interpreted what they saw as signs from God (or the Devil!) during the Middle Ages, fantastic airships by secret inventors during the latter part of the last century, and phantom weapons and rockets from Nazi Germany during and immediately after World War Two. 1947 appears to be a watershed merely because it is the time when the current social myth (that UFOs are spaceships) took hold of the evidence and turned these same simple light phenomena into sightings of alien spacecraft. *This social myth has masked a very real atmospheric phenomenon and we may now be seeing the incorporation of the crop circles into an updated version of the same cosmic myth.* This is why we face a crucial time in which we suggest Terence Meaden has pointed out the scientific phenomenon at the heart of all these myths. As it may now lie in transition (from alien spaceships to cosmic forces creating mystic crop marks) we have an opportunity and a responsibility to establish this evidence within our society as a scientific fact, not as a continuing science-fiction fantasy.

We must remember that science is not at the summit of knowledge. This is a mistake every generation makes, only for its folly to be demonstrated when new facts, new theories and new phenomena are discovered and become integrated into a consensus world view. Let us take an example.

For many years astronomers denied the fact that people saw meteorites fall to earth because, they insisted, stones did not exist in the sky and could therefore not fall to earth. It took someone from another branch of science entirely to *prove* that meteorites were extra-terrestrial and so *had to come* from space. This realisation was a paradigm revolution, because it rocked established ideas about the solar system and opened up a new field of astronomical research. Yet meteorites, like many other phenomena, obviously existed even before they were understood or adopted as part of scientific dogma. Rainbows were seen long before mankind had the physics to explain them. The sun was deified long before we came up with a theory of nuclear reaction to show how it functioned.

This is the reality of the UFO mystery. We believe that it may take meteorology to play the role of devil's advocate and show many other fields of science that UFOs represent novel new phenomena of potential scientific value.

Section B. BUFORA's Crop Circles Research

BUFORA first became involved in the crop circles mystery almost by accident, when the first modern circles appeared at Westbury (Wiltshire) in 1980). From the very beginning, both the media and UFO believers began promoting them as the result of an 'intelligence', despite a complete lack of supporting evidence. This demonstrates how a large section of modern-day society *wants* to believe in the impossible, even without evidence to support such beliefs, and how other groups take advantage of such needs for possibly more selfish motives, e.g. promotion of their ideology.

For this reason, we have always been very conscious that hoaxing must be an important factor in our understanding of the phenomenon, and would grow alongside the escalation of media attention. This is because the myth that UFOs are alien spaceships is very appealing and several groups exist which have powerful vested interests in promoting this and opposing any rational solution.

Ian Mrzyglod, of the PROBE team (an erstwhile sister group to BUFORA) first contacted Dr. Meaden in 1980 and began exchanging information about the crop circles that were appearing in the West Country. Mrzyglod discovered and later exposed the first major crop circle hoax in 1983, although he gave up the subject around that time, when he realised that his attempts to bring rationality to corn-circle research was being completely ignored by the British media. Jenny was first widely quoted in the national press *(Daily Express)* that same summer supporting the embryonic research of Terence Meaden, and so our involvement predates that of certain self-styled 'experts' who have recently begun to attract huge media attention. Our concern from the very start was to challenge the media claim that UFOs in the mythical sense were responsible and so encourage a more rational approach to the problem.

We have both always considered that there must be a 'natural' solution to the phenomenon, and we have spent a decade trying to educate the media towards that view. This has resulted in a long-standing battle with other ufologists who are reluctant to consider less exotic solutions to the mystery. At times this has been acrimonious and we have been widely accused of spoiler tactics and both jealousy and rivalry with these ufologists. Frankly, we reject that claim as we have no personal grievances, as such. However, we believe it was our duty to speak out and that the evidence is what matters, not what some more esoteric-minded ufologists choose to read into that evidence. We have no desire to descend into personality squabbles, but cannot apologise for pointing out what we perceive as fallacies when made in public view by influential pundits.

We have successfully promoted our point of view via many media sources. Our success has, however, been completely ovewhelmed by the current wave of publicity surrounding the phenomenon which frequently makes both absurd and demonstrably untrue statements about the circles. It seems that all our efforts, dating back over the past decade, have been largely swamped by the typical desire (of media, ufologists and many members of the public) to *want* an exotic explanation for the circles to be proven.

We should stress that, although our work has often been conducted through the medium of BUFORA and possibly represents a consensus view amongst our investigators (certainly a quite widely held one), our stance is *not* a position that is adopted by all members of our group (which holds no corporate opinions). We recognise that there are BUFORA members who disagree with our views and we are happy for this disagreement to continue along with fair and reasoned debate.

During the past decade, BUFORA members have monitored crop circle sites, conducted on-site investigations, followed up spurious UFO reports that have been associated with the appearance of the crop circles, and carried out the first major survey of the crop circles with the Tornado and Storm Research Organisation in 1987. In 1986 we produced a 28-page booklet *Mystery of the Circles,* which we circulated free to every newspaper in Fleet Street and which attempted to dispell the myths that the media were foisting on the phenomenon. In 1989 we produced a much expanded report *Controversy of the Circles,* which examined the social history of the subject, the characteristics of crop circles, and independently evaluated all the major theories that have been proposed to account for the phenomenon. We have also been responsible for investigating a number of associated anomalous events, such as the Marple 'Hay Fall' and the Little Hayward case, which we believe have direct relevance to our understanding of the natural atmospheric mechanism that lies behind the crop circles.

Our decade of crop circles research has resulted in the following findings:

1. A Minority of Crop Circles are Hoaxes

We know that some crop circles are proven hoaxes, with the culprits confessing to their hoaxes after their activities have been exposed. These proven hoaxes include:–

– Westbury 1983 (a quintuplet formation), which was created by a national newspaper in an attempt to fool a rival newspaper into falsely reporting a 'UFO landing';

– the 1986 Cheesefoot Head number 2 formation (a ringed circle), which was created by four farmhands in less than twenty minutes next to a major road in broad daylight (their hoax was sufficiently convincing that it passed off as 'too uniform and perfect to be part of some hoax' to a certain researcher who examined it shortly afterwards);

– a number of other formations that appeared during the 1989 media hype surrounding the launch of a popular book on the subject. We believe the media publicity inspired copycat hoaxing at an unprecedented level during that year.

We also suspect that a number of hoaxes are appearing that are not being identified as hoaxes, because of the difficulties serious researchers of the subject have in locating circles before they are harvested or well trampled by visitors. Our understanding of these hoaxes and media demonstrations of circle-making have convinced us of our second finding, although tempered by the knowledge that at least one superficially genuine-looking circle has been privately admitted to us (and we accept the admission) as being a hoax.

2. Hoaxed Circles are 'different' from Genuine Circles

We believe that although there are proven hoaxes occurring (probably several every summer), a genuine primary phenomenon is being reported throughout Britain (and indeed, the world). This genuine phenomenon seems to differ from the man-made creations across a range of characteristics:–

TABLE 2: Differences between hoaxed circles and the "real" circles.

	Genuine Circles	*Hoaxed Circles*
1. Swirl Pattern	Always present in one form or another	Not Present or only partially covers affected area
2. Layering Effects	Usually Present	Never present
3. Banding Effects	Always Present	Present but not very uniform
4. Condition of crop	Usually undamaged	Stems usually broken Heads damaged
5. Shape	Usually 'elliptical' or almost circular	Either perfectly circular or clearly misshapen (e.g. kink outer ring)
6. Position of Spiral Centre	Usually offset from the geometrical centre, but can be dead-centred	Usually dead centred

Continued on next page

7. Type of Formation	All Types	Some evidence of restricted range
8. Damage to Ground ?	No	Sometimes hole is apparent at centre; sometimes evidence of footmarks
9. Residual electromagnetic effects	Present	Absent
10. Conditions of Surrounding Crop	Undamaged	Tracks marks and footprints evident
11. Degree of publicity	Only 10% are reported	Most receive wide-spread publicity
12. Time of discovery	Usually overnight	Usually during the day

We would also like to say that our conclusions here differ somewhat from Dr. Meaden's because we believe that hoaxing is a rather more important aspect of the phenomenon than he recognises and may be responsible for some of the complex formations that seem to become 'fashionable' during any given summer. It must surely be relevant that some of the best known UFO hoaxes involved the manufacturing of circular marks (e.g. the 1968 Ohio College hoax, which achieved nationwide publicity within 48 hours). Again, the fact that hoaxers create circular "ground traces" clearly demonstrates that hoaxers know what UFOs are supposed to be (spaceships) and what shape UFOs are. We wonder how significant it is that a recent well-known, supposedly bona-fide UFO case in America involves an unassuming man taking dozens of photographs of 'spaceships' and thus provoking an enormously lucrative debate about their nature (with books, TV series and media features already generated). This case – whatever its status ultimately proves to be – included a burnt circular patch in a field.

3. The BUFORA/TORRO Survey

In late 1986 we recognised that our assessment of the genuine crop-circle phenomenon was being distorted. We were particularly concerned with the apparent "evolving" of formation types, from simple single circles (1980), to linear triplets (1981), quintuplets (1985) and circles with rings (1986). Although we were happy to consider Dr. Meaden's meteorological explanation for the primary phenomenon, we maintained that a 'natural' phenomenon would not "evolve" in this manner. We suggested that unless examples of the more complex formation types could be discovered before the advent of the modern crop-circles problem (1980), then this could be indicative of hoaxing for the more complex formation types.

In early 1987 we carried out a sample survey of cereal holdings in the English County of Hampshire (where many circles were being reported), with a complementary sub-survey at other locations known to be producing circles. The survey produced the following findings:

(a) The media report a *biased sample* of those crop circles that are actually appearing (i.e. they tend to report only the more exciting formation types at the expense of single circles, because single circles are not as evocative as quintuplets, triplets and ringed formations and are also 'old news').

(b) We discovered accounts of two formations that had not been previously reported (a triangular triplet and a regular quadruplet), thus suggesting that further formation types existed which had yet to be reported (a finding that has been proven by the discovery of many new formation types since 1987 and one type which we found in our historical literature survey of 1989 – a quintuplet of rings – which appeared once in the USA but not so far in the modern data).

(c) We produced a statistical estimate for the mean frequency of the mechanism that creates crop circles (one mechanism every 349 square kilometres per year).

(d) We found that only ten per cent of the reported formations had been reported to investigative agencies (the media, police, or meteorologists), thus implying that large numbers of crop circles were appearing but were not being reported (landowners rightly fear a media-inspired invasion of their crops).

(e) We uncovered evidence that the farming community were HAPPY to accept both a meteorological solution and hoaxing, despite claims being made by certain other circles researchers that 'no farmers accept' a meteorological solution.

TABLE 3: Numbers and proportions of responses to the question "The following explanations have all been proposed for the 'mystery circles'. Please indicate by ticking which explanations you believe are the most likely".

	Hoaxers	*The Weather*	*U.F.O.s*
Yes	29 (32%)	19 (21%)	3 (3%)
No	8 (9%)	9 (10%)	15 (17%)
Don't Know	18 (20%)	15 (17%)	16 (18%)
No Response	35 (39%)	47 (52%)	56 (62%)
Totals	90 (100%)	90 (100%)	90 (100%)

(Respondents could tick more than one box)

A chi-squared test of the difference between the proportions of farmers accepting the Weather and Hoaxers proved Not Significant. Chi-squared tests of the difference between the proportions accepting the Weather and UFOs, and the proportions accepting Hoaxers and UFOs were statistically significant at the five per cent level. These results were true when the Non Respondents were both included and excluded.

We suggest that these findings based on the opinions expressed by responding farmers, were consistent with our hypothesis that the crop circles are created by a rare 'natural' phenomenon being mimicked by hoaxing.

4. Other Findings

Throughout our decade of research we have tried to evaluate Meaden's developing meteorological mechanism to the best of our ability. We have made constructive criticism where we felt that the theory was lacking and we have searched for historical evidence that might support it. In particular we have:

(a) researched a hay fall case at Marple, Chesire (June 1988), where a standing vortex sucked up hay into a discus-shaped mass (resembling a 'flying saucer') and then transported it over a distance of at least a kilometre before dropping it on astonished local residents. This event reputedly left a single circle in long grass and was associated with sensations of air pressure felt by witnesses;

(b) researched the 'Mowing Devil' case of August 1678, reported to us first by a reader of our work, and which appears to be a historical account of a multiple crop-circle formation in Hertfordshire;

(c) discovered accounts of at least a dozen other crop circles in Britain which predate the modern crop-circles myth and which were all reported to UFO organisations or the press at the time (thus excluding the possibility of retrospective hoaxing). Significantly, every one of these pre-1980 formations was located away from Wessex, thus proving that the alleged concentration of circles in the "Wessex Triangle/Corridor" is an illusion fostered by the media and some researchers. Many of these formations were complex patterns, thus proving that the alleged evolution of formation types is also a result of media bias and sampling errors;

(d) discovered more than 20 'new' cases of crop circles from around the world. These included crop circles in Australia, Brazil, Canada, New Zealand, South Africa, Sweden, Uruguay and several states in the USA.

Our 1989 report *Controversy of the Circles* discussed a number of agricultural factors that we believe may have affected the ability of mature arable crops to record the presence of what we call, for expediency, the Meaden Vortex, thus leading to the apparent upsurge in reported formations. These factors are discussed in our new book *Crop Circles, A Mystery Solved,* where we suggest that the introduction of winter crops, with more closely packed stems, higher head-to-stem weight ratios and more intensive pesticide-treatment levels have all contributed to this greater vulnerability of British crops.

Although we have questioned Dr. Meaden's atmospheric vortex theory in the past, we now accept that he has provided the only scientifically-falsifiable theory that is:–

– backed up by consistent eye-witness accounts of a revolving mechanism that hums or buzzes,

– appears under consistent meteorological and topographical conditions,

– is supported by independent observations of wind vortices remaining stationary and forming in multiples,

– has historical and international precedents for most reported formations,
– has the cautious backing of other meteorologists!

5. The "UFO" Connection

Although we have emphasised that most UFO reports are explicable, and that the few reports which remain unexplained are NOT spaceships, we have come to realise that Meaden's Vortex Mechanism is – at least technically – an unidentified flying object. Remember (section A), UFOs are really just unidentified atmospheric phenomena (UAP). A previously unrecognised vortex mechanism with unusual electrical properties clearly meets this definition, and puts paid to the unjustified dismissal by science of UFOs per se in the wake of the Colorado University Report. We have published a book which dispells all the recent media hysteria surrounding the crop circles and which applies Dr. Meaden's challenging new theory to those remaining unexplained cases. We believe that he has discovered a novel atmospheric force which clearly accounts for a major part of – and possibly all of – the unexplained UFO evidence including its more bizarre aspects. *Quite simply, we suggest UFO research in its own right is now dead and has become a part of meteorology!*

Section C. How Meaden's Theory Explains the UFO Phenomenon

In Section A we demonstrated how most UFO reports have relatively mundane explanations. In this last section we take a look at the reports which – until now – we have been unable to explain, and which seem to be genuine observations of novel new phenomena. We divide this section into four:

1. Ball Lightning and Super Ball Lightning
2. Car Stop Cases
3. CE IIIs and CE IVs (Abductions)
4. Summary

There are many strange things occurring in our atmosphere which currently defy proper scientific explanation. These events are in a very different class to the UFO reports we discussed earlier in this paper. They invariably include:–

– UFO events where ground traces are recorded, this includes circular patterns of the crop-circle type as well as other types of ground trace;

– UFO events where witnesses report severe physiological symptoms such as burns, headaches, nausea and amnesia; and

– UFO events where motor vehicles and other electrical equipment (e.g. radios) are impeded or affected in some way.

Usually these effects are transient and it is rare that ufologists have the opportunity to record permanently what has occurred. However, these cases offer real probative data which we suggest the scientific community has ignored at their peril. Skeptical ufologists use the term UAP – Unidentified Atmospheric Phenomenon – which is far less presumptive, as already discussed. We are convinced that the unexplained UFO evidence is really composed of several varieties of UAP, and that anything on the fringes of the atmospheric sciences is shunted into this area (and reported as a 'UFO') where science ignores its.

1. BALL LIGHTNING

UFO groups have hundreds of cases of objects that resemble ball lightning but which have been reported instead as UFOs. Here is a selection:–

(a) Shetland Islands, World War II

In the transmitter room of a secret radar station following a major thunderstorm a ball of fire entered via the feeder lines. After slowly drifting around the room it disappeared through the bulb on a metal lamp-bracket. The glass envelope surrounding the bulb simply evaporated (without any trace of molten or broken glass in its wake). The engineers were all puzzled as to why the ball – if normal electrical energy – did not 'earth' on the extensive and adjacent metal casing of the transmitter and instead traversed the length of the room to a small lamp-bracket.

(b) Katong, Singapore, 1953

This case came to our notice when Jenny had an article published in the *AIR UK* in-flight magazine. The witness had been in the RAF for 27 years and was with his wife and two other witnesses when the event occurred. Following a tropical storm which led to heavy flooding, the weather suddenly cleared (as dramatically as if they had passed into the eye of a hurricane). Suddenly, an orange 'cricket ball' appeared, nestling on the telephone wires behind their house. It was fuzzy-edged and made a loud hissing or fizzing sound. The object rolled gently along the wires and then curved off – floating through the sky and passing straight through the open louvre-shuttered windows. At such close proximity all four witnesses were able to observe the ball, which appeared more blueish-white than orange, with fluidic yellowish patches inside. The ball moved at slow walking pace about four feet off the ground and traversed the kitchen. As it passed within 10 feet of the refrigerator the motor began to shudder, accelerating and decelerating strangely. Also, despite the fact that all the house lights were switched off, they glowed a peculiar dull orange while the object was in the house. Even the fluorescent strip-tube lit up as the object drifted by. This UAP was inside the house for about 20 seconds and then arced back and disappeared through the same window. The four witnesses inspected the house but found no damage or scorching to windows or walls. All electrical equipment continued to function normally.

(c) Exhall, Warwickshire, 30th December 1977

At 16.30hrs on a cold, cloudy day, a golden ball of light appeared from a cloud and seemed to hover above some electricity pylons. It was surrounded by a shimmering haze and remained stationary for several moments before suddenly accelerating upwards into cloud. At the spot where the ball vanished, a distinct hole formed in the cloud cover and persisted for some minutes before gradually filling in. The hole was several times the diameter of the ball of light.

(d) Coniston, Cumbria, May 1980

Two well-qualified witnesses (husband and wife) were examining rocks on an iron-ore quarry site when an oppressive feeling akin to the approach of a thunderstorm came from nowhere. It was approximately 14.00 GMT on a sunny day. Coming down the hill slope was a small round object described as resembling a steel ball-bearing and covered by striations on its surface and surrounded by a hazy aura. This followed the precise contours of the land a few feet off the ground and emitted a penetrating humming sound which was almost at sub-audible levels. One witness said that the noise generated a terrible sense of doom and foreboding and was very painful. After hovering for about two minutes the ball suddenly shot upwards at terrific speed and the sound and oppressiveness disappeared instantly. The man (who was an engineer) went straight to the car and drove home, refused his wife's suggestion that they report the incident to the police and never discussed it again. His wife told the story to Jenny Randles for the first time when she appeared on BBC television discussing UAP some ten years after these events.

(e) Ilkley Moor/Wharfedale, North Yorkshire, November 1980

The location was Otley Chevin and the time 03.30 hrs. The witness was on his way to work when he observed a glowing egg-shaped object heading south-west over the River Wharfe. The object made crackling sounds "as if surrounded by lightning" and the treetops over which it floated glowed orange, indicating how low the object was. The object accelerated up into a cloud and disappeared. The witness immediately reported his observation to Otley Police and they confirmed that a patrol car had also chased the object that same morning.

(f) An Airfield in East Anglia, April 1984

Three air-traffic control officers observed an object in the sky which they at first thought to be an aircraft on approach. It was late afternoon on a sunny day and the reflective glow was taken to be sunlight from the metal frame of the aircraft. However, the object was 'landing' on the wrong runway and only after a few moments observation via binoculars did it become clear that this was not the aircraft (which was elsewhere in the sky making a correct approach). Some moments of panic ensued when it was thought that two planes were landing on intersecting runways at the same time. However, before a warning could be issued the 'UFO' (now visible through binoculars as an intensely-bright round ball that was generating its own light and looked like "a mass of crinkled paper rolled up") touched down on the runway and then immediately bounced upwards at a steep angle, streaking away into the sky. The incoming aircraft reported seeing nothing and made a safe landing minutes later. One of the air-traffic controllers became very distressed by this experience. Another tried to seek radar confirmation from a nearby military base (the airfield itself had no radar). However, the base was closed. After great discussion the officers decided *not* to file an air incident report because they considered this would be disbelieved. For this reason the precise location of the airfield cannot be revealed.

Meteorologists may or may not consider these reports to represent 'ball lightning'. However, our main point is not affected by this. Nearly all meteorologists will have never even *heard* of these cases, because they have been tainted with that emotive term UFO, and thus been ignored and discarded into the wastebin of science. We contend that this is a mistake on the part of science, although we recognise the reason why this has occurred.

These cases involved objects that glowed, moved independently, were sometimes associated with unusual electrical effects and were frequently seen to possess structure of some sort. Our concern is that some reports reported in a UFO context may contain data that would clarify the properties of ball lightning. It may be that extreme varieties are reported as UFOs, whereas meteorologists do not even realise that such extreme varieties exist because they were reported outside their scope and so never taken into account when drawing up what constitutes the parameters of ball lightning.

2. CAR STOP CASES

Vehicle Interference Cases are amongst the most fascinating UFO events being reported to UFO organisations. BUFORA compiled a catalogue of over 400 such events as long ago as 1976, from all over the world and dating back to the 1940s. These accounts normally involve moving automobiles, occur predominantly during the early hours of the morning, and frequently involve severe physiological effects on witnesses. The event normally begins with the sighting of an unusual luminous object (frequently egg-shaped), which 'homes in' on the witnesses and their car. This is quickly followed by the car engine losing power, headlights dimming, and static on the radio. Despite desperate attempts to regain power, car engines frequently stall and cannot be restarted whilst unusual luminous phenomena are observed close by. Here are some typical cases.

Case 1: Levelland, Texas 1957

Perhaps the most interesting car stop on record occurred at the small town of Levelland, Texas, on the night of 2/3 November 1957. Just before 23.00hrs, the duty police officer Patrolman A. J. Fowler received a telephone call from a farmhand, who had been driving about four miles west of the town when he suddenly saw a flash of light in a nearby field. The witnesses observed a strange luminous object rise from an adjacent field and move towards his vehicle (perhaps it was attracted by the metallic bodywork?). The UFO was torpedo-shaped, estimated to be 200 feet (60 metres) in length, and coloured white and yellow. As the object approached, the truck's lights went out and the engine died. The witness and his companion jumped out of the truck and hid underneath as the UFO passed overhead making a sound like "thunder" and "a rush of wind". Such was the disturbance that the truck itself rocked back and forth whilst both witnesses felt a sudden blast of heat. As the UFO disappeared into the distance, the truck's lights returned to normal.

Patrolman Fowler dismissed the call, thinking that the witness must be drunk. About an hour later, he received a second call, from one Jim Wheeler, who encountered a brilliantly lit 200-foot long egg-shaped object resting in the centre of the road four miles *east* of Levelland. As Wheeler approached, his car lights and engine failed. As the UFO ascended, his lights came back on again.

During the next two hours Patrolman Fowler received an additional eight reports of the egg-shaped UFO. In total ten vehicles stalled in the presence of unusual luminous phenomenon within a twenty-mile radius of Levelland in less than three hours. That ten vehicles should stall in the presence of an unusual luminous phenomenon in such a small location is unprecedented even in UFO lore, yet unless we resort to suggesting some massive conspiracy between apparently unconnected witnesses these events certainly seem to be consistent and totally independent observations of a genuine atmospheric phenomenon. In particular we note that the 'object' was associated with unusual winds, roaring sounds, and heat effects. It stalled car engines and dimmed their lights.

The weather conditions on the morning of these encounters were misty with slight rainfall. Astronomer Donald Menzel has pointed out that early November 1957 was one of the wettest periods on record for the Levelland region, with an unusually high number of electrical storms recorded. Menzel attributed the sightings to 'ball lightning' and the car stops to 'wet electrical circuits'. We contend that a Meaden Vortex is a more realistic explanation than the suggestion that ten independent motor vehicles all independently stalled due to 'wet electrical circuits' within a few hours of each other in the same general area.

Case 2: Aston Clinton, Buckinghamshire, 9th February 1962

A Mr. Ronald Wildman, who was delivering a new car from Swansea, was passing through Aston Clinton and Tringford, Bucks, at night when he saw a white oval light surrounded by a hazy mist and with dark blotches around the rim. His car suffered only partial impedance and the object brushed frost particles off nearby trees as it shot away. Nearly thirty years later, crop circles appeared less than three miles from this same location. Dr. Meaden has demonstrated that this car-stop case, the 1989 quintuplet at nearby Aylesbury, and the 1989 quintuplet west of Tring, all appeared in the lee of the Chiltern escarpment that traverses the location. (Ref: *The UFO Encyclopedia,* Margaret Sachs, Corgi Books 1981, pages 177-178).

Case 3: Hook, Hampshire, England, 26th October 1967

This case involved an engineer and manager of a transport firm, Mr. W. Collett, who was driving a converted Ford Transit minibus with a load of metal castings on the A32 north of Hook when the entire electrical system – engine, lights and radio – cut out. Presuming the cause to be a loose lead, Collett examined his car engine and checked the battery, spark plugs and distributor wires, noting that everything seemed to be connected properly.

However, the witness noticed an unusual dark mass in the sky ahead, but was more preoccupied with his engine fault and tried unsuccessfully at first to restart his engine. A minute or so later the engine did restart, but only a few hundred metres along the road the engine and lights again cut out. Again Collett got out of his cabin to check the engine. On this occasion he noticed something strange about the atmosphere, an oppressive feeling similar to the kind of sensation that we experience before a thunderstorm. Collett also described a kind of pressure which hurt his eardrums.

He was able to remedy this problem by blowing his nose, as one can do to avoid air-pressure difficulties in the ear. He then noticed an unusual smell, which he likened to arcing electrical equipment, or bakelite, but which he soon established was *not* coming from the engine (which still would not start).

The witness finally turned his attention to the object hovering immediately ahead of him. He described it as "like a squat ice-cream cone" (i.e. a typical vortex funnel shape), with a rim separating the domed top of the UFO from the tapered base. After a few moments the UFO drifted away over adjacent trees and Collett was able to resume his trip to the Midlands (a distance of almost 200 miles), which was completed without further incident. This event occurred at 04.30 hrs, when the weather was cold, clear and frosty. Again electrical impedance was associated with changes in air pressure, and after the encounter was over the witness reported a tingling numbness in his nerve endings and that a toothache from which he suffered had completely disappeared! We suggest that this UFO was surrounded by a strong electrical field which may have affected his nervous system.

Case 4: Sopley, Hampshire, 6th November 1967

Carl Farlow was driving a Leyland Comet diesel truck on a night-time delivery run down the A338 in Hampshire. He was between Avon and Sopley, heading south, and the weather was fine and dry, although it had been raining earlier in the day. As Farlow's truck approached a crossroads, his headlights began to dim and after a couple of seconds they faded altogether. Alarmed, Farlow brought his truck to a stop but left the engine running. At this point he noticed a large, purplish-red oval object to his right, moving slowly over the river across the road in front of him. The object was at the height of a telegraph pole and estimated to be about 80 feet long (say 24-25 metres. The

UFO made a continuous humming noise as it passed by and Farlow noticed a distinctive pungent burning odour, perhaps indicating the presence of ozone.

At this point the witness noticed that another vehicle was also involved in the encounter. This was a Jaguar with two occupants that had been approaching from the opposite direction. As the UFO disappeared the driver of the Jaguar (a vetinerary surgeon) approached Farlow and told him that his car had lost both its engine and lights as the object approached. His passenger had become hysterical. Both men rang the local police from a nearby telephone box, noting that the vet's hand-held torch failed to function (it had worked properly earlier that same evening).

When the police arrived both witnesses noticed that adjacent scrubland appeared brown and burnt, and that the tarmac road surface seemed to have melted at the spot where the UFO had hovered. Both men were taken to Christchurch Police Station and asked to sign statements, although the woman witness required overnight hospitalisation because of severe shock. The two men were later interviewed by officials from the Ministry of Defence.

The next day Farlow returned to Ringwood (north of the encounter) to collect some personal effects. He was driven past the scene of the encounter by the police, and was astounded to see that a bulldozer was levelling the ground where the grass had appeared burnt, two men were using a theodolite to take measurements of the road, and that the telephone box had been freshly painted. A week later Farlow returned to the spot and discovered that the road surface had been freshly covered for a distance of about 200 feet.

Thirty-six hours after the incident Farlow was allowed to collect his truck from the compound at Christchurch. The engineer told him that his electrical system was burnt out and that he needed a tow to start the lorry and had to drive very carefully to get home without mishap. The truck subsequently needed a new dynamo, starter motor, regulator, ammeter, battery and bulbs. The entire bill cost £400. (Ref: *Science and the UFOs,* Randles and Warrington, page 105-8).

Once again, two vehicles were involved in a car stop associated with a humming oval object. Like many of the other car-stop cases in the UFO literature, the event involved unusual smells (ozone?) and occurred in the early hours of the morning (when Meaden Vortices are most likely to form).

Case 5: Higher Chisworth, Derbyshire, 4th March 1968

The witness, a Mr. Burnell, was driving his new Triumph Spitfire sports car at about 21.00 hrs on a clear, dry night. A small golden ball of light appeared in the south (from the New Mills direction) and sped across the valley northwards towards the Longendale area. As the light passed by, the radio set became silent, the headlights failed, and the engine cut out suddenly. Moments later, with the light now receding into the distance, the witness was able to restart his car, although the radio set refused to work (and eventually had to be replaced). The location of the car stop was on the slopes of a prominent hill, less than two miles from where the Marple hay fall was to occur twenty years later (allegedly producing a small crop circle). Researchers Devereux, Clarke and Roberts note numerous UFO events in the Longendale area in their study *(Earthlights Revelation,* Cassell, 1989). South-west of here is Werneth Low, another prominent hill where at Christmas 1974 a vertical 'cloud cigar' was reported. The object had a flattened end and a tapering base, and changed shape several times before disgorging several small spheres "like soap bubbles being blown". Can it be a mere 'coincidence' that a major car-stop case and a crop circle all appeared in the same area, and on the lee of a prominent hill slope?

Case 6: Key West, Florida, USA, 1st January 1969

Two witnesses reported a sudden 'deep' sound overhead as a shower of needle-like hailstones struck their car. This shower was extremely localised and was immediately followed by a peculiar blast of warm air. The witnesses reported a sensation of "weightlessness" (i.e. as if they were in an elevator) and they also reported tingling, electrical vibrations all over the body (due to the electrostatic field?). Above their car they observed a silver glow and "a tapering funnel-like stream of light" descending on to their car. Again, all attempts to start their car during this event met with failure. We contend that contrary to the more popular interpretation that this was an encounter with a 'spaceship', these witnesses encountered an electrically-charged vortex accompanied by a fall of ice-needles and some peculiar suction effects.

Case 7: Nelson, Lancashire, 9th March 1977

At 03.10 GMT on the morning of 9th March 1977, shift workers Jeff Farmer and Brian Grimshawe drove home along the deserted streets of Nelson, a small industrial town set in the Lancashire hills. The two witnesses first observed a light drop from a cloud above nearby Pendle Hill, a location with a long-established tradition of witchcraft and supernatural events. The light descended and then moved slowly towards the witnesses, who halted their car to watch but left the dipped headlights and car engine running.

They later described the object as resembling a giant cigar, with beams of light at either end, which was surrounded by a 'grey mist' with thousands of multi-coloured lights or sparks glowing in the centre. As the UFO approached, the car headlights dimmed until they were almost out. Both men reported that the UFO emitted a low 'humming' sound followed by a noise 'like the tide coming in and out'. The light hovered directly above the car while the two witnesses desperately tried to restart the car engine. When this failed they both got out of the car and stood directly beneath the light. They described an unusual sensation of (air?) pressure pushing down on them 'like the wind'. They also reported a strange 'tingling' sensation which made their hair stand on end.

By now, both witnesses were panic stricken and got back into the car, which they still could not start. Slowly, the UFO drifted away, the car's headlights eventually regained their full power, and then the engine spluttered into life as the object disappeard. Both men subsequently developed nausea, pounding headaches and watery, reddened eyes, which lasted for several hours. It was later shown that the car radio had burnt out during the encounter. Scores of independent witnesses observed unusual lights in the Pennine region on the night of 8th-9th March. The car had been fully serviced only five weeks before the encounter. What kind of force stalls car engines, makes a low humming sound and causes severe physiological reactions to people who get too close? (Ref: *The UFO Conspiracy*, Jenny Randles, Blandford Press, 1987, pages 137-9).

Case 8: Barnard Castle, Co. Durham, 6th June 1977

At 23.30 hrs on a very wet night Mark Henshall, a young motorcyclist, was paced by some purple (nearly ultra-violet) lights and then, as a Jaguar car overtook him on an incline, he was struck by a dazzling beam from a purple-pink oval mass directly overhead. Both car and motorbike began to lose engine power and headlights, but neither failed completely. They seemed to be dragged *up* the hill for a couple of hundred yards by some unknown force and steam began to rise from the motorcycle as rainwater on the surface was rapidly heated. The rider took off his leather glove and felt the tank which was too hot to touch. Then, after only a few seconds, the light vanished and both vehicles regained normal power. They pulled to a halt and the two strangers discussed what they had seen. Unfortunately, the car driver was never traced but due to his more restricted view had reported to Henshall that he only saw the glare not the object itself. Next day the motorcyclist found that his brakes (which he instantly applied the moment the light appeared) were so worn as to be irreparable. His leather jacket and gloves had been 'steam-dried' to a wrinkled appearance by the heat. Upon arrival home the rider's mother commented immediately on how hot and flushed his face appeared. Over the next few days he suffered from headaches and sickness.

Case 9: Bellwood, Pennsylvania, USA, 15th October 1983

Catherine Burk was driving near her home in Bellwood at approximately 21.00 hrs. The weather was dull and threatening rain. While driving at 35mph, the witness became aware of "a loud, whirling sound" coming from her right side. She looked through the passenger window and observed a bright, silvery, saucer-shaped object that was flat on top but had a protruding hemisphere on the middle of the base. As the UFO passed slowly above the car, the vehicle was lifted off the road by several feet and the witness was thrown against the side door while she desperately tried to regain control of the vehicle. This 'levitation' (suction effect) only lasted a few seconds, and when the UFO released its grip the car fell back to earth with a bump and the engine cut out. The witness took twenty minutes to restart the car. She subsequently suffered hearing loss (due to air pressure?), severe headaches (as with the Nelson and Castle Barnard car stops), itching blisters (due to the electrostatic field?) and eye disorders. Perhaps the worst effect was that parts of her hair fell out, as if she had been exposed to an excessive dose of radiotherapy. All these effects are consistent with the strong electrically-charged mechanism being proposed by Dr. Meaden.

Case 10: Launceston, Tasmania, 14th December 1987

This case, investigated by Keith Roberts, of the Australian UFO Centre took place at 21.30 hrs. A grey egg-shaped UFO swooped down and 'landed' on the road ahead of a Mercedes car. Both engine and lights failed instantly, and the witness had to slam on the brakes to avoid running into the object. The UFO was so bright that the witness found it difficult to stare at the object for more than a moment or two. He then jumped out of the car and fled behind a tree, where he began to vomit (a symptom that persisted until the following day). The terrified witness watched his car being dragged along the road towards the UFO from behind the safety of his tree. The car left rubber tread and scuff marks on the road surface as it was dragged by some force towards the UFO.

It is time the ufologists and the meteorologists dropped their prejudices about these cases. They do not represent encounters with an alien intelligence. Neither are they the product of deranged minds and confabulation. Witnesses all round the world are reporting a consistent and perhaps disturbing (even dangerous) event, which involves a mechanism that hums or buzzes, often appears to be revolving, nearly always produces tingling sensations due to the presence of an electrostatic field, is sometimes accompanied by unusual odours, and which occasionally involves strong 'suction' effects caused by some force. We suggest that these accounts are entirely consistent with the mechanism Terence Meaden has proposed to explain an entirely different kind of effect – the crop-circle forming plasma-vortex. Little wonder that the Ministry of Defence reputedly took such a strong interest in the Sopley car stop. Imagine what useful applications there must be from gathering a scientific understanding of whatever natural force can stall car engines, levitate heavy objects and generate physiological effects on anyone who chances to get too close.

3. CLOSE ENCOUNTERS, THE ULTIMATE UFO CASE

This type of case is the most controversial in ufological archives and the link between Meaden Vortices and CE IIIs may not be immediately obvious. We mention them with some trepidation but do point out that they represent the most extreme form of ufology – the key element in the armoury of the ufologist who claims that UFOs are alien spacecraft. If the Meaden vortex can account for these very tough cases – and we believe it can – then absolutely no aspect of the UFO evidence is immune and nothing remains that will allow the responsible investigator to leap beyond natural forces into the realms of the supernatural.

Even the most prized UFO cases will have been scientifically explained and the spaceships will have been permanently grounded.

(a) The Alan Godfrey Case, 28th November 1980

This has been described as the most significant UFO case on record in Britain. It involved a West Yorkshire police officer, Alan Godfrey, and occurred in the small Pennine town of Todmorden – scene of many UFO cases over the years. The time was 05.05 hrs, and the weather was wet but clearing (as a frontal system passed overhead). Godfrey was in a patrol car searching for some cows that had disturbed a housing estate. He was driving along Burnley Road when he observed an object hovering just above the road surface and spanning the road ahead. The UFO was like a glowing, spinning top separated by a line of dark blotches (which Godfrey interpreted to be windows). The base of the UFO was clearly rotating and nearby trees were bending in the wind despite the fact that it was calm elsewhere. Godfrey tried to contact his base, but both UHF and VHF channels were indecipherable.

What took place next is difficult to describe, but is typical of the so-called alien contacts that ufologists document. Godfrey next remembers being past the UFO staring into the dark but empty sky. The UFO had disappeared and Godfrey could not remember driving past the object. The policeman doubled back, met up with a colleague, and they both inspected the spot where the UFO had been seen.

Despite the earlier rain, the road surface at this point was dry and both men discovered *a swirled circular pattern identical* to that being discovered in crop circles. Subsequent investigation established that police officers from an adjacent force had seen a blueish glow in the same general area at about the same time. Investigation also established that a period of some ten minutes was 'missing' in the testimony of the witness. Some ufologists immediately leapt upon this "time lapse" as suggestive that Godfrey had been 'abducted' by aliens, and Godfrey was eventually persuaded (rather reluctantly) to undergo a series of hypnotic regression sessions to discover what had "really" happened during the missing ten minutes. During these sessions, Godfrey recounted a typical "abduction" scenario, in which his car engine cut out, he was 'floated' into the UFO, suffered head and body pains, and was examined by a group of robots (who were accompanied by a leader called 'Yosef' and a large black dog!). All these features sound very unlike alien beings and are indicative of cultural conditioning.

We recognise that meteorologists might find the pressure of a story like this to be quite unacceptable in the scientific proceedings of a conference debating unusual atmospheric phenomena. We disagree. In 1988, during a live TV show, Godfrey himself expressed his view that the testimony he produced under hypnosis was very possibly just a dream, but that the initial encounter with the spinning UFO was 'real'. Godfrey pointed out that in between the original encounter and the hypnosis sessions he had assimilated a great deal of UFO material via books and talks with ufologists. While he was positive that he had seen something real above the road, and of course we have independent testimony to support this evidence, Godfrey was willing to accept that his subconscious memory could well be an unconscious mix of the material he had read *after* the encounter. We believe that this is one of the most significant statements eve made by a UFO witness in the entire history of the subject.

We suggest that Godfrey observed a Meaden vortex – an electrically-charged spinning vortex – which formed as a frontal system passed over the area (which is very hilly. Todmorden lies within a steep valley overlooked by rugged terrain). The vortex impeded radio contact and left a swirled pattern in the drying road surface. The 'time lapse' (if real) could have been a brief period of unconciousness induced by the interaction on the brain cortex of the electrical field surrounding the vortex. Some on-going medical research suggests that this kind of effect can occur.

(b) The Port Talbot case, 1972

This case came to Paul Fuller's notice when lecturing at an Open University seminar on UFOs, at Port Talbot in South Wales in 1989. The witness (a taxi driver in his late 30's) apparently believed that he was the only person in the world who had undergone an experience like this, although we know that this is certainly not the case. The date was possibly October 1972 and the time approximately 23.30 hrs. The witness was driving along the A48 trunk road (a very busy road, even at this time of night) from Port Talbot to Swansea after visiting his girl friend. After crossing the Ferry Bridge, he became aware that his car was being paced by a dark flattened saucer with a rim of reddish light on the base. The UFO passed over the top of his car as the witness slowed down and stopped in a lay-by overlooking what was then a major industrial complex.

The witness observed the UFO through his windscreen before getting out of his car. It was from this point on that the witness reported a number of unusual sensations . . . a sense of air pressure pushing down on him from above (identical to that reported by the witnesses of the Marple hay fall, and numerous car stop cases) . . . a rhythmic pulsation (which suggests the presence of a rotating air disturbance) . . . and most significant of all, a tingling sensation on his face and arms (due to the presence of an electro-static field).

Like many of the other cases discussed in this paper, everything that has been reported up to this point seems fully consistent with the observation of a spinning vortex associated with a strong electro-static field. However, what the witness reported next again proves how the UFO Myth distorts a relatively straightforward case and turns it into an encounter with an 'alien intelligence'. The witness reports that just above the glowing rim, he saw "three dark grey shadows" that were "jostling" each other. Although the witness could not see any details, he was convinced that these shadows were UFO entities, who he believed were watching him and trying to communicate with him. In the Alan Godfrey case, these patches were interpreted as the windows on a spaceship (a frequently-made claim in such cases), although in *both* cases these were simply dark patches on luminous, spinning objects. The location is at the base of some very steep hills, again indicating a topographical effect similar to that already demonstrated for the crop circles.

Like many close-encounter cases, the witness was puzzled by the very sudden disappearance of the object (which streaked straight up) and by the total isolation of the encounter, despite being parked on one of the busiest roads in South Wales! This sense of isolation has been reported in a high proportion of close encounter cases and is termed the Oz Factor (after the strange fantasy-land in the Disney film 'The Wizard of Ox'. We suggest that witnesses in close proximity to the Meaden vortex hallucinate and lose all sense of time due to the presence of a strong electrostatic field. We believe that had the Port Talbot witness been subjected to regression hypnosis, he would have produced a similar story to the Alan Godfrey 'abduction'. We suggest four reasons why we should dismiss the literal reality of these alleged 'contacts' with 'aliens':

(1) In forty years of UFO research, no close-encounter witness has yet to produce a single piece of evidence that proves the objective reality of such a contact (e.g. a photograph of the alien, any extra-terrestrial artifact). By contrast the car-stop cases and the initial phases of the contact cases *do* produce such evidence (e.g. the independent confirmation of the swirled pattern on the road in the Alan Godfrey case).

(2) At least three 'abduction' cases exist where the witnesses were observed by third parties during the 'abduction' in such circumstances that a 'real' abduction would have been physically impossible.

(3) All the alleged 'abduction' cases involve absurd features (e.g. the Jewish overtones in the Alan Godfrey case), unnatural time jumps and other 'impossible' features (e.g. in one case the witnesses – involving a family of five – were 'floated' into the 'spaceship' but saw themselves in their car at the same time as they were inside the 'spaceship').

(4) The nature of the close-encounter case changes over time, i.e. the first 'contact' cases (in the 1950s) involved meetings with 'aliens' who took their human contacts to the moon (where they saw non-existent rivers and trees), 1960s 'abductions' involved medical examinations with 'aliens' who were concerned about their technological achievements (atomic experiments, pollution etc), and now, in the 1990s, abductees report ecological warnings.

4. CONCLUSIONS

We believe that the force Dr. Meaden has discovered in connection with naturally-formed atmospheric vortices can account for a substantial proportion of the unexplained UFO data, and we urge the scientific community to drop their prejudices about the phenomenon and open up channels of communication with serious UFO researchers. We predict that the mutual advantages could be far beyond the expectations of many within both fields and that together there is real hope of finally laying those ET spaceships to rest and replacing them with new and useful scientific discoveries about the earth and its environment.

About the authors:

Both authors are Directors of the British UFO Research Association (BUFORA), which is the oldest and largest national UFO research body in the UK. Jenny Randles has been Director in charge of field investigations since 1981 whilst Paul Fuller co-ordinates BUFORA investigation in the Wessex area and has from 1985 supervised the research programme by the organisation that has been examining crop circles from as early as 1981.

They are both outspoken opponents of the media-inspired myth that UFOs are 'alien spaceships', favouring more mundane (yet fascinating) scientific explanations. They have lectured widely on the subject throughout Britain, with Jenny Randles also speaking at seminars in the USA and Europe. Both have appeared on TV and radio programmes about crop circles since 1985.

Professionally, Paul Fuller has a BA in Geography, a postgraduate diploma in statistics and works for Hampshire County Council as a statistician. Jenny Randles trained as a science teacher and has qualifications in geology and a diploma in media communications. She is now a professional writer and broadcaster, having written and presented radio documentaries for the BBC.

Jenny Randles is the author of 14 books, including *Science and the UFOs* (with Peter Warrington: Basil Blackwell, 1985), based on an article in 'New Scientist' magazine (1983) which was the first to be accepted for publication by a UFO researcher. She has also had an article on Crop Circles published by the American science journal OMNI (1987).

The two authors published their first research report on crop circles in the booklet *Mystery of the Circles* (BUFORA, 1986), which was greatly expanded into *Controversy of the Circles* (BUFORA, 1989) – 112 page booklet which concentrated on the social history of the phenomenon.

This summer they have published *Crop Circles: A Mystery Solved* – a full length book objectively examining the crop circles mystery and appearing from the international publishers Robert Hale.

OBSERVATION OF A CIRCLE IN PROCESS OF FORMATION, NEAR DUNDEE, SCOTLAND, AFTER DAWN IN LATE AUGUST 1989

By G. T. MEADEN

The eye witness of this rare, spectacular phenomenon seen in eastern Scotland in August 1989 was Mr Sandy Reid of Dundee, Tayside. The account given here results from an interview effected by the author on 13 November 1989. This is an extrememly important addition to the literature on crop-circle observations, only three good descriptions of crop circles in process of forming having been seen previously. The three earlier accounts of circle-formation were all from Wiltshire. Other reports exist as well but they give less detail.

Sandy Reid, a naturalist, has for many years studied foxes and their habitats and territories in his Tayside locality not far from the north and east of the town of Dundee. He chanced to view a cropfield circle during those precious moments of creation, when he was following a trail along an embankment between two fields. Not only are eye-witness accounts of circle formation uncommon, but Tayside is one of only two Scottish counties from which crop circles have been reported in the last few years (the other is Morayshire).

Mr Reid gave the date as late August 1989 (or just possibly early September); the time 0425/0430 GMT. After a calm, pleasant night dawn had broken to reveal a fine morning sky. Mr Reid was used to recognising the importance of wind-blown scent, so he was especially aware that there had been an absence of wind that night. He noted too that the night had not been cold, meaning that there was no wind-chill. As we shall see below, these and other clues indicate that the date was either Sunday 27 August or Monday 28 August 1989.

At a critical moment Mr Reid was progressing along an embankment between two fields planted with spring barley which he said was 'green and turning yellow'. Deer use the embanked track as well as foxes; from its low elevation Mr Reid had a good view into the sloping fields. Suddenly his attention was drawn to an unusual noise and violent rustling of the corn. Thinking perhaps there might be a deer in the barley he froze immediately, from which he moved into a crouching posture. Very soon he knew that instead of deer there was quite a different sort of commotion taking place only a few metres away. Although it was still windless where he was, he saw that the corn over a circular area was being buffetted by a highly-localized movement of air. Indeed, this part of the field appeared to be waving about as if suffering from flowing air currents such as could be caused by a vortex vertically above it *because the motion did not progress across the field but remained fixed to the same small area.*

This continued for some time, between half a minute and one minute, (he reckoned). Then quite quickly the crop went flat over a *circular* region, with a sharp perimeter, which he estimated had a diameter of 50 to 60 feet (i.e. 15 to 18 metres). He remarked that it was extraordinary that the nearest part of the circle was no more than 15 metres distant, yet he felt no wind himself. He then entered the flattened circle noticing what he called 'an unusual condition of the atmosphere'. He could not express this in words but sensed a peculiar sensation in the air. Everything had gone quiet, the noise from the air and moving corn had ended, and the birds had stopped singing.

Being ignorant of the circles problem, and unaware of the significance of his observation for circles research, Mr Reid did not pay attention to the lie of the barley, but he did recall that the crop was not laid down as a spiral, a series of rings or a radial blast. He merely remembered that when crossing the circle he noticed the straws were laid first one way then the other. Although incomplete, his description suggests that the lying straws may have adopted a lie that we have not yet encountered during our ten years of circles research. One pattern which might approach this description to a greater or lesser extent is a variation on the quadranted array noted in a circle at Winterbourne Stoke (South Wiltshire) at the beginning of August 1989.

Mr Reid went home to return later with a friend, except this time he approached the field from the opposite direction. In doing so he encountered a second circle some 7-10 feet in diameter (three metres across, say) which he had not spotted earlier. The two circles were over 50 metres apart. The national grid reference for the area is NO 4535 approximately, but at the request of Mr Reid the exact location is not given because he "does not want his foxes disturbed by sightseers".

The circumstances of this account fit well existing ideas on hill-induced vortices. 1½ km to the north and west of the circle site is Duntroon Hill; a few kilometres beyond are the Sidlaw Hills. The first stage of Mr Reid's observation testifies to the presence of a vertical vortex 'stationary' above the field. The secondary stage relates to the descent of a breakdown state of this vortex perhaps in the manner of a ring-vortex as discussed by Snow and Kikuchi (1990).

Weather maps show that the weather on the night of Sunday 27th August to Monday 28th August was quietly anticyclonic and clear with a weak north to north-westerly airflow over eastern Scotland. 24 hours earlier the speed of the north/north-west wind was also light but locally more erratic with parts of eastern Scotland suffering light showers. In this part of Scotland no other nights between 20 August and 10 September could be described as fine or clear and *not* cold (i.e. neither intrinsically cold nor devoid of noticeable windchill). Besides if we move too far beyond 27-28 August it is increasingly difficult to reckon on the barley crop being only 'green and turning yellow' at the time of the incident (because before mid-October the crop had completely ripened and had been harvested). Also the fact that the witness saw the circle being made at around 04.30 GMT means that daylight was adequate for this, which is more likely for a date that is earlier than a September one. Lastly, it is highly probable that a weekend was involved, and that the fox watch took place on a

Saturday night or a Sunday night.

In short, it is likely that it was the early hours of either 27th or 28th August when the atmospheric conditions for circle-forming vortices were developing. After 0001 GMT on one or both of these nights the north-west wind, which had already fallen very light (down to force 1), died away altogether. We then deduce that at about 0425/0430 GMT on one of these mornings a minor gust front in a rising, light north-westerly or northerly wind (possibly on 27th, rather than 28th, in connection with advancing cumuliform cloud?) picked up sufficiently to throw out to the lee of Duntroon Hill a vortex system, whose breakdown state in the air which by then was stably stratified, was Genetrix of the Tayside circles.

FURTHER NEWS ON THE CIRCLES EFFECT FROM CERES

By G. T. MEADEN

INTRODUCTION

Since 1980 the proof that the quixotic circles are caused by a peculiar species of natural atmospheric vortex has become ever clearer. The probability is that the majority of circles are formed by airflow across undulating or hilly terrain by vortices developing in the downwind shear zone. The circles appear when rotating forces, such as result from instability at the time of vortex breakdown, reach the crop canopy. There the outcome is a short-lived burst of activity, lasting only seconds, during which the main circle is created, a process which is immediately followed, on maybe 5 - 15% of occasions, by visible rings and/or satellite circles. Furthermore in recent years a link has been established between the vortices that make circular damage impressions and the atmospheric ball-of-light phenomena that have been occasionally observed in non-thundery conditions and which for want of an available name have sometimes been put into a broad 'ball-lightning category' of unexplained atmospheric lights (Meaden 1989: *The circles effect and its mysteries*). The consequences that this has for the so-called UFO problem have been discussed by Randles and Fuller (1990: *Crop Circles: A mystery solved)* [cf also Meaden, Proc. Lyon Conference, April 1990].

Therefore besides being of momentous importance to workers in boundary-layer meteorology, circles research is an area of concern to workers in the general 'ball-lightning field' because this research may ultimately lead to an understanding of those numerous ball-lightning reports for which there was previously no framework around which to erect an explanation. In this regard one may cite in particular: (a) long-lived 'ball lightning' (lifetimes exceeding a few seconds), (b) giant 'ball lightning' (diameters greater than a metre or so), and (c) 'clear-air' and non-thunderstorm 'ball lightning'. The present report summarizes progress in research made during January-December 1989 season with some remarks about the 1990 season added as it stood at the end of May.

NATURE OF THE PROGRESS

Substantial advances were made in circles research during 1989 on all fronts of activity. Formation dates at several circle sites were known exactly (together with the associated weather conditions), more than ten new circle *formation patterns* were discovered, two circle-making electrified or plasma balls were sighted descending into wheatfields at night, one circle was watched as it formed during daylight hours, further reports of previously-unknown circles from earlier years came to hand (including new patterns), and extremely useful theoretical progress was effected. In addition, on the conventional ball-lightning research front, a ball-of-light phenomenon in Kent was recorded on video film the anaylis of which might provide significant support for theoretical ideas based on the concept of natural atmospheric plasma vortices. However, it is not certain that this event was due to ball lightning. The provisional report on our anaylsis of this film is given in a book *Ball lightning studies* published in April 1990 by Artetech.

CIRCLE DATA

The total number of circles known in Britain for 1989 was 305, of which 233 were found in Wiltshire, 16 in Buckinghamshire, 13 in Dorsetshire, eight in Hertfordshire, eight in Hampshire, four in Devonshire, and four in Gloucestershire. There were three each in Kent and Staffordshire, two each in the counties of Tayside, Berks, and Essex, and one each in Avon, Shropshire, Suffolk, Cambridge, Leicester, and North Humberside. Circles were found in wheat, barley, oats, rapeseed, and tick beans (cattle beans). One circle, about eight metres in diameter, was incomplete because it overlapped a roadway. Omitted from these totals are experimental and highly doubtful cases including the Polperro (Cornwall) quintuplet and the Mansfield (Notts) circle.

The big total of 305, from 18 counties, is partly the result of increased public awareness and the increase in flying hours spent searching for circles, and partly because so many (about 72 in Wiltshire) seem to be associated with the jumbo daytime-outbreak on 9th May 1989 when a weak cold front struggled southwards in essentially anticyclonic conditions.

Circles were also reported from countries besides Britain. In December there was an outbreak of twelve circles on a Victorian farm in the south of Australia including at least five circles on one farm. The same farm also had a well-attested visit from a luminous plasma vortex in midwinter (August 1989). At least five circles were reported in four separate events in Manitoba, Canada, and a circle was also found and photographed in Florida in November 1989. Newspaper cuttings refer to circles in other American states too, but no surveys are yet known to have been done.

A large number of additional pre-1980 events came to our attention during the period of January 1989 to May 1990, some involving vortices and/or spinning lights in addition to circular ground traces. Most impressive because of its antiquity was a circle, probably ringed, which happened in Hertfordshire in August 1678 complete with effects of luminosity. This arose through the discovery of a seventeenth-century pamphlet four pages in length entitled "The mowing devil: or, strange news out of Hertfordshire". It was noteworthy that on the night of circle formation the field in question was seen to be all aglow (J. Randles, R. Skinner, *J. Meteorology*, Vol. 14, November 1989).

From Japan we learnt of a well investigated case for 1979 which formed in a ricefield in Ibaragi prefecture. The pattern was of a new type – the "doughnut". There was a broad, clockwise ring, diameters 2 and 4m, with a tiny anticlockwise circle 0.3 m across at the geometric centre (J. Takanashi 1980). Among the several old cases newly brought to our attention was another from 1980 consisting of an anticlockwise *ring* 8.6m across and 0.7m broad, having six internal spokes, apparently made by a descending light-form. Details of these events and many others are being published elsewhere.

SOME OF THE SIGNIFICANT EVENTS OF 1989

One of the important events of 1989 was the quintuplet circle formation east of Aylesbury in July. This 5-circle pattern appeared on a level site downwind of a hill spur of the Chilterns six kilometres to the south-east. These circles are important for demonstrating how far from the creator-hill circles-effect vortices may develop (cf *The circles effect,* p.38). When told of this case, Paul Fuller informed the author that not far from Aylesbury, at the village of Tringford, there had been a well-investigated ball-of-light event on 9 February 1962 in which a huge luminous ball descended to road level, interfered with the performance of a vehicle, and 'brushed' frost from trees as it departed. Reference to weather charts for that occasion showed that following the calm winds of a ridge the rising wind direction (south-east) corresponded with the compass bearing of the nearest part of the Chilterns four kilometres distant.

In December 1989 Robert MacKenzie wrote from Buckinghamshire to say that while overflying in a hot-air balloon in July 1989 he had photographed a second quintuplet in this same part of the county. His pictures revealed a new form of the quintuplet array – a species of 'flattened' five-spot pattern. This was near Tring which helps to confirm that this area just north of the Chiltern Hills is a circle-rich region like the Westbury Hills of Wiltshire. A similar, more exaggerrated, form of 'squashed quintuplet' was photgraphed in Dorset in July and reported to me in December. The existence of such patterns leads us to predict that formation of 8, 12, perhaps even 16, circles surrounding a bigger central one might be an optimum situation which in combination with annular rings could be theoretically possible. Three-spot and six-spot satellite systems surrounding a central big one were predicted many years ago (*J. Meteorology* 1982), since when the three-spot type has been seen (Oadby, Leicestershire in June 1988).

At Bratton/Westbury (West Wiltshire) circles formed at night on 19 July 1989 in a south-west wind along what is likely to have been 'a line of separation 'between one and two kilometres from the creator-hillspur to the south-west. The biggest of these circles which was anticlockwise had a diameter of 26 metres. Later in July and August even bigger circles were formed in north-central Wiltshire. These were clockwise, single-ringed circles with main-circle diametres of 32 metres (105 feet), the biggest we have ever found (Figure 1). Elsewhere – but this time in Avon County near Bath – the smallest ringed circle so far known to us was discovered. The circle's

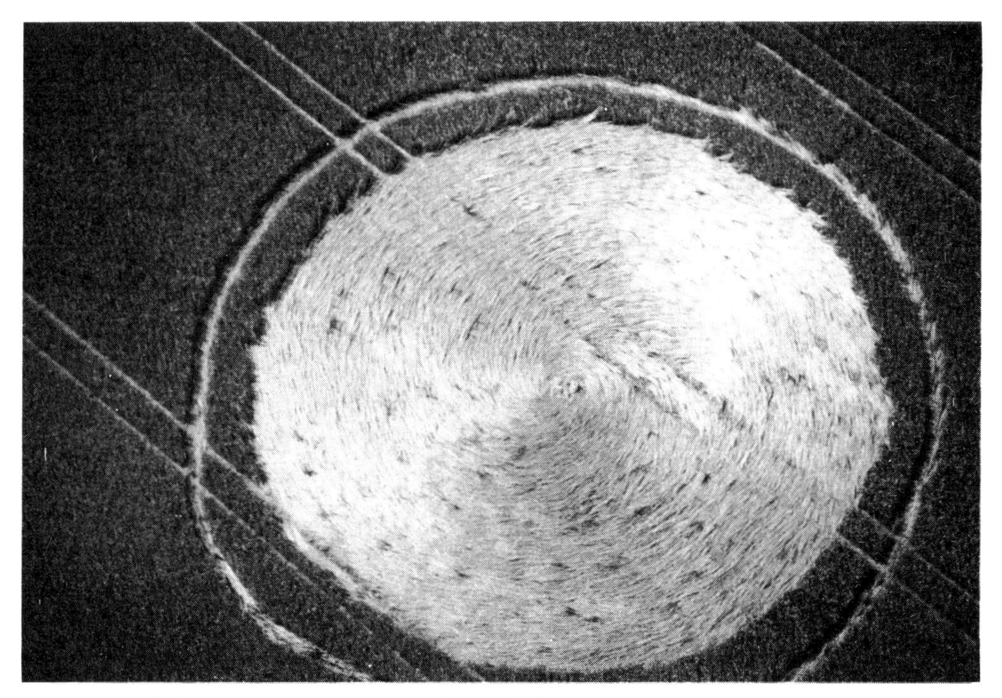

Fig.1: Anti-clockwise ring round the clockwise giant, Beckhampton, Wiltshire, August 1989. Photograph by the author.

internal diameter was only four metres and the concentric ring diameter was approximately six metres.

An unexplained power cut affected the farm and village at the presumed time of formation around dawn (the circle was in a field near overhead 11000 volt cables).

On three occasions in 1989 a clockwise circle was found with a *clockwise* ring around it. For a couple of these, subsidiary evidence suggested that between circle and ring there existed an additional, concentric but effectively-invisible ring directed in the opposite sense to the others. Also in central Wiltshire south of Lockeridge a triple-ringed circle occurred, the rings alternating in the usual fashion. A double-ringed circle was studied at Bratton, West Wiltshire.

Altogether in 1989 sixteen circle sets based on the quintuplet design were discovered. One of these was modified as an unusual septuplet and another as a nonuplet. In addition, three others out of the 16 had extra circles (sometimes one, sometimes two) which gave the patterns a 'cruciform' appearance. The Cherhill one was really a septuplet, five of the seven circles being nearly in line. The distance measured across the 'great diameter' of this linked formation was 72 metres. A photograph is reproduced on the front cover of the new edition of *The Circles effect and its mysteries.* The so-called 'crucifix' is imperfect, the misalignment of circles 6-5 being nine degrees out of true with circles 5-1.

Two of the circles discovered in South Wiltshire by Mr F. C. Taylor during airborne reconnaissance in early August were remarkable for their complex, overlapping, concentric-ring character. One had a curious quadranted structure combined with circular symmetry (see author's main paper for sketch plans). These amazing findings are to be discussed on another occasion.

At Woolstone in Gloucestershire one morning *J. Meteorology* subscriber Michael Rawlinson was amazed to find a quadruplet group of circles in a field opposite his house in the Cotswolds. His barograph displayed significant changes at the presumed time of formation in the early daylight hours. Other barographs in the locality (and as far away as Gloucester) confirmed this, so it seems that the circles were created in conjuntion with a minor frontal passage. Two circles in the group had outstanding characteristics which we shall describe elsewhere.

Fronts were detected in connection with circle appearances at sites in other counties on various days too. On one occasion in June what amounts to a retrograding sea-breeze front may have been involved (the original sea-breeze had passed through earlier in the evening but later appears to have been repulsed by a rising gradient wind). In all cases the air was still or nearly still before the arrival of the frontal boundary.

Also theoretically important is that ten, at least, of last year's circles had a bunch of damaged and undamaged stalks at their centres structured into prominent pyramids. Several other instances were noted in which pyramids had formed but had subsequently been bent and blown over. This is plain proof of a *ring vortex* striking the crop, which signifies the development of a *breakdown state of a primary vortex condition* such as a hill-sourced trailing vortex or eddy vortex. In this connection Prof. John Snow (U.S.A.) drew attention to a paper by N. Tamai, Asaeda and N. Tanaka (Japan) published in *Boundary Layer Meteorology* in 1987 (vol. 39, 301-314). These researchers performed fluid-flow experiments involving laminar motion over a hemispherical hill, and showed how stable, arched vortex tubes develop in the downsteam turbulence. Flowing water coloured with dye was used, but a similar result would be expected for laminar airflow across a real hill. Dr Tokio Kikuchi pointed out the relevance that swirled vortex rings could have for the situation, citing the theoretical work of Prof. H. Keith Moffat (Generalized vortex rings with and without swirl, *Fluid Dynamics Research,* Vol. 3, 22-30, 1988). John Snow and Tokio Kikuchi have intiated discussions based on ring-vortex descent in a vortex breakdown situation. The introduction of swirl can explain beautifully the outflowing multi-spiral bed patterns so familiar to circles-effect researchers. A joint paper is in preparation. George B. Bathurst independently arrived at related spherical ring-vortex ideas via aerodynamical principles and hypothesized how it might work for annular-ringed and quintuplet-circle production too.

Another paper pertinent to the new concepts of atmospheric vortex stability appeared in *Nature* in April 1989 'Tripolar vortices in a rotating fluid'. The authors G.H.F. Van Heijst and R. C. Kloosterziel, demonstrated by means of laboratory experiments how a monopolar vortex in the sheared environment of a rapidly-rotating fluid re-forms into a previously-unknown stable, tri-polar state. Although this is not the same as the circles-effect vortices, there may be some relevance to vortex stability-instability transitions that *do* apply to our vortex species (cf straight-line triplet formations in the circles effect). It is certainly curious, and worthy of remark, that such a simple observation as triple-vortex stability was unknown previously. How many other multiple-vortex combinations might equally be stable?

In addition to the considerable progress effected in crop-circle research, further proof was forthcoming that conditions can arise under which land devils can leave circular traces as well. This was presented by Peter Rendell who investigated land-devil/whirlwind circles at Pucklechurch, Avon County, in August (*J. Meteorology,* Vol. 14, 414-415). A similar observation seems to have been made on Roundway Hill, Devizes, Wiltshire in August 1989 by Miss Jackie Pearson (*J. Meteorology,* vol. 15, May/June 1990 issue). The suggestion is now proposed that the circle flattening could have resulted from a type of 'drowned vortex jump' as studied by T. Maxworthy for land-devils (On the structure of concentrated columnar vortices. *Astron Acta* 17, 363-374, 1972).

CIRCLES AND BALLS OF LIGHT

On two occasions, well viewed by witnesses, circles formed in the presence of glowing balls of light. In one of these (North Wiltshire) a big orange-coloured ball was seen to sink into a wheatfield and extinguish itself. Next morning a 15-metre ringed circle was found at that spot (*J. Meteorology,* Vol. 15, 5-7, 1990). The other happened in the middle of the night in East Kent. A great ball, described as a 'spiralling vortex of light' which made a loud humming noise, descended into a wheatfield and vanished. This was watched by two men who immediately investigated by the light of the moon and found an 18m diameter circle. Near it was a smaller circle whose presence (a little to the right with respect to the witnesses's line of sight) allows one to understand the remark that the observed vortex of light 'blinked out to the right' (i.e. the men were regarding two self-illuminated vortices which were nearly but not exactly in line with one another). A report was prepared by Paul Harris (*J. Meteorology,* Vol. 15, 3-5, 1990).

Aerial archaeologist James Pickering of Leicestershire, reported an amazing species of circle from Staffordshire which was subsequently visited by CERES investigator David Reynolds. This unusual 'toothed' ring or swathed circle, some 70 metres in diameter, gave the impression that a non-swirling ring-vortex or microburst may have disintegrated explosively above the crop canopy. A similar, smaller pattern on the other side of the field displayed a prominent anticlockwise swirl, as did a partially-formed third one. Two similar 'toothed' circles were seen on a Kent beach in 1980.

Attention was again given in 1989 to some elementary dowsing experiments inside and outside circles using bent metal rods. The positive response obtained was very encouraging and additional electrical and magnetic instrumental work is now under way.

Finally in view of the theoretical circle-research now being undertaken on ring-vortices and how they can be formed naturally in the atmosphere, the video film obtained by Mr Ray Cahill of Kent on 10 September 1989 takes on a significance which goes beyond that of ball lightning alone. If his film really is a movie record of genuine ball lightning, then it proves that luminous toroidal or ring vortices are natural products of our atmosphere, and encourages us more than ever in our determination to mount regular nocturnal and daytime circle watches next season. Visible on the film for a total of 1.5 seconds as it crosses the field of view is a reddish-orange torus – a species of oblate spheroid with an axial hole. The torus is composed of 8, perhaps more, segments, and is surrounded by an aureole tinted greeney-white. The event has been accepted as genuine by Professor R. C. Jennison (University of Kent) and Ron Lobeck (TVS Weatherman) who propose a diameter of 0.20m for the ball which they say was travelling at about 1 ms^{-1} (*Weather,* Vol. 45, 151-152, April 1990). Independent examinations of the video recording by Terence Meaden and Mark Stenhoff however raise doubts concerning the reality of the event as caused by ball-lightning (see *Ball Lightning Studies* (also *J. Meteorology,* April 1990)). Optical test experiments on video cameras by Dr. Arne Bergstrom of Scientor, Sweden confirm these doubts. The results of these tests are being prepared for publication.

CIRCLES WATCHES

A week-long circles watch called Operation Green Hill was undertaken at a site in Wiltshire in the neighbourhood of Silbury Hill at the start of July 1989. On most nights manning was continuous, but regrettably no observers were present when circles appeared in full view of the main watchpoint between midnight and 10 a.m. on 4th July. Voluntary observers will be welcome this summer on Operation High Hill, especially those who can bring along or attend to scientific and photographic apparatus. Please write for details.

Last summer one person, in Scotland, was lucky to witness a circle while it was being formed in daylight, but as with previous known sightings this was an unplanned observation. The date was late August in a field of barley which was turning from green to yellow. Full details are given in a paper in *Weather,* Vol. 45, pp 273-274 1990, and in the present book. In England in 1989 the season ended a month earlier than in 1987 due to the good weather and early harvesting. Most of the known circle fields were cut by the end of July, but in Scotland the potential for crop-circle appearances continued for a month or two longer.

THE NATURE OF DAMAGE TO PLANTS IN CORN CIRCLES

By JOHN A. GRAHAM

INTRODUCTION

Naturally-occurring physical damage to cereal plants, the main forms of which are known as lodging, is a widely recognised and common phenomenon. Lodging and its associated factors are well documented for wheat and barley crops (Anon, 1968 a, b; Pinthus, 1973; Graham, 1983). It has been investigated in other cereals including maize (Fakorade and Mock, 1978; Remison and Akinleye, 1978; Zuber et al., 1978), rice (Khan et al., 1978; Kobayashi and Hitaka, 1969: Wells and Johnson, 1970) and in sorghum (Boonsue, 1967; Esechie et al., 1977; Van Arkel, 1978). Like crop circles, lodging is not confined to cereal crops and may be found in cotton (Brown and Hyer, 1955), flax (Gubbels, 1976), soybeans (Blomquist et al., 1973; Johnson and Pendleton, 1968; Woods and Swearingin, 1977) and many other crop species too.

Whereas lodging damage often appears to have a directional component, the areas within fields have irregular rather than geometric configurations. This is the chief difference between lodging and circles.

The consequences of lodging for cereal farmers are variable. Yields within damaged areas can be depressed by over 25% (Stanca et al., 1979) prior to harvesting. The actual amount of grain recovered will depend on the efficiency of the harvesting system. In cases of severe lodging very little grain is recoverable and this will often be the situation within circles too. Should the damage occur prior to growth stage 75, individual tillers in both lodged sites and in circles are able to exhibit some powers of recovery due to geotropic cell elongation at the nodes. This will counteract the yield depression slightly and improve the efficiency of grain recovery by harvesting equipment.

Cereal farmers are likely to be penalised financially because of poor grain formation in damaged areas lowering specific weight values, and due to the higher levels of moisture associated with laid crops increasing the risk of alpha-amylase generation and therefore low Hagberg Falling Numbers in milling varieties of wheat. The crucial factor determining the value of lost produce is not the degree of damage in any damaged area, but the total amount of damage in a field. In fields which have suffered irregular lodging damage, the areas affected could range from a few small patches to over 95% of the crop. In fields where there is no other damage apart from that in circles, the direct financial penalty is normally therefore not great.

FORMS OF DAMAGE

A cursory inspection of a lodged area or a circle will show that the damage to the crop in either area, certainly as far as the farmer is concerned, is identical. That is, all the plants are laid over tending towards a horizontal rather than a vertical habit. This results in the ears lying close to the ground, many buried beneath other damaged plants, interfering with ripening and posing a major challenge for mechanical harvesting techniques.

More detailed examination of stems, however, reveals one of two modes of mechanical failure. One is a direct failure of the stem itself, while the other involves soil failure with the stem maintaining its mechanical integrity intact.

i) Stem Failure

Stem failure is brought about by some external force causing local buckling in the basal internodes. Under windy field conditions stems may also be at risk of Euler buckling, where the critical buckling force **Fe** is given by

$$\mathbf{Fe} = \mathbf{n}\,\pi^2\,\mathbf{EI/L}^2$$

Since the critical load is solely dependent on the flexural rigidity, **EI** and the elastic limit of the material is not exceeded during buckling, the stem will return to its vertical habit once the displacing force has been removed.

Local buckling occurs at a stress that is generally taken as being given by

$$\beta l = \mathbf{kEt/D}$$

ßl is the buckling stress, **E** is Young's modulus, **t** is the thickness and **D** is the diameter. **k** is a constant normally taken as 0.5 for imperfect cross-sections like plant stems (Wainwright et al., 1976).

In many corn circles *ßl* has already been exceeded for the majority of stems, which is why they are laid over. A number of studies have suggested the wind speed necessary to cause local buckling of cereal stems in the field. Neenan and Spenser Smith (1975) suggest that a contact wind speed of 21.75 m/sec for wheat and 15.4 m/sec for barley would be necessary. Laboratory and wind tunnel data published by the author in 1983 showed that a mean 2m wind velocity in excess of 60m/sec would be required to cause local buckling in wheat, assuming a logarithmic profile. For stems of barley this figure would be somewhat less, perhaps half, due to barley having a significantly smaller second moment of area, **I.** It is therefore perfectly feasible for air moving at such velocities in a circular configuration to cause flattened circles in cereal crops.

ii) Soil Failure

In many instances of lodging in cereal crops the stems themselves do not suffer any form of mechanical failure. Rather, they have become permanently displaced from the vertical as a result of the displacing force overcoming the resistance offered by the plants' anchorage system. The author has shown that surface soils with low specific volumes, characteristic of many cultivated agricultural soils, whose tensile and shear strengths diminish by several orders of magnitude when wetted, can be brought to critical state failure by relatively small forces when wet. The forces could be as small as a few grammes. This explains why conventionally lodged crops always fail in this manner in association with wet weather and yet frequently the rainfall is not associated

Fig. 1 Dr. John Graham with Terence Meaden at the Upton Scudamore 4-ringed quintuplet on 10 July 1990. Tests with an ELE cone penetrometer showed negligible differences in compaction inside and outside of the circles.

with notably windy conditions.

Circles differ from conventional lodging in that they will often occur when soils are quite dry. Under these conditions the forces necessary to cause failure are likely to be several orders of magnitude greater than when the soil is wet, with approximately an order of magnitude increase per 5% reduction in moisture content for most U.K. soils (Towner, 1974). However, it is evident from the damage caused at sites such as the ringed quintuplet in green wheat at Morgan's Hill, Bishops Cannings, Wiltshire (July, 1990) that such forces can be exceeded during the formation of circles because in these circles the laying of the crop has been as a result of soil failure even though the soil was quite dry. On this particular site there was in fact a notably uncompacted surface soil layer (cone penetrometer readings were too low to be significant). This was evidenced by an area of natural lodging (again due to soil failure) which was triggered by, and adjacent to, the main circle.

In some circles it may be observed that a few plants immediately adjacent to tramlines have remained standing. This is likely to be due to the fact that the soil there has been compacted significantly by wheeled traffic, and its specific volume and thus its strength properties vastly increased.

CONCLUSION

The mechanical failure of plants in a corn circle can take one of two forms, although it is likely that both forms will be found on many sites. On this basis, corn circles may be classified as a form of lodging.

Failure is as a result of either local buckling of basal internodes or of soil failure causing loss of anchorage of the root crown. From this we can draw some conclusions about the nature of the forces causing the damage and the environment from which they arise.

It may be possible that some damage is caused by forces which could be quite small if circles, where the mechanism failure has been soil failure, were formed under high soil moisture conditions. However, field observations tell us that circle formation appears to be associated with settled, dry weather and so the formation of circles by an agency generating a force of a few grammes on cereal plants is likely to be the exception rather than the rule. In many instances circles are formed in cereal crops under dry soil moisture conditions. They occur too when crops are senescing and plants' basal internodes have their maximum Young's modulus and therefore maximum resistance to local buckling. Despite this, the damage sustained by individual stems is very frequently due to local buckling.

One must therefore conclude that *the causal agent is an external force related to the aerial environment rather than a soil related phenomenon.*A perfectly viable scenario for this causal agent would be air moving in a circular configuration of velocities in excess of 50m/sec.

REFERENCES

ANON. (1968) a) *Lodging in wheat: Annotated bibliography.* Commonwealth Bureau of Crops and Pastures.

b) *Lodging in barley: Annotated bibliography.* Commonwealth Bureau of Crops and Pastures.

BLOMQUIST, R.V., KUST, C.A. and SCHRADER, L.E. (1973) Effect of ethrel on seasonal activity of three enzymes and lodging resistance in soybeans. *Crop Sci.* 13,4-7.

BOONSUE, B.(1967) A diallel analysis of lodging resistance and associated characters in *Sorghum vulgare* Pers. Ph.D thesis, Purdue University, U.S.A.

BROWN, L.C. and HYER, A.H. (1955) Chemical defoliation of cotton. 4. Lodging in bottom defoliated cotton. *Agron.J.* 47,378.

ESECHIE, J., MARANVILLE, W. and ROSS, W.M. (1977) Relationship of stalk morphology and chemical composition to lodging resistance in sorghum. *Crop Sci.* 17,609-612.

FAKORADE, M.A.B. and MOCK, J.J. (1978) Relationships between grain yield and agronomic traits in five maize variety hybrids. *Iowa State J. Res.* 54,355-360.

GRAHAM, J.A. (1983) *Crop lodging in British wheats and barleys.* Ph.D. Thesis, University of Reading.

GUBBELS, G.H. (1976) Growth retardants for control of loding in flax. *Can.J. Plant Sci.* 56,799-804.

JOHNSON, T.J. and PENDLETON, J.W. (1968) Contribution of leaves at different canopy levels to seed production of upright and lodged soybeans [*Glycine max (L.) Merril*] *Crop Sci.* 8,291-292.

KHAN, R.A., DUBLE, B.P., KASHYAP, L. and CHANDRAKER, B.L. (1978) Prevention of lodging losses in rice. *Oryza* 13, 129-130.

KOBAYASHI, H. and HITAKA, N. (1969) Studies on the lodging of the rice plant. *J. agric. Met., Tokyo* 24,15-23,67-74.

NEENAN, M. and SPENSER SMITH, J.L. (1975) An analysis of the problem of lodging with particular reference to wheat and barley. *J. agric. Sci., Camb.* 85,495-507
PINTUS, M.J. (1973) Lodging in wheat, barley and oats: the phenomenon, its causes and preventative measures. Adv. Agron. 25,209-263.
REMISON, S.U. and AKINLEYE, D. (1978) Relationship between lodging, and to a growth regulator. *J. agric. Sci., Camb.* 93,449-456.
TOWNER, G.D. (1974) The assessment of soil texture from soil strength measurements. *J. Soil Sci.* 25,298-306.
VAN ARKEL, H (1978) The forage and grain yield of sorghum and maize as affected by soil moisture conservation, lodging and harvesting losses. *Neth. J.agric. Sci.* 26,181-190.
WAINWRIGHT, S.A., BIGGS, W.D., CURREY, J.D. and GOSLINE, J.M. (1976) *Mechanical design in organisms.* Edward Arnold, London.
WELLS, B.R. and JOHNSON, T.H. (1970) Differential response of rice varieties to timing of mid season applications. *Agron.J.* 62,608-612.
WOODS, S.J. and SWEARINGIN, M.L. (1977) Influence of simulated early lodging upon soybean seed yield and its components. *Agron.J.* 69,239-241.
ZUBER, M.S., COLBERT, T., SCHULL, C. and CHANG, H. (1977) Stalk quality improvement studies in corn. *Rep., Dep. of Agron.*, Missouri University, U.S.A. 43-46.

REMARKS ON REPORTING AND RECORDING CROP-CIRCLE PHENOMENA: AN AGRICULTURAL VIEWPOINT

By MONTAGUE KEEN

I am responding to your suggestion that I might write to amplify my suggestions for improving the system of reporting and recording crop circle phenomena. My suggestions take the form of questions to be asked, or facts to be ascertained, in a department of inquiry which, on the basis of the evidence recorded in the three books published last year on crop circles, I think has been generally neglected. Before listing them, however, a word about the rationale of my proposals.

The first task of a scientifically-based inquiry into unexplained phenomena must be an impartial and complete record of all available relevant evidence. That duty poses the question: relevant to what? Clearly, relevant to any possible explanation of the phenomenon under investigation. But since a satisfactory explanation is precisely what is being sought, we must first have a hypothesis, or a number of them. Aware of it or not medical doctors face this dilemma every time a diagnosis is attempted. Should we record on what day of the week the circle is believed to have been formed? Surely not, because there seems unlikely to be a causal link. Should we try to discover the time of day or night the circles were known or suspected of having been formed? Almost certainly yes, since it is reasonable to suppose that factors like ambient temperature, wind speed and direction, and relative humidity, all of them subject to diurnal variation, appear relevant. They seem relevant to a hypothesis based on almost any sort of air movement, especially vortices, but not so apparently relevant to one based on extra-terrestrial force and intelligence. Most of us would instinctively accept the former and reject the latter, in accordance with Occam's razor; but the *selection* of hypotheses is essentially arbitrary, preconditioned by our individual intellectual prejudices.

For practical purposes we have to whittle down the theoretically infinite number of recordable facts (based, for example, on acceptance of the possible validity of astrology, numerology or the existence of ley lines). To have a reasonably digestible number of questions for our investigator-recorders, we have implicitly to reject what might be considered the more outlandish. These become subjective judgements. For example, you might consider that the reactions of a dowsing rod over a circle site *might* provide some relevant evidence. A large number of your scientific colleagues might ridicule dowsing, let alone the possibility that it might yield evidence. (I may say that I would not: I make the point for illustration). On the other hand there are those who find the vortex theory inadequate to account for all the known facts, and might suggest parallels with the type of force postulated by Professor John Hasted (in his classic work *The Metal-Benders, 1981)*; and with this in mind might urge the merits of assays by a university or governmental laboratory to establish whether unexpected changes in the molecular structure of smitten plants have taken place.

Just suppose there were such evidence, then two things follow: first, the obvious need for several further checks to establish whether or not this is a normal feature of pressurised stems; secondly, assuming confirmation is forthcoming, whether this structural change can be replicated by laboratory tests. If so, we would begin to know more about the type, strength, speed, etc, of the force responsible, and this might have evidential value, negative or positive, to the vortex theory. To reject such tests on *a priori* grounds, in the belief that such changes are inconsistent with a vortex-type explanation, would in my view be unwise, because unduly limiting. Others may disagree. My point is that we all need to reach broad agreement on what evidence may be relevant; and my instinct is to press for the widest range of facts even if they appear to pre-suppose explanations hostile to established beliefs.

One further point: disregarding the one well-publicised hoax of July 1990, the most recent aerial photographs (including some of my own) show further, astonishing, developments in the complexity of patterns, well beyond even the remarkable picture taken at Cheesefoot Head, and shown at the June conference. Where anything other than a circle, oval or ring is evident, e.g. square or oblong shapes, or arcs or segments, there is in my view an additional burden on the investigator to establish or eliminate hoaxing. I was impressed by the twelve criteria appearing in Table 2 of the Fuller and Randles paper on pp 104-105 of these proceedings and I would hope that something along these lines could be routinely employed. Indeed, in order to end up with a hoax probability score, it should be possible to apply an assessment mark to most of the differences listed. My suggested questions are designed to ascertain the physical parameters of the force responsible; and ideally this should be done in a form susceptible to statistical analysis by computer, and with a sufficiently large number to enable chance deviation assessments to operate. To this end it is not good enough simply to record what type of crop is affected, or the date(s) on which the circle (or circle pattern) was discovered, or known to have been caused. In addition, one needs to know:

(a) identity of the crop, i.e. spring wheat, winter barley.
(b) the name of the variety: some are earlier, shorter or longer stemmed, heavier, etc, and date of sowing (earlier sown crops are more prone to lodging).
(c) the height of the standing crop.
(d) the quantity and type of fertiliser applied: extra nitrogen, or a high organic manurial content of the soil, could result in lusher growth and weaker stems, more susceptible to windblow.
(e) whether the crop has been treated with a growth regulator or straw-shortening chemical, e.g. Cyocel, which has the effect of stiffening the straw and reducing the height.

(f) the date when first observed, and the growth stage of the crop: there are two recognised growth stage scales: Zadoks and Feekes. An accurate record of the growth stage reached at the moment of impact is crucial to any estimate of the turgidity, brittleness or flexibility of the stem. If the degree of straw dessication has reached Zadok growth-stage 94, for example, it is difficult to conceive of any natural wind force which could knock it flat without fracturing the stem - or, for that matter, shedding the seed. That might even apply to the so-called hard-dough stage (87 Zadok's when harvesting would normally be imminent. The full scale is for the botanist or specialist. An abbreviated version would probably be adequate. Some expert advice on this would be useful, with a simple, illustrated chart prepared for investigators. What is important to note, however, is that when the lignification of the stem as sap-rise ceases and dessication starts is of critical importance to any attempt to assess the strength of the knock-down force. I do not know how many circles have been noted in grass for silage-making, or (later) grass standing for hay. In either event a record of the grass mixture is desirable, since heading dates, which are a key to stem rigidity, are very precisely known for pure varieties. I should add that, outside Britain, crops like cotton or sugar cane have very much tougher stems. Any record of a crop circle in such crops would be of great interest, and would highlight the importance of the growth stage record.

I am assuming it to be common ground that investigators will also make a careful note of the direction(s) of the laid crop, the sharpness or roughness of the circle edges, the degree and nature of any damage to the grain, assuming it to be a grain crop, whether the stem is bent or fractured, damage to the soil, moisture content of the soil surface, measurement of any residual electromagnetic effect, and so on, in addition to topography and all ascertainable meteorological factors.

I trust these observations may prove a useful contribution to the pool of advice you are receiving.

IONIZATION, AND ITS POSSIBLE EFFECT ON CORN CIRCLES

By GORDON W.C. GARROULD

As the study of the 'Corn Circle Phenomena' unavoidably involves the thinking of several different disciplines, the possible involvement of ionization is worth investigation, as Terence Meaden has pointed out in the *Circles Effect and it's Mysteries.*

To start with some of the earliest demonstrations, the Faraday Dark Cloud Test is worth recalling. Over a century ago Michael Faraday slowly evacuated a tube into which were fixed anode and cathode conductors charged just enough to provide a faint crackle of discharge as the pressure fell. As the atmospheric pressure fell in the tube, the crackling quietened to a light streamer effect, and by the time the pressure had fallen to a half a light pink colour (for air) was noticeable at the cathode, i.e. the beginning of the sort of aura, noticeable as ionization increases. Evacuating the tube further to one-third atmospheric pressure greatly increased these effects and the colour, if anything, became more blueish.

This would not seem to be particularly relevant to our consideration until one realizes that one only has to travel in a high-altitude aeroplane to physically experience this little Faraday experiment. The atmosphere at 18,000 feet is already halved in pressure, and before the top of Mount Everest is reached the pressure has dropped to one third of that at sea level.

Thus one quickly realizes that an ionized atmosphere is not particularly rare, in fact it is only at cloud level above our heads, and the really vast thunder clouds can tower right up to 30,000 feet and above.

"Why cornfields?" is the question so often asked in the Press, and then "Why are these circles so much more frequent in recent years?"

The answer to both questions may to a great extent lie in the modern farming of grain crops. No longer do we see, as was so common in pre-war years, the farm cart toiling up the field with the animal manure being forked out of the back. Nor do we see the small patch-work fields, surrounded with hedge and ditch and often tall mature trees.

The present day farming of corn, 'prairie-farming' as it is sometimes described, presents the clouds above with a wide sea of regular spaced corn ears, crowded together far nearer than before, and of remarkably even height due to careful seed selection and much more accurate spread of fertilizer. As the ear ripens it is heavier and larger, with the well-developed vertical bristles peculiar to ripening corn. These bristles in themselves need careful thought, for they are needle sharp and are ideal for the discharge of static electricity. In fact we have in the cornfield a vast sea of tiny 'lightning conductors', each with its classic sharp-pointed form above, held above the ground by a dry hollow cornstalk but sufficiently damp inside to provide the conductor from ear to root.

Looking at the whole cornfield, as it were in 'cross section', we have in fact a form of 'double condenser'. The clouds slowly passing overhead provide more than likely a light spikey negative charge or negative plate. The corn bristles below discharge through their bristles a continuous stream of electrostatic charge i.e. the typical lightning conductor situation. Yet approximately 80 cm below the ear we have the earth carrying equal and opposite charge, making a third plate to our condenser system.

For those who like a simple experiment, thread 12 to 15 cottons through a sheet of corrugated cardboard, and cut them off say 7cm long. A sheet of ordinary window glass is now placed with a neat pile of books at each end to hold it say 12cm above the 'cornfield'. Choose a bright dry sunny day. Nothing happens in the damp. See that the 'cornfield' and glass are bone dry, and then rub vigorously the top of the glass with a *dry* silk cloth (not art-silk), and very soon the first of the 'corn-stalk' cottons will start to move and then stand up.

If the silk is now balled up and brought near the surface of the glass as if it were a mini-cloud, the cotton corn-stalks will duck away, i.e. they are electrostatically repelled. If a Malvern-water-type plastic bottle is now rubbed hard with the silk cloth, and brought near the glass surface, this mini-cloud, being of opposite polarity will attract the corn-stalk cottons instead of repelling them.

This simple experiment shows how easily an ionized condition can be established in very dry air, but as the books are only at each end, a light breeze from door or window will soon dissipate this tiny ionized zone and the cottons will sink back again. Thus in the real cornfield a steady breeze over even dry corn will keep ionization to a minimal level, and it must be a *still dry* atmosphere above the corn to allow ionization to accumulate.

Below the corn ear of course, the forest of tiny corn stalks make such ventilation almost impossible because light breezes merely wave the corn into ripples without ever penetrating to the roots some 80 cm below. In this still dry atmosphere trapped amongst the corn stalks, we must consider another ionizing condition, all too often overlooked, and yet perhaps throwing light on the perplexing way in which these circles seem to be more prevalent in our Wiltshire area and often near ancient sites.

The fact is that in Cornwall the various granite formations have been weathered down and exposed, but as one moves east the granites dip down under broken alluvial rock formations, with in many cases overlaying chalk, and so many of our Wiltshire cornfields are on chalky soil. The 'prairie farming' of corn goes on just the same in East Anglia, but here the many fields starting from Hertfordshire into Essex and beyond are on deep clay.

As is well known but often forgotten, granites the world over are slightly radioactive, and it is only when one reads HMSO publications recommending the proper ventilation of buildings to prevent the accumulation of radon gas, that one realizes how widespread this situation extends. There is little fear under normal circumstances, as the breezes blow the heavy gas away and dilute it, but in the still atmosphere around the corn roots it can accumulate for several weeks during growth and ripening.

Radon gas is itself radioactive, and continuously decays, although slowly, to polonium, which is itself radioactive. So the rays given off at each decay generate ionization in the atmosphere around. Here, however, the atmosphere cannot be ventilated, and so for several weeks on land with granites below them this accumulation is unavoidable.

There is little health risk, as the whole field is swept with dusty winds as soon as the corn is cut, but the Meaden Effect relies on static charge as well as vortices, and so by the reasoning above, one is setting up quite naturally, if unintentionally, the ideal circumstance for corn-circle phenomena to occur regularly.

WAS A HILL'S SPHERICAL VORTEX SIGHTED AT CROP LEVEL ON 24 JULY 1989?

By GEORGE B. BATHURST

Abstract: The familiar vortex-ring is known to expand diametrically in the course of distance and time, but the more compact variant known to aerodynamicists as the Hill's spherical vortex could penetrate further without expanding and be more ready to accept spin. Such an entity helped by chaff ingested from the stubble appears to have been sighted by three members of the Pearson family, in 1989. It's relevance for understanding the crop-circle phenomenon is discussed.

Since their fortunate sighting of a spherical whirlwind atop Roundway Hill on July 24th last year, the Pearson observers have been convinced that this was the agency responsible for the crop-circle recordings. The main reason was that when the spherical whirlwind touched down even on the stubble from which it ingested the chaff, it left a 'flat circular impression' visible from the nearby track. The initial reaction of experts on the crop circles has been that either the Pearsons must have seen a dust-devil, or that it is unlikely that a visible impression would be left in the much shorter stubble. On the other hand, the observant Pearsons may have been able to see something left behind as an impression, if not flattened straw then an area of local condensation indicating that the air responsible was cold. One difficulty has been that a suitable theory has been lacking to explain such an unusual sighting as this.

The lengthy silence between the mid-1989 description conveyed originally by Mrs. Betty Pearson, and the letter published in the May/June 1990 edition of the *Journal of Meteorology* this year, was not due to the three female members of the Pearson family who reported the sighting as soon as possible. The original letter was to David Garmston, BBC South West, producer of a series on the crop circles, of which she sent me a copy. In it she wrote "Further to my telephone call to your office, I am writing as promised re your recent programme on crop circles around Wiltshire. We were visiting Melksham last weekend, and on Monday July 24 (1989) took a picnic up to Roundway Hill, near Devizes. On our way back (i.e. southward along the track above the western face of Roundway Hill) my elder daughter exclaimed "What is that?". We stopped the car and watched absolutely fascinated as a sort of whirling globe about 15 feet across swished away a few feet from us over the stubble field. The reason that we even saw it was that the cornfield had been recently cut (perhaps that same day by 4.00 p.m.), with the result that this (spherical) whirlwind was pulling up the chaff from the ground - hence we were able to see its perfectly formed globe shape. It stayed in one place for a few seconds, moved rapidly up and across towards the right, stopped there and dropped down again still swirling, bounded up again and then fizzled out into the air, leaving a flat circular impression where it had touched down nearby on to the stubble surface. We did wonder whether this was the explanation for the forming of the circles, and thought that you might be interested in our

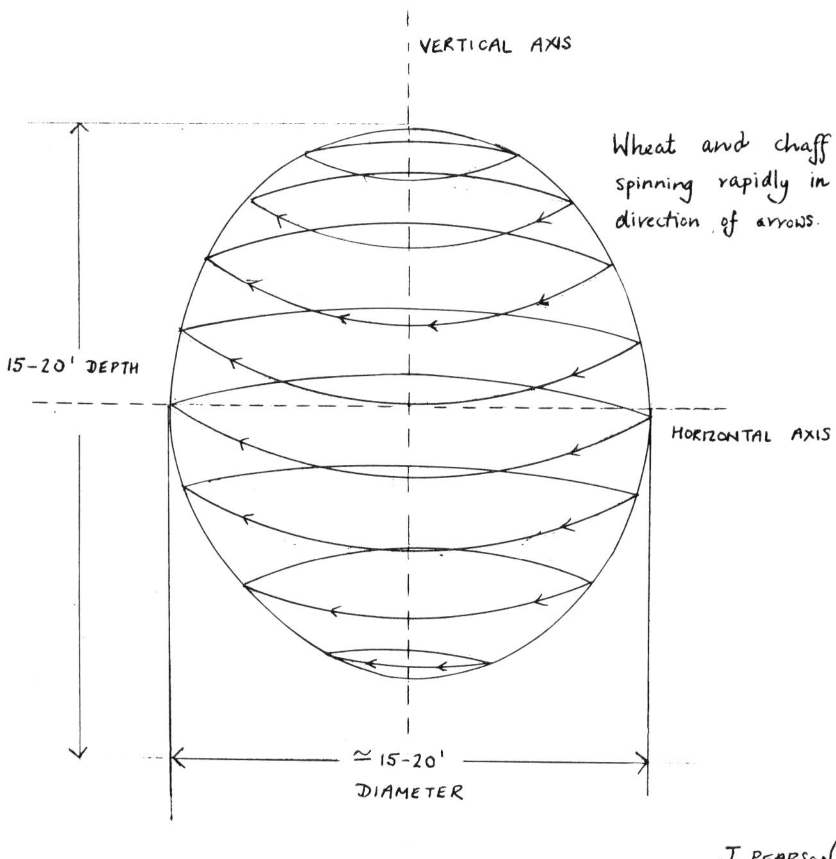

sighting".

This description is the same as that of Mrs. Pearson's elder daughter, Mrs. Anne H. Marson the former WRAF aircraft controller, except that the latter added a diagram which includes the circular impression on the ground below the sphere. This was harder to print than that of her sister, Miss. J.F. Pearson B.Sc., because her diagram comprised coloured inks, yellow for ingested straw tailings and red for directional arrows. Of special interest were her comments: "It was a perfect globe shape, rotating very fast in horizontal planes, and less so in vertical planes (about a loop or vortex-ring axis?). This appeared to give it (or was at least in sympathy with) movement across the field. Anything loose or light seemed to be whirling around inside it. After the second bounce it whirled away into the corner of the stubble field and over the trees. By now it was very high and of the more traditional funnel shape, but still containing all the chaff". Understandably enough, having no familiarity with spherical vortices, Mrs. Marson's diagram might be taken to suggest a downflow component on the leading side matched by upflow component on the opposite side. It seems more likely that there was downflow component all round the outside matched by invisible upflow close to the vertical axis. This could still result in horizontal translation with axis tilted in the direction of motion. It would remain compatible with the sphere converted into a funnel or pear-shape aloft, as actually transpired. Probably, the initial downflow component was near the centre, as typical of vortex-rings, until the ground was reached. This direction could then reverse, if only to account for the apparent loitering and ingestion of chaff which then centrifuged to fill the volume. On leaving the surface suction-loop, this component could reverse again leading to descent and repetition. Only a spherical vortex could aspire to such reversals without immediate loss of energy although its decay into the funnel shape prior to final dissipation might be accelerated.

The reasons why the Pearson family are thought to have sighted a Hill's spherical vortex initially aspirating chaff might be summarised as follows:

(1) The conviction and competence of the Pearsons who have all along suspected that crop circles are formed in this way.

(2) It seems to be accepted that vertical components in dust-devils are uniformly upward except perhaps within the extreme central core; for example, one was seen from a glider to raise coal dust high above a railway depot, and pilots from a nearby airfield reliably gain lift by flying tangentially into them. Three-dimensional motion is not usually apparent in their vicinity, unlike the sighting here.

(3) Dust-devils do not usually rise or bounce into the air over level ground, as happened twice in this instance. Their trail is untidy and not thought to amount to 'flat circular impressions' in stubble fields in particular. Because they comprise warmer or drier air than their surroundings, there is no mechanism whereby they can be seen descending, as happened twice in the case under discussion.

But what theory might explain this case, if only with the wisdom of hindsight? The answer is surely that on perhaps rare occasions, a rotary thermal forms as a result of heat being stored and released from corn fields. Southern England, where the circles total is said to reach seven hundred during the hotter summers of recent date, must be especially prone, including its high percentage of circles on chalk soils and the steep rolling hills of no great heights. Once such rotary thermals form, they may well be accompanied by the rotary or vortex-tube heat-exchanger action usually known as the Ranque-Hilsch effect after the names of the French inventor and subsequent German investigator. As is well known, the vortex tube has reached the market in its smaller duct-contained form - more noted for its simplicity than efficiency when friction of the walls has to be taken into account. With the ducted version, the inner helical current or core is found to be colder due to the more energetic particles being centrifuged into the outer and thus hotter helical sleeve. Counter-flow between the two helical currents is normal with each being tapped by small tubes at opposite ends. In the event of a rotary thermal 'exploding' silently and lacking structural rigidity, the heat-exchanger effect must be temporary as centripetal forces associated with curvature of an entrained secondary flow in vertical planes are overcome. Any such silent exploding might well discharge radially a number of spherical vortices at some height such as 2000 feet, or on occasions lower down with the damage pattern observed to a cornfield in Staffordshire and a beach in Kent (as described to the Oxford Conference by David Reynolds). Some rotary thermals may well lead to tornadoes or even vortex-breakdown instability, but the majority over southern England must not. One of these latter is thought to have been sighted by me as long ago as 1962, as the subject of some description in the April 1989 edition (pp 123-125) of *The Journal of Meteorology*.

There was no reference on this occasion to a spherical vortex being seen, but they easily could have been present in position "B" in the sketch (p. 125 *loc. cit)* where long branches reached down to a low level over moorland rather than responsive crops. These branches were visible radiating from the rotary thermal, first horizontally just above cloud base, and then vertically downwards. At the time they were assumed to represent sub-vortices but they could equally well have been the trails of spherical vortices prolonged in one favoured direction.The sense of the parent rotary thermal was cyclonic, and that of the inversions naturally anticyclonic. The wind driving slowly along the rotary thermal was from the east, which would mean that it would follow the direction of the rotation on the right-hand side, as observed. The vertical array of vortex-rings is hard to justify by counter-flow alone but may imply a cooling effect.

But would a descending and previously chilled spherical vortex initiate some of the stranger forms of crop circle, such as the satellite patterns, the contra-rotating sets of rings, the radial outflow spurs, and perhaps the rare or localised rectangles that have been recorded? The answer seems to be that they well might, given that a spinning spherical vortex could itself continue or develop the Ranque-Hilsch effect. Thus, the satellite patterns probably represent splashes on impact, two, three or four in number at roughly equal spacings. Academic specialists on vortex-ring theory have suggested that counter-rotation could be the result of an impact and spreading over the surface when spin has been added to a vortex-ring. Another possibility is that this represents the operation of the third law of motion in horizontal planes, with action and reaction becoming equal and opposite. The radial spurs may represent a line of yield or weakness before wind pressure or perhaps the further tilting of a vertical axis. The presence of parallel rectangles on these occasions is baffling (if they are not hoaxes or additions), but they may mean that the air of a Hill's spherical vortex has acquired and carried earthwards a charge of static electricity of no great voltage. Each symmetrical pair of rectangles might represent a bridge like a rainbow-band crossing the core extension at a particular radial distance. Excrescences or claws are even harder to explain at present, but again they may represent another effect of an electrical charge. Yet another type of charge action may be the quadrants or swastika divisions of one crop circle impression, or this could have a more aerodynamic explanation.

The author can claim to have seen aloft only a total of four rotary or eddy thermals, the first of which is described and dates from 1962. The second was quite near the west coast over South Wales a year or two later. The third was over north-western Wiltshire and lasting long enough to be photographed as not unlike a tail dangling below a cumulus cloud. The fourth was caused by a stubble fire or fire-whirl, and seemed to draw down a cone of cool air from aloft, say five thousand feet overhead. None of the three latter displayed smoke-rings of cloud matter or acted as vortex tubes; these may well be infrequent or perhaps largely limited to the night hours.

OPERATION HIGH HILL – CERES'S CIRCLES WATCH OF 1990

Lights and Noises in the Atmosphere

Operation High Hill, organised by CERES, took place from Friday 13 July to Saturday 11 August 1990, chiefly on the Beckhampton Downs in central-north Wiltshire, but with additional watching at Bratton and Upton Scudamore (West Wiltshire) in the period 13 July to 20 July. The hope was to obtain eyewitness and photographic evidence of either circles forming or their associated light-forms appearing, together with instrumental data regarding the condition of the atmosphere as a function of time. Alas, we were out of luck this year, as also last year (Operation Green Hill), but one of our observers did at least have a sighting of a luminous form above a field in which circles were found when daybreak came.

The key to our operation was mobility. Instead of setting up the entire team in front of a single field for the whole period of the operation, the team was split in order that different zones could be monitored simultaneously, the choice of zone depending upon recent developments and present and predicted weather variations. On Friday nights, when observer numbers were at a maximum, as many five or six hillside or hilltop observation posts were each manned by one or two carloads of circles watchers.

The operation was intended to be a quiet affair without sought-for publicity. However on the first night, the 13th July, the meeting of some thirty observers at Silbury Hill car-park was attended by several press reporters and ABC Television of the U.S.A. who were making a documentary programme on the circles effect. Among the scientists present were Dr John Graham (chief agronomist at Shuttleworth College, Cranfield Institute of Technology), Dr Robin Allen (Department of Physics, Southampton University), Dr Chris Nash (Southampton University), David Reynolds (Lancaster University), George Bathurst, Maxwell Woosnam, and Gordon Garrould. Other keen circle watchers included Paul Fuller, Peter Rendall, Roger Davis, Jacqui Pearson, Richard Flaherty, Busty Taylor, Michael Dimmock, Stanley Morcom, Una Dawood, and Alan Rayner.

The ABC television crew assisted that night by filming with their infrared night-vision camera at Bishops Cannings and Alton Barnes. At Bishops Cannings adjoining the Calne Road a four-ringed quintuplet had appeared on 1st June. Its arrival had been heard in the darkness of the night by farmhand Andrew Woolley as an extraordinary whistling sound which woke him up before it stopped soon afterwards. A further quintuplet hit the same field on 6th July, partially overlapping the first quintuplet. At Alton Barnes the now-famous circles complex appeared on Thursday 12th July and was fresh and undamaged when the CERES team inspected it on the evening of the next day and the following morning. The night of Wednesday-Thursday had been calm except of course for the particular location of the "vortex sheet" where the descending vortices struck, but the night of Friday-Saturday (the first crop-watch night) was unfortunately rather windy and no circles appeared anywhere that night. However, the next night (14th–15th) when only one witness was present (and he was an unsuspecting but observant member of the public, not an intended circles watcher, who was on the road near the top of Walker's Hill, Alton Barnes) a marvellous orange-yellow light form manifested itself by hovering close to the hilltop. In the morning wheatfield circles were found close by (for details, refer to the article on eye-witness sightings, pages 181-2).

One of the circles observers working with the CERES team was Richard Flaherty, an experienced wildlife photographer. He spent three weeks camped on the downs, and was out watching practically every night from 20 July onwards, choosing sites according to the wind conditions. One starlit night at 2.30 in the morning (BST) he was walking along a track at SU 076095. This was slightly below the ridge along which the A4 passes, and was between the A4 and Windmill Hill, Avebury. Richard was moving westwards when he saw in the distance to the south-east a single column of light coming from high in the sky into what he realised must have been Stephen Horton's wheatfield the other side of the A361 around 1.25 km away (SU 083685). Unfortunately he could not see the lower end of the column because the ridge intervened and there was no quick way of attaining the ridge. The column seemed to be the result of weak self-illumination and in particular was entirely different from car headlights in character, brightness and direction. In fact the luminous column, which was nearly vertical, definitely had nothing to do with aircraft, there being none about anyway. He watched the unusual light for six or seven seconds not fully aware of its importance, but nevertheless decided that in the morning he should look to see whether any circles had appeared below - which he did. The date was Wednesday 25th July, the morning when Stephen Horton, like Richard Flaherty, found that the field contained circles linked by curving paths (the so-called 'scrolls'). This observation of a luminous column or tube is very important being the third time in three years that such a report has come to our attention. The other occurrences were at Silbury Hill (June 1988) and Bratton (July 1988) when the witnesses were able to specify that they definitely saw *tubes,* not beams, of light.

During the four weeks of Operation High Hill a number of circles appeared on the Beckhampton Downs but not within sight of our waiting observers. There were some near misses. For instance, one of our observers arrived at Silbury Hill the morning of 1st August to find that numerous circles had appeared in the opposite wheatfield from the A4 overnight. His photographs of these circles (page 166) were among the few ever taken of these circles because the farmer set about harvesting the crop next day. Indeed, as inevitably happens every year the crop-circle season terminated itself by the disappearance of the cereal crops. In a mainly rainless, warm July-August, as in 1989 and 1990, harvesting starts early and is completed early. We hope for better luck on the next circles watch (Operation Blue Hill) when we plan to return to the same general area for a more detailed and persistent monitoring programme of the Beckhampton Down-Pewsey Vale circles region. The starting date is likely to be Friday 21 June 1991.

THE RIDDLE OF THE RINGS: DEVELOPMENTS IN CROP-CIRCLE RESEARCH IN 1990

By G.T. MEADEN

Abstract: The latest research into crop-circles undertaken between April 1990 and April 1991 is summarised in this article. Besides reporting a considerable amount of observational work some of the first analytical results are reviewed too. It is important to emphasise that all the fresh evidence continues to support the generalised atmospheric vortex theory as the cause of the circles in the crops; that is to say, the circles owe their origin to nothing more than natural aerial vortices interacting with crops on the ground. However, the details of these vortices, the vortex-crop interaction and the resulting crop-circles display many extraordinary features *which denote an extraordinary phenomenon at work* - one which will have very considerable consequences for physics, meteorology, archaeology and prehistory. New features not previously noted include double-circle systems joined by a spur or "corridor" and sometimes accompanied by rectangular marks and rings or semi-circular arcs. Many of these systems were found aligned exactly along or parallel to tractor marks or "tram lines". At Alton Barnes and Stanton Saint Bernard in Wiltshire there were linear arrays of this type consisting of *twin pairs* of double-circles with additional single circles in the same line. A discussion is held on the possible reason why the implied vortex sheet should seemingly be attracted to tractor lines in this way. Also, this year further reports were forthcoming on acoustic and optical effects associated with circle-making vortices, and there were fresh accounts from eye-witnesses who had watched circles as they formed from the effect of vortices.

1990 proved to be the most exciting season for circles research since studies began ten years ago. So many discoveries were made, and in such diverse and wholly unexpected ways, that this present report on the season's work is to be regarded as simply a provisional, condensed summary of the major observations. Further details together with a start on the analysis may be found in issues of the monthly *Journal of Meteorology.* At the same time it is a pleasure to take the opportunity to acknowledge the help of so many investigators ranging from enthusiastic amateurs to research scientists at the professorial level who have so willingly and usefully co-operated with CERES. It is by such collaboration and teamwork that we shall eventually arrive at amassing the precise data that are needed (circle types and surveys, places of occurrence, exact times and dates of formation, video and photographic sequences of circles and vortices happening by night and by day) in order to resolve this challenging and endlessly fascinating problem.

THE SEASON'S TOTALS

Over 700 circles were found in Britain in 1990, the earliest in April, the latest towards the end of August. They were spread across 30 counties, including Wales and Scotland, besides which there were good reports of circles from Ireland, Holland, Bulgaria, Japan, Canada and the U.S.A. This large total was made possible because of the co-operation of so many enthusiasts via the nationwide CERES organisation. As usual for Britain most circles were found in wheatfields, but there were some reports from fields of barley, rapeseed, linseed, and silage grass.

The circle distribution was spread across thirty counties. In 1990, as in 1989, Wiltshire dominated the scene with about 70% of the year's total. This year the leading counties were Wiltshire: over 400; Hampshire: over 50; Norfolk 18; Devon 17; Sussex 16; Oxfordshire 13; Buckinghamshire: 12, and so on.

THE FIRST CIRCLES

Britain's first circle of the year was spotted on 28 April in a field of rape south-west of Windmill Hill near Avebury, Wiltshire. This field formed part of R.A.F. Yatesbury until station and airfield closed down in the 1960's and the fields reverted to farmland. Another circle of apparently similar age was found by Mr. Busty Taylor a few days later. Judging by the age of the circles a formation date of 20-24 April may be surmised, the wind being approximately north-east in this period. The next circles, seven in all with one of them ringed, were found on Beckhampton Down in Wiltshire on 3rd May only a few kilometres from Yatesbury. Their slightly aged appearance suggested they had formed in April like the others.

Next, on 13th May, Mr. Taylor found a new formation: a triple-ringed quintuplet - main circle diameter 31 metres, satellites about 4.2m, ring diameters 36m, 47m, and 61 metres (or 200 feet). Within the group lay a half-metre baby while a seventh circle lay a little to the north. Three more lay to the east further down the slope and seven were randomly dispersed in a neighbouring field. Thus by 13th May we knew of 26 circles for Wiltshire. The first Hampshire case of the season came from the famous Cheesefoot Punchbowl and could be described as a circle surrounded by a "doughnut ring". Beyond the perimeter of a 12-metre solid circle was a narrow undamaged band and then a ring some 12 metres in width.

After the next happening we were back at Bishop's Cannings. On 19th May Busty had found the biggest circle so far known to circles investigators: a 61-metre diameter giant. Three rings were noted to surround it at the time, their diameters 68, 79 and 85 metres. Also in this big field were the circles of a *vortex shower* (defined below) numbering 28. Then between 22nd and 27th May another vortex shower added 35 to the fast-escalating total. The new circles were tiny, many about a metre across, the biggest 2-3 metres, and they were peppered about the field seemingly at random. It was on 27th May that a fourth, larger ring - diameter 92 metres - was spotted around the three-ringed circle. Its authenticity is admittedly a puzzle. It could have been fashioned by two people working together, the first walking round at a constant distance from a second who followed either ring 2 or ring 3 holding the end of a tape six or twelve metres in length. Alternatively, and perhaps more likely, the crop may have been weakened at the usual bending place a few centimetres above the ground at the time of the original incident by a force circulating in "ring 4", although the crop did not topple domino-fashion until vibrated by general gusty winds a few days later.

Circle reports rolled in steadily from Wiltshire, Hampshire and Oxfordshire. By 1st June the 1990 total was 160 and CERES's overall databank total had passed the 1000 mark. The May total had escalated away rapidly because such a large number of "vortex showers" had been spotted from aircraft. This new word, "vortex shower", appropriately recognises the role behind the meaning of multiple occurrences, which either happen in a widely-dispersed fashion across one or more fields, or sometimes in a more limited, quasi-linear fashion.

Short, quasi-linear rows were found on several occasions, as on the curving summit of Furze Knoll, a part of Morgan's Hill between Bishop's Cannings and Calstone-Wellington. This place was visited the day before the Oxford conference by the visiting professors, and identified as an example of marks made by boundary-line vortices. (Spinning vortices along such boundaries have been described by Professor Scorer in his *Clouds of the World* although vortices involving descent were not then recognised). A similar example had been noted the previous August beneath Beckhampton Hill in a wheatfield (of which one is shown in Fig.2 of Snow and Kikuchi's paper and another in Fig.5 of Meaden's opening article). This is a vital observation, as Professor Snow stressed in his lecture, because each row plainly points to a line of separation of a fundamental kind crossing the hilltop and continuing downwind. Other vortex-lines turned up during May-June 1990, notably at Yatesbury in the lee of Windmill Hill, on the slopes of Overton Hill (east of Avebury), and further away in Oxfordshire (towards Childrey), and vortex showers were quite widespread later in the summer too.

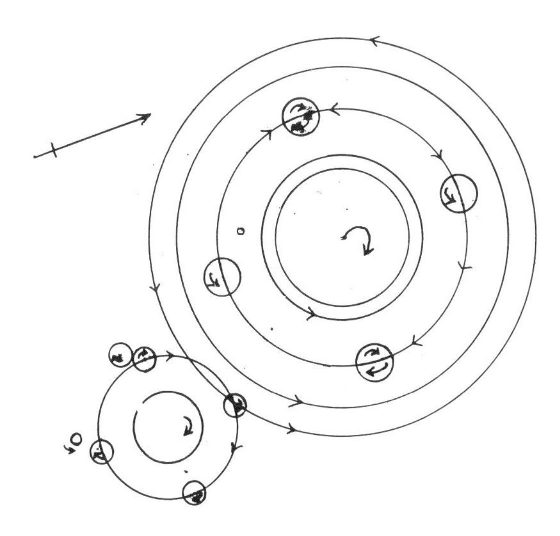

Fig 1. Bishop's Cannings, along the Calne Road. A four-ringed quintuplet formed on 1 June and single-ringed quintuplet which appeared on 6 July 1990. Some additional small circles seen on this drawing appeared as part of a vortex shower on 1 June.

QUADRUPLE-RINGED AND TRIPLE-RINGED QUINTUPLETS

Early on 1st June a four-ringed *quintuplet* system appeared in the parish of Bishop's Cannings along the Calne Road (Figure 1). Some time after midnight the occupant of the nearby farmhouse, farmhand Andrew Woolley, was awoken by a screaming, whistling sound. This was probably the moment, half-a-kilometre away, when the circles appeared, as we have plenty of evidence from other occasions to indicate that circle-making vortices are accompanied by whirlwind-sounding acoustics. In fact, a similar statement was made seven weeks later to Jenny Randles who was investigating the 22-metre diameter Cheshire circle at Preston Brook. She was told of a "high-pitched screeching wail coming from the direction of the field" at 1 to 2 a.m. on 28 July. In Pyecombe, Sussex, a local woman was "woken up by noises the night the crop circles turned up". These were the circles of a "classic triplet" which appeared in the first week of August.

Quintuplet sets with a faint ring connecting the satellites have been known since 1983 (Bratton, Wiltshire – c.f. *Circles Effect and its Mysteries* Fig. 33. p.65). Early study of the satellite-ring overlap at Bishops Cannings showed that ring formation had preceded every one of the satellite circles. Close study of the westernmost satellite further revealed the peculiarity that the ring (diameter 58m) had entered this circle from *opposite* directions, and that the anticlockwise part of the ring *became* the swirling anticlockwise flow of the satellite (Figure 2). For this circle at least one may conclude that the air or ionised air flowing in the 58-metre diameter narrow ring was constrained to recirculate as the 7-metre diameter satellite circle. On 6 July a single-ringed quintuplet (ring diameter 33m) affected the same field, overlapping the 92-meter diameter fourth ring of the four-ringed quintuplet.

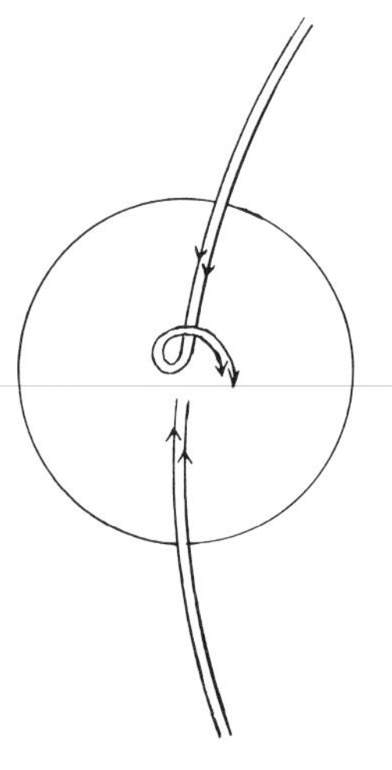

Fig. 2 Detail of the westernmost satellite of the four-ringed satellite at Bishop's Cannings showing how the motion within the ring appears to have redirected itself to create the satellite.

Another *four-ringed quintuplet* appeared at Upton Scudamore 20 km to the south-west in West Wiltshire near Warminster at the end of June (Figure 3). This one had a small satellite on its outermost or fourth ring (not visible in this photograph) in addition to four big satellites on the second ring. Two fields away was a *three-ringed quintuplet,* formed the same day. This system could even be named a *septuplet* because the outermost ring entertained two small opposed clockwise satellites in addition to the four big anticlockwise satellites on the first ring (Figure 4). An eighth circle lay on the second ring but this one may have descended as part of a vortex shower rather than as an integral part of the main system. Another array of circles formed the same day at Upton Scudamore was a linear triplet in which the middle circle was triple ringed.

THE FIRST HAMPSHIRE-AREA DUMB-BELL SET WITH RECTANGULAR FEATURES

On 23 May a circle pair appeared in the county parish of Chilcomb and near to Cheesefoot Punchbowl (Figures 5 and 6). Its unusual features were: (1) the spur from the bigger circle which in effect became an avenue uniting the circles, and (2) the four rectangular trenches which were variously called troughs, squares, boxes, coffins and other names during the course of the season.

The wind that night fell calm having been from an easterly quarter, and became westerly after the passage of a ridge. The corridor linking the circles lay east-west. This was also the direction of the tramlines, the lower field-boundary a hundred metres away, and the orientation with respect to a hill close to the east.

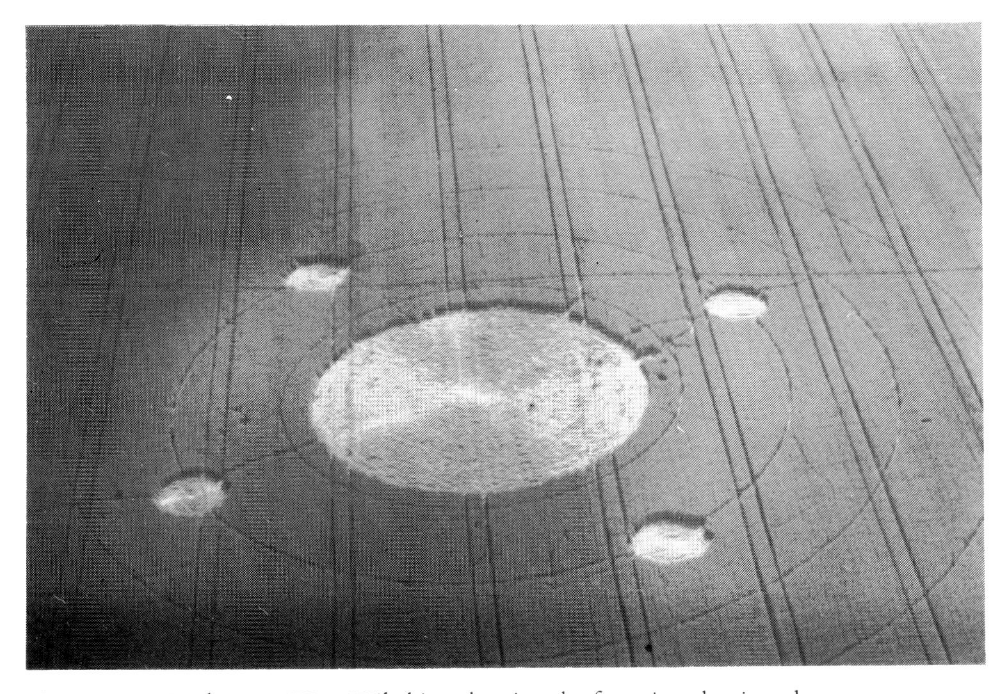

Fig. 3 Upton Scudamore, West Wiltshire, showing the four-ringed quintuplet.

Fig. 4 Upton Scudamore, West Wiltshire, showing the three-ringed quintuplet, three additional circles on the second and third rings, and six circles from a vortex shower.

Fig 5. "Dumb-bell" arrangement with spur and rectangular markings. Chilcomb, Hampshire, 23 May 1990. In 1989 when this field was planted with rape a single circle was formed (to the right of the picture). In 1987 a huge ringed circle with radial blast centre formed in the middle distance of this wheatfield.

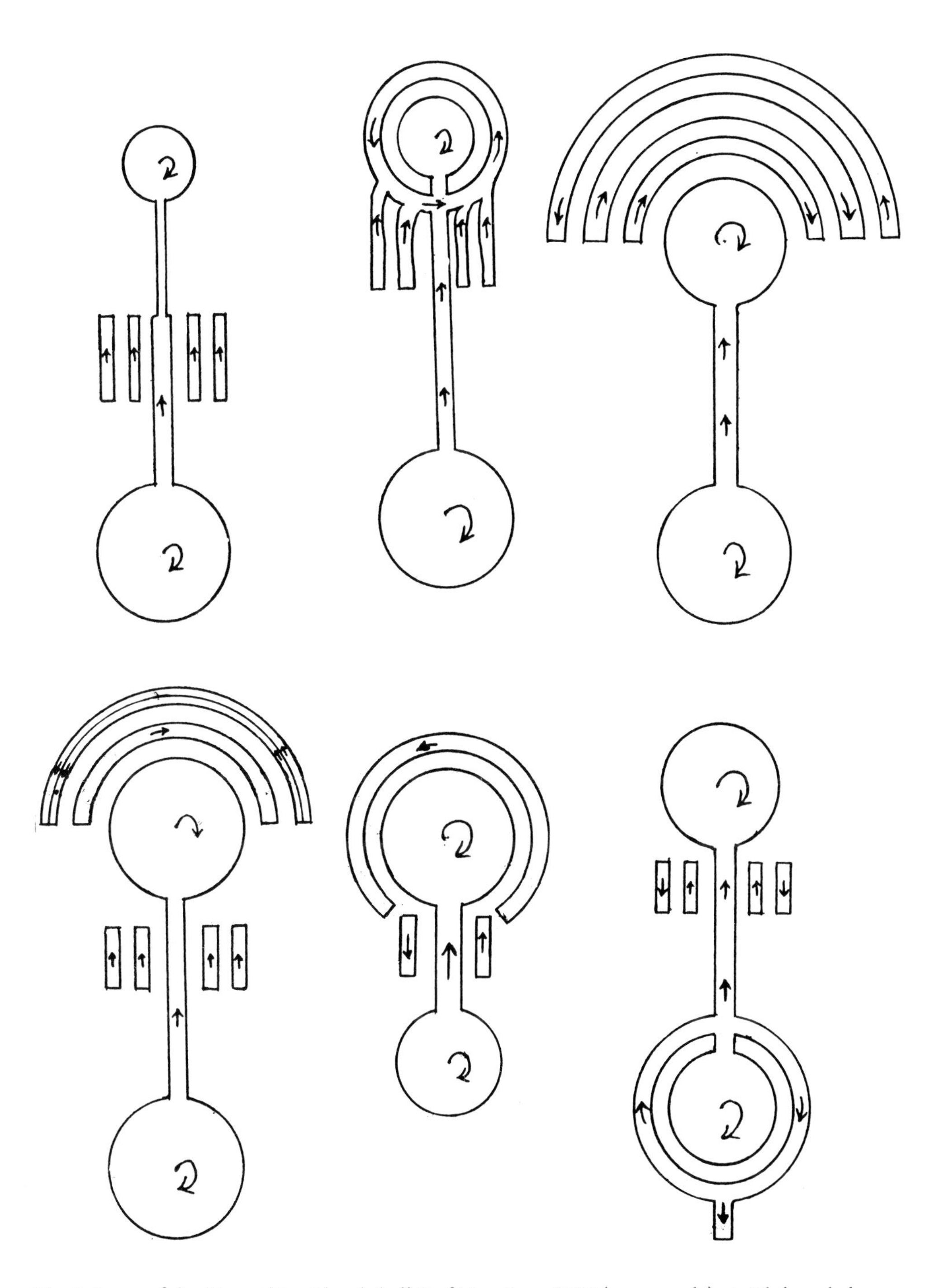

Fig. 6 Some of the Hampshire "dumb-bells" of May-June 1990 (not to scale). 1. Chilcomb, lower field; 2. Near Cheesefoot Head; 3. Chilcomb, upper field; 4. Near Litchfield/Seven Barrows; 5. Near Morestead; 6. Near Cheesefoot Head.

While an understanding of such a pattern will not be possible for some time, it may nevertheless be suggested that the pattern is the result of instability, a consequence of an unstable and complex vortex (or double vortex) making a powerful impact with the crop and the ground. The mirror-image symmetry noted within the trenches is remarkable. Each trench from a pair on one side is mirrored by its opposite number with regard to the internal lie of the crop (Figure 7). In fact, despite the rectangularity of shape the quintessence of vorticity *is* present within the beds of these trenches. Because a rectangular mark in the crop is what would result from the translatory motion of a "rainbow arc" or semi-circular arc across the field, trenches do in any event retain the quality of the vorticity which drives the system.

DUMB-BELLS WITH TRENCHES, AVENUE AND RING

A related circle system appeared a few days later on high ground a kilometre from the top of Cheesefoot Head (Figure 8). In this the smaller circle was surrounded by a ring, the spur being so long as to constitute a complete avenue or corridor uniting the circles. In the trenches the felled corn displayed the same mirror-image tendencies as in the previous case but the trenches were elongated towards the ring, turning slightly on the approach to the ring so as to follow the direction of motion of the ring. This shows that the

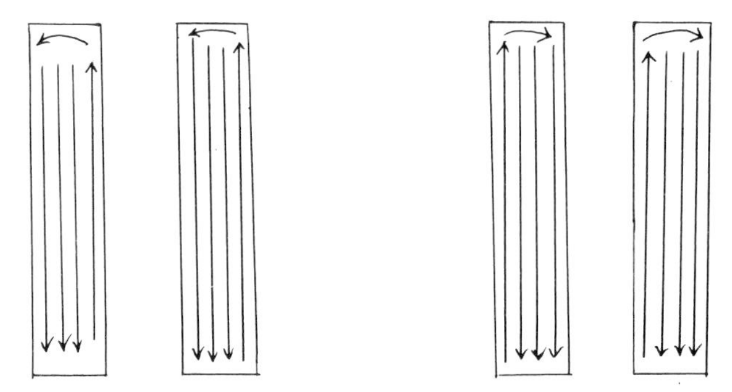

Fig. 7 Detail of the lie of the fallen wheat in the rectangular areas of the Chilcomb dumb-bell.

ring formed first, even if only by milliseconds, with the resulting distortion to the proximal ends of the lengthening trenches. Dumb-bell alignment was this time from west-east, at an acute angle of about 45 deg with the tramlines and also angled wth regard to the downslope direction. The weather that night (May 31st-June 1st) had fallen calm, after which the wind picked up from a westerly direction.

Another system which attracted much attention was a triple-ringed circle in which the innermost rings were composed of interrupted arcs as in the Figure 9. This appeared in Dog Leg Field on the Longwood Estate on 6th June a week after a conventional triple-ringed circle had manifested itself 700 metres to the east. These formations were easily seen from the Petersfield-Winchester road. One should pay attention to the directions of motion within

Fig. 8 George Bathurst (left) and Paul Fuller studying the dumb-bell circles (number 2 of Fig. 6). They are standing in the ring where the lefthand pair of trenches meet the ring. The trees of Cheesefoot Head may be seen top left of the picture.

Fig. 9 Ringed circle with two pairs of interrupted arcs on Longwood Warren, near Cheesefoot Head, June 1990.

the 90-degree arcs as indicated by the lie of the wheat. The character of these discontinuities reminds us that the rings form at the moment of impact, the result of a short-lived boundary interaction. Although the rings are found interrupted at the surface, they were not necessarily incomplete when they were a short distance above the crop canopy.

VARIOUS HAMPSHIRE DUMB-BELLS, JUNE - JULY 1990

In Figure 6 which is not a scale drawing we summarise *some* of the complex shapes known for Hampshire in 1990. Whereas they differ from one another, they have the basic dumb-bell base as a common feature.

The one with its three 170-degree arcs appeared at the upper end of the same field of wheat as the first Chilcomb circles in May but it arrived three and half weeks later on steeply-sloping ground near the top of the hill.

The next was at Seven Barrows, north of Litchfield, in Hampshire near the A34 road to Newbury. On the evening of 22 June I pointed out this featureless field to conference members as we drove past following our circles tour, that this was a 'repeater' region for circles events (circles are known for this area for 1976, 1978, 1981, 1982 and 1985). The circles were a hundred metres from a group of Bronze Age barrows which had been there for over three thousand years.

At Morestead, south of Winchester, a related dumb-bell combination appeared before the end of June, as did another on Longwood Warren in a field not distant from the eminence that is Cheesefoot Head. Yet another formed on Chilcomb Down on land belonging to the Bruce Family, near the A31 junction with the B3404.

In southern England the crops remained green until the middle of June. As always happens within each circle the felled wheat or barley, being green, quickly responded to the geotropic effect, the means by which the youngest nodes turn upwards until the top of the stem becomes vertical. An example from Exton (Hampshire) is provided in Figure 10. There is no truth in the rash statements being put out in 1989-1990 by certain non-scientists that a fallen crop continues to grow sideways.

THE ALTON BARNES CIRCLE COMPLEX

The magnificent array of circles which formed in East Field between the village of Alton Barnes and Walker's Hill overnight on Wednesday-Thursday July soon became the best-known crop circles in the world (Figure 11). These circles lay in the Vale of Pewsey, immediately south of the chalk downs and a few kilometres south-east of Devizes in Wiltshire. After a week of tolerating good-humouredly a degree of trespass in his field Farmer Tim Carson decided to receive visitors at £1 a time, a sensible reaction which allowed many thousands of interested researchers and non-scientists their first glimpse of these magnificent, wholly genuine circles.

The difficulty of understanding this wonder of nature was, if anything, *aided* by the discovery that a similar but non-identical set of circles appeared at

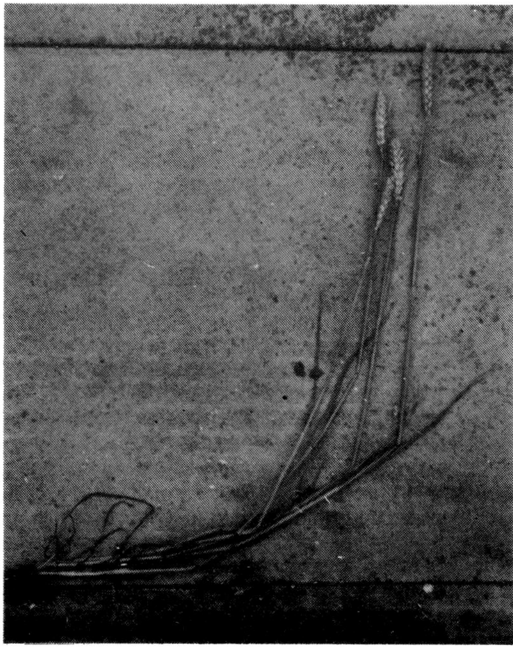

Fig. 10 Within three days of the appearance of the Exton quintuplet the wheat was straightening up again by the normal process of nodal bending. A few plants were removed in order to be displayed more clearly in the second photograph. While the lower part of the stem is horizontal to the ground, the upper part has turned through 90 degrees by bending at two nodes.

Fig. 11 Alton Barnes: the spectacular 9-circle complex comprising two dumb-bell pairs having fin-like features, possibly the result of unstable vortices impacting the ground on 12 July 1990.

about the same time a couple of kilometres to the west in the parish of Stanton St Bernard. Both sets of circles were aligned in the direction of tramlines, which for Alton Barnes meant 346 deg magnetic and for Stanton 098 deg. Indeed at Stanton St Bernard the circles were centred exactly *along* tramlines (Figure 12).

Of all the remarkable features built into these circle systems the first to note are the duality of the paired circles (dumb-bells), the rectangular trenches, and the curious claw-like fins or arms protruding from some circles and rings. The near correspondence of certain features between the one group and the other must carry clues about their origins. In fact, a couple of weeks later some kilometres to the north yet another circle group of the same classification appeared on land between the East Kennet and West Kennet long barrows. The mutual resemblance was uncanny (Figure 13).

Clearly, a common underlying agent is responsible for the longitudinal array of patterns and their primary oddities like the three-fingered examples. The curious claw effect appeared too on a *solitary* circle at Stanton St Bernard (Figure 14) and another on Allington Down three kilometres to the north (Figure 15). Analysis is under way.

SOME OTHER BIZARRE CIRCLE SETS

Of the several other circle complexes of the linear-spur type found in July

Fig. 12 Stanton Saint Bernard: an equally dramatic circle complex three kilometres from Alton Barnes but not so much publicised.

we may cite the linear four-circle set from the punchbowl beneath Pepperbox Hill, South Wiltshire (Figure 16), and the triple-circle set on Crawley Down, north of Winchester (Hants), south of Cheesefoot Head (Hants) (Figure 17). The three main circles in the field opposite Silbury Hill this summer were linked linearly by spur-like corridors (Figure 18). As this complex arrived late in the season (1st August) when the corn was ripe, the farmer made a point of harvesting the field the next day.

Other interesting Wessex complexes included ones behind Wilton House (South Wiltshire), on the side of Stone Pit Hill (Central Wiltshire) and near Bramdean (Hants). More conventional were a regular quintuplet at Exton in the Meon Valley (Hants) and two regular quadruplets composed of three 120-deg satellites spaced about a bigger central circle (Oxfordshire and West Wiltshire). Triplets were reported from Sussex and Devon among other counties.

THE CURVING CIRCLE SETS AT BECKHAMPTON AND BRATTON

At Beckhampton, Wiltshire, the night of Tuesday-Wednesday 24th-25th July 1991 produced some amazing circle patterns in a wheatfield of Farmer Stephen Horton. It is possible that the appearance of one or more of the patterns was related to the occurrence of a self-luminous column or tube of light seen pointing into that field at 2.30 a.m. on the 25th.

Fig. 13 East Kennet circle complex which formed a couple of weeks after those at Alton Barnes and Stanton Saint Bernard.

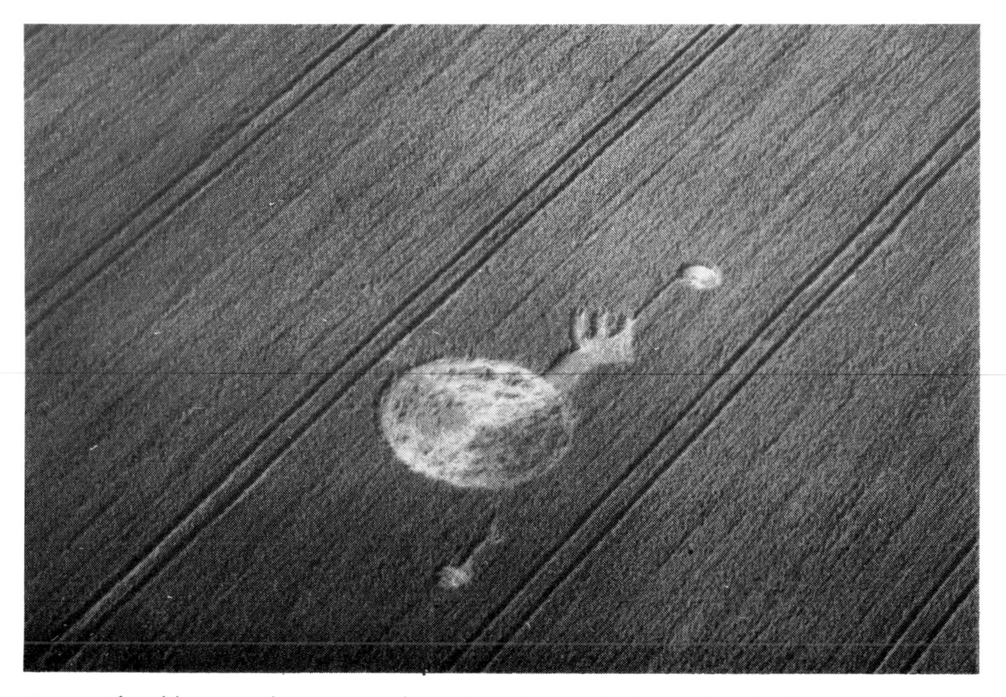

Fig. 14 Claw-like appendage to a single circle at Stanton St. Bernard, Wiltshire.

Fig. 15 A single circle with a claw-like feature on Allington Down, Wiltshire.

Fig. 16 Triple circle set in the punchbowl area beneath Pepperbox Hill, south of Salisbury.

Fig. 17 Linear arrangement of circles on Crawley Down, north of Winchester, Hampshire, displaying the strange-attractor effect.

Fig. 18 Circles opposite Silbury Hill, photographed on 1 August a few hours after their formation.

Fig. 19 Circles at Beckhampton, Wiltshire, lined by curving paths. The anticlockwise circles had standing tufts at their centres.

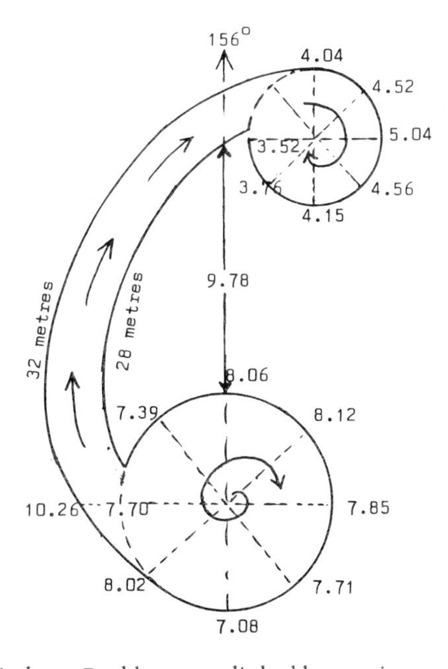

Fig. 20 Survey of two circles at Beckhampton linked by curving paths. Flow lines in the bigger one were outwards, in the smaller one they were inwards!

A general view of the field is given in Figure 19. Altogether there are thirteen circles (some joined to each other by curving corridors) together with one of quasi-triangular shape and some other but smaller geometrical elements of interest in themselves.

Figure 20 provides a sketch, not to scale, of two of the circles with some of the survey points showing. The circles are joined by a curving path thirty metres long. The bigger circle was clockwise outwards and the smaller circle clockwise inwards. Both circles had tufts at their centres. These elementary observations accord with vortex theory in which a ring vortex is envisaged as descending into a field before "spinning up" again. This is not the first time that a curving arc has been seen. In July 1989 there was a long curving path into a single circle in a field close to Cheesefoot Head, Hampshire, and on a smaller scale entry paths of a related type have been spotted elsewhere (1987 Bratton, 1988 Firs Farm, Beckhampton).

Also visible in the photograph (Figure 19) is a series of three linked circles. All were anticlockwise, each with a central tuft, and were joined by a four-metre broad curving corridor. In order, the circle diameters were 14, 7.5 and 7 metres. It was in the biggest of these circles that Paul Ferguson and Terence Meaden performed various *proton magnetometer tests,* parts of which were also filmed for an ITV farming programme and a BBC children's programme. Similar magnetometer tests were carried out on two occasions at Upton Scudamore in the four-ringed quintuplet and its satellites.

Next we mention the tuft-centred quasi-triangular shape, with sides 10-11 metres long, shown in Figure 21. This was likely produced by the descent of a ring vortex which expanded in the usual fashion up to a diameter of eight metres. Beyond this a distortion of the circulating forces set in which led to a quasi-triangular shape with rounded corners. The flattening of the corn within these corners was regular, being no more than an extension of the outward flattening initiated by the primary spiral-circle. Some non-scientists have tended to regard non-circular shapes like the quasi-triangle as wholly anomalous, but the triangle is nothing other than an imperfect circle. It is only to be expected that non-circles and curving paths should occasionally result from the vicissitudes of wandering vortices - that not all the short-lived vortices are perfectly quasi-stationary during their momentary impact with the crop and ground.

Of the other unusual patterns noted in this field there was a mini-triangle with sides 4-4.5 metres long and a rectangle four metres by one metre which displayed the characteristic 'combing' effect into the corn at its remote end in the way commonly noted for the distal end of natural rectangles (like those in Figure 6). The origins of these and some other small cropmarks in the vicinity seem to be linked to the presence of a tractor lane from which they exit. This serves to emphasise the role that tractor marks can play in modifying the earth's local electric field possibly by acting as *strange attractors* (defined overleaf) for vortex descent and hence circle-patterning on some occasions at least. We go into more detail on this later and in other papers. One should note that swirl-centred triangles, dated to July, were also found at Cullompton (South Devon) and Seaburn, Sunderland (Tyne and Wear).

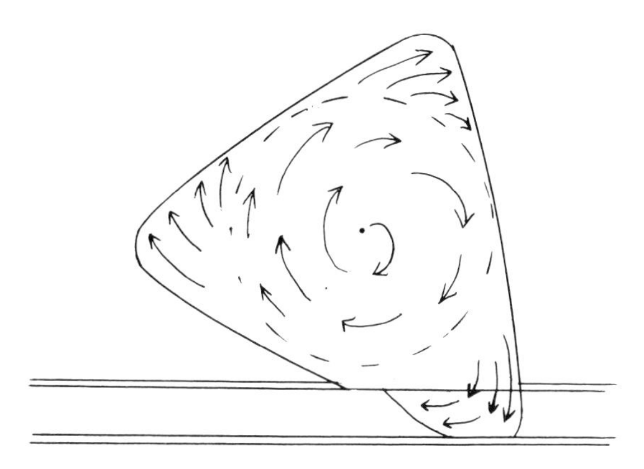

Fig. 21 Sketch of the triangular form at Beckhampton with its outward swirling flow.

THE DAISY PATTERNS - INCLUDING A BALL OF RED LIGHT

Circles in a daisy pattern were reported from Devonshire and Somerset County, the first a centre circle with seven regular satellites from Bickington in June, the second a circle with six satellites from Butleigh Wootton, near Glastonbury in mid-July.

A third daisy-pattern system, one with ten ringed satellites surrounding a central ringed circle, turned up at the end of July in East Anglia (Figure 22). This last was formed on the night of 30-31 July, possibly in the late evening of 30 July at the time of the observation of a glowing ball of red light. It was seen by the farmer shining above his field at Hopton as viewed from his house on the edge of Gorleston (Norfolk). "He looked at it through his binoculars and described it as a red central glow with a thinner red outer ring." [Rather than ring he really meant "shell"]. "By the time he had passed the binoculars to his son the thing had gone" *(Eastern Daily Press).*

This beautiful system may be added to half-a-dozen other groups known for flat coastal regions. These include the intricate Seaburn circle-system of July 1990 studied by Dr. Dennis Wheeler (but about which doubt as to authenticity exists) and the Deal (Kent) swathed circles of 1980 (ref. David J. Reynolds, this book).

We should here emphasise that *hills are not essential prerequisites* for circle formation although, as the author has said on many previous occasions, the presence of hills makes the likelihood of circle formation very much greater. In fact, a relationship with hills has been demonstrated for distances up to six kilometres downwind of the hill. But, whereas the majority of circles are formed quite near hills or on hills, there are indeed a few percent which appear in the absence of any obvious hills. The point to stress is that circles *can* form *anywhere where vortices develop* provided that the vortices 'spin up' or move down to interact with the ground. One obvious source of non-hill vortices is the marine-air/land-air boundary between air-masses known as the sea-breeze front. These fronts produce large numbers of whirlwinds in the right conditions (Meaden *Weather* vol. 36, 47-48 1981), from which it can be surmised that a few of them will occasionally lead to crop-circles. It is for this reason that some fair-weather whirlwinds may be expected to create crop circles if for some reason they undergo vortex breakdown or metamorphose into a descending spherical vortex. This year, once again, we have received reports of real whirlwinds carving out true crop circles in the middle of the day (details reproduced elsewhere in this book and also in the *Journal of Meteorology*).

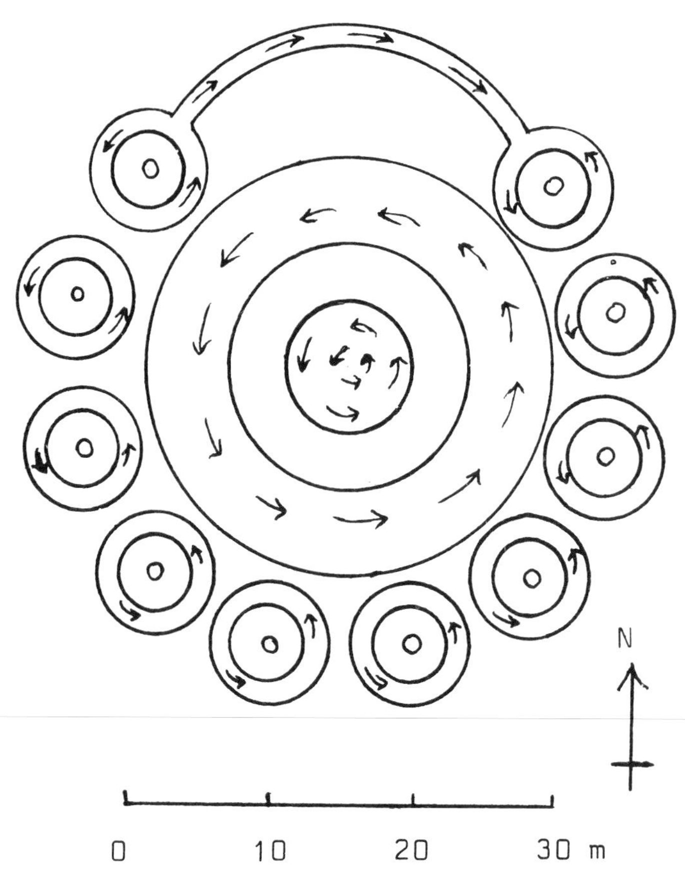

Fig. 22 The so-called daisy-pattern at Hopton near Gorleston, East Anglia (after Bryan Haylett).

Single spurred circles were reported from near West Kennett Long Barrow, West Kennet Stone Avenue, Normanton Down (Wiltshire), Wilmington (Sussex), Beddingham (Sussex), Clifton Campville (East Staffordshire border), and Rawmarsh (South Yorkshire). Opposed double spurs were found at Amport (Hants). On Etchilhampton Hill, Devizes (Wiltshire) the main circle of a dual complex had six radiating spurs. Neither this nor a four-spurred example from Chorley near Litchfield (Staffs) had been fully authenticated at the time of writing.

The main circle at Halton, Wendover (Bucks) had four spurs radiating from it in various directions. Robert Mackenzie surveyed this circle-spur complex and also a neat 11-m diameter ring at Little Missenden in a field of linseed and a marvellous six-circle complex at Amersham with odd-shaped spurs and avenues (Figure 23).

In Devon Douglas Cooper surveyed an extraordinary 7-circle complex at Bulkworthy. Details were given in the first issue of *The Crop Watcher* (Figure 25). Unusual features were the two rectangles whose flow structures diverged from the centre of each rectangle and ended in tight swirls at the southern ends. The largest circle had opposed fins protruding from it. A circle with a fin or a "hook" found at Preston-on-Stour was well described by Nigel Knight.

Other ringed circles were surveyed at Preston-on-Stour (Warwickshire), Linby (Notts), North Walsham (Norfolk), Hampton Bishop (Herefordshire) [this one had opposed spurs as well], Culver Down, Brading (Isle of Wight), Winterbourne Stoke (Wiltshire), Haydon's Coalbach, Radstock (Avon County), Cheesefoot (Hants), Upton Scudamore, and Bratton (Wiltshire). Pure rings were reported from several sites in Britain. Various other circles, some non-simple were found and/or surveyed in Isle of Wight, Leicestershire, Essex, Lincolnshire, Warwickshire, West Midlands, Worcestershire, Herefordshire, Staffordshire, Shropshire, Cheshire, Lancashire, Nottinghamshire, Yorkshire, Humberside, Durham and Northumberland. Welsh reports included Cwm Belan (Llanidloes) and Dyffryn Farm near Cardigan (Dyfed). In Scotland there were circles in silage grass at Blairgowrie, Perthshire, concerning which CERES has received two photographs.

From Ireland we have reports of circles from Ardee (County Lowth) [a 12-m diameter circle in wheat] and Malahide, County Dublin. An aerial photograph of the latter above Biscayne shows a distorted ring 2-m broad and 22-m diameter surrounding a 4-m diameter ring. Alongside was a crook-shape consisting of a 2-m broad path.

OPERATION HIGH HILL AND THE LIGHT OBSERVATIONS

On Friday 13th July began CERES's task to witness circles in the natural process of formation: Operation High Hill. This was centred on the Beckhampton Downs and it ran for a month, ending on Saturday 11th August by which time few unharvested fields were still remaining. The high point of each week was the Friday evening meet at Silbury Hill when numbers rose to a couple of dozen or so. Different hills were manned depending on numbers and the character of wind and weather. The operation was run as a low key affair with no overt publicity. ABC Television News (U.S.) attended for the opening night, together with their night-sight cameras. No-one was

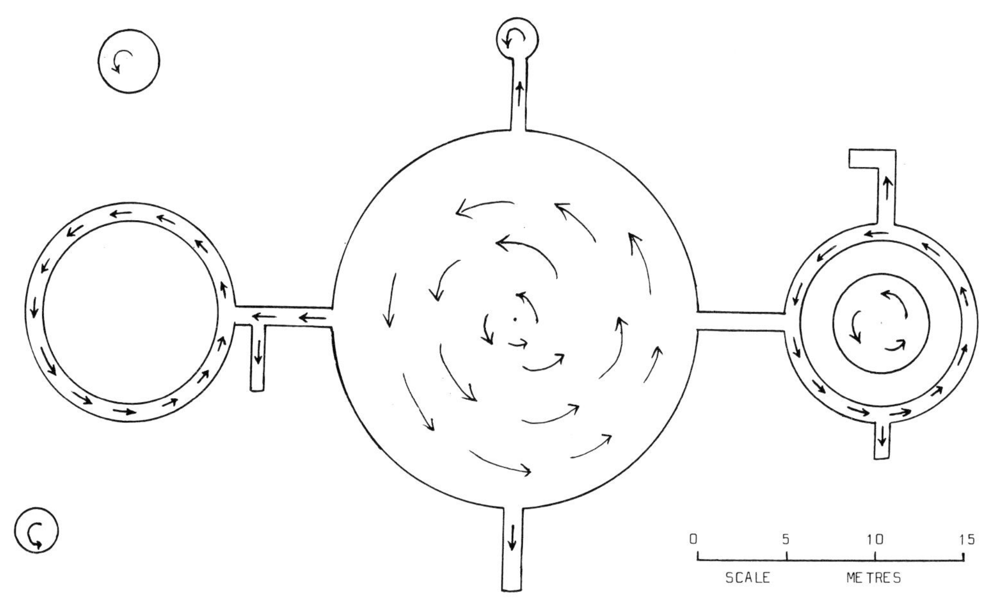

Fig. 23 Circle complex in the Chilterns at Amersham, Buckinghamshire (after Robert Mackenzie).

fortunate to witness circles forming during the month-long operation but one observer, Richard Flaherty, who camped out for three weeks did see a distant column of light shining from a starlit sky into the Beckhampton field where the scroll-like features were found in the morning. The time was 2.30 a.m. on

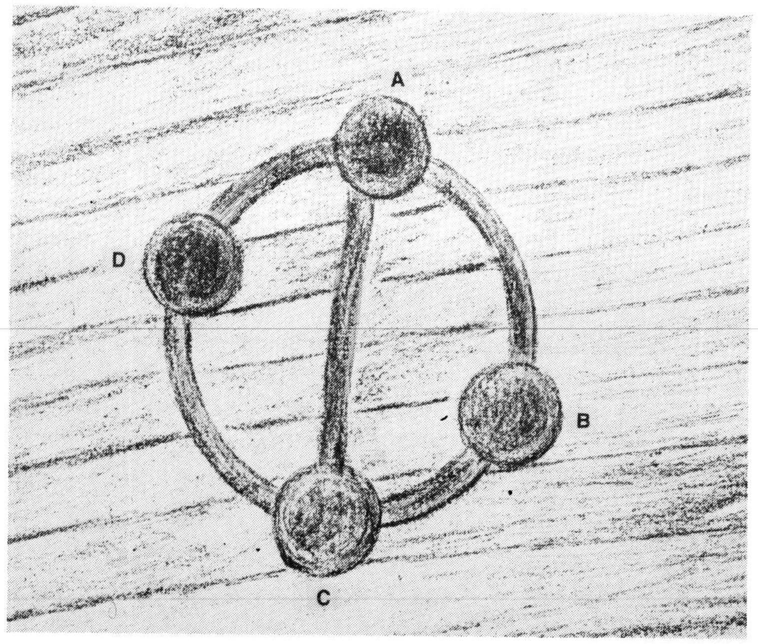

Fig. 24 Circle complex from Bulgaria, July 1990 (after S.G. Taneb).

Wednesday 25 July. He watched the light column for about seven seconds. This description recalls similar Wiltshire light-tube events at Silbury Hill in June 1988 and at Bratton in July 1988.

Following an article in a Bulgarian weekly *(Orbita)* in July several circle reports were received from that country. A four-circle set which appeared on 22 July 1990 is drawn in Figure 24. Main ring diameter was 23-23.5 meters and the satellites 3.5-4 metres across. Another Bulgarian reader reported spiral-centred circles which appeared in the period 14-19 June near Drujba, Sofia.

In Japan there were at least twenty circles. More than twenty occurred in Canada as well, and a even bigger number were reported from the U.S.A.

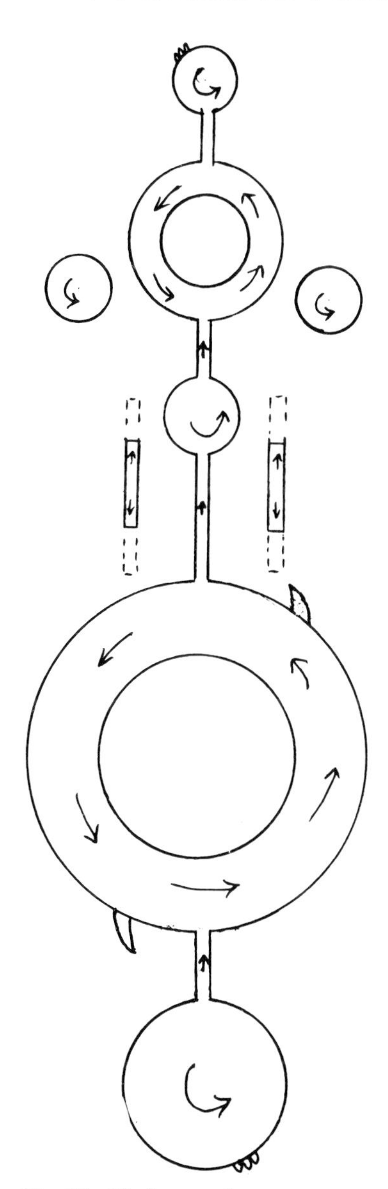

Fig. 25 Circle complex at Bulkworthy, Devonshire (after Douglas Cooper).

SOME THEORETICAL CONSEQUENCES

All in all the 1990 season was outstanding. Many new, wholly unexpected circle types and groups were formed by natural means. The evidence continues to support a natural atmospheric origin for the circles - chiefly via the occurrence of electrified descending vortices capable of producing sound and light - and it is expected that considerable theoretical advances will follow as analyses continue, especially of the more extraordinary groups. The much-publicised Alton Barnes circles demonstrate aberrations from circularity which positively help the generalized vortex theory. For instance, it has been suspected for some time that some vortices have complicated but symmetrical internal structures which lead to the well-known quintuplet formations or broad multi-ringed systems, but at Alton Barnes the crop and ground impact of unstable vortices gave rise to less regular patterns and exposed for analysis something of the satellite-forming and ring-forming elements in a 'miscarriage' situation. By studying imperfect cases like these we are learning more quickly than expected the working details of the complex vortices, and are also demonstrating how effective a research tool the study of imperfect circles can be.

In this context one further circle requires

particular mention because although it was only a single circle it had the unusual characteristic of being a circle of the 'radially-inward suction' kind. This, the first 'truly radial inward' circle in our records of circles which now total 1700, happened at Braishford, Hampshire in August. The 5-m circle was characterised by a ring of bare earth created by an inward parting of the wheat whose heads all lay "towards the centre as though it had been combed". This directional motion produced a conical centre of unflattened wheat protruding upwards from the bed *(Romsey Advertiser).* The circle therefore demonstrated the whirlwind phenomenon of vortical spin-up, in the manner already explained by John Snow.

Strange Attractors. Whereas prior to 1990 due caution demanded the conclusion that there was then *insufficient* evidence to make statements about the possibility of circle-system alignments with tractor lines, enough additional data emerged in 1990 to permit such an announcement. In fact, a surprisingly large fraction of the linear circle-sets (spurred singles, dumb-bells, triple sets, and Alton-Barnes type extended complexes) were found aligned parallel or perpendicular to tram lines. A few were centred precisely along tramlines, and some others were angled at 45 or 60 degrees to tramlines (while others, to be sure, were not).

Analysis is incomplete but one can already say that it appears that a degree of circle alignment with some sort of inherent, largely veiled, regularly-spaced *grid system* can occur (Figure 26). The right-hand drawing is an approximate scale drawing of the six circles in the Stanton St Bernard complex which form the *linear part* of the chain (cf Figure 12). The smallest circle is "out of step" being centred 6.5 metres from the next, but after that the next five centres give inter-centre distances of respectively 17.4, 27.2, 18.3, and 36.6 metres which correlate well with points on *a nine-metre network* or a semi 18-metre network.

For Alton Barnes the correspondence, which is less good, was first tested by Mrs. Julie Blay. From bottom to top the first four inter-centre distances give 10.0, 18.4 and 27 metres, a reasonable start for a basic nine-metre grid (or semi 18-metre grid), but then comes a non-'integral' spacing at around 21 metres, followed by a quasi-nine multiple at 35 metres. For the purpose of the drawing, instead of deforming the grid at this point we have, for convenience, reduced the non-integral spacing of 21 metres to 19 metres to allow for this single 'eccentric?' offset. We should point out that 17-17.5 metres commonly corresponds to the spacing between adjacent pairs of tractor marks, which leads to an overall repetition distance approaching 19 metres when adding on the tractor-line widths themselves (the tractor's width of about 1.6 metres creates pairs of lines up to 1.8 metres across). Wider spacing of 21-23 metres arises from the use of longer boom lengths. On some farms the spacing was 18 metres for many years and then a switch to longer booms was made.

The overall centre-to-centre length of the *principal five* circles at Stanton was 99 metres compared wth 101 metres for the Alton set. It should be recalled that the two circle sets were located three kilometres apart and were angled in quite different directions with regard to the magnetic meridian (098 and 346 deg respectively). Despite this, the circle complexes have remarkable similarities as noted here, and others besides. The clawed fins for instance egress primarily at around 30, 45 or 60 degrees to the main axes (which may suggest they aimed at various network points on the inferred grid system). Also there are four circles or rings in each set, eight in all, each having a diameter close to 15 metres. This tends to suggest the existence of a preferred diametral size related perhaps to a well-defined Larmor radius, the consequence of the magnetron effect (the spiralling of high-velocity charged particles in the direction of an external magnetic field). The suggestion that preferred circle sizes exist seems supported by the observation that so many of the big circle diameters and ring diameters found in 1989 and 1990 were clustered about diameters of 31, 62 and 93 metres, while a tendency for clustering at around 4, 8 and 15 metres had been noted many years earlier.

It would seem that the proposed *grid* (which sometimes corresponds to the visible tramlines) could act as *a wave guide for the local orientation of a vortex sheet.* This would further intimate that electrical effects play a major role in this singular correlation. I propose that the primary vortex if electrified - as indeed I have inferred it to be for other reasons anyway - sometimes finds itself attracted to tractor-line regions because of local electric field anomalies initiated by the repeated passage of tractors up and down the field. Tractors of the same axle width return to the same fields year after year. They begin by working parallel to field boundaries, as a result of which the boom lengths of the planting, pesticide and fertilising machines assure, in some field systems at least, a repetition of the same tractorways up and down the field. Ploughing and planting at right angles in alternating years yields a species of square-based grid. To this novel phenomenon - the electric-field anomaly link with tramlines - I have given the name *strange attractor (J. Meteorology, vol. 15, 317 - 320, 1990).* Reasons for the development of electric-field anomalies, if that is what they are, have yet to be evaluated. I suggest that one is that repeated passage of heavy farm equipment leads to compaction of the thin chalk-dust laden soil to depths approaching the bedrock. This would affect the flow of sub-surface water and hence modify the electrical conductivity of the comparatively dry chalky soil. Besides this, a phenomenon could be operating such as the one proposed by George Nehls (see his article). If a link with the 11-year sunspot cycle exists, then either 1991 or 1992 could be a peak year for circle numbers and their complexities.

Circles in Prehistory The foregoing argument helps to explain why the circles effect in its advanced form, i.e. as evidenced by recent complex-circle discoveries, is a modern development in what is otherwise an age-old problem. Plain circles and simple ringed circles date back to the prehistoric era; the complex circle sets could be a recent manifestation related to farm-machinery usage in the field, especially over dry chalky soils, combined with a peak in

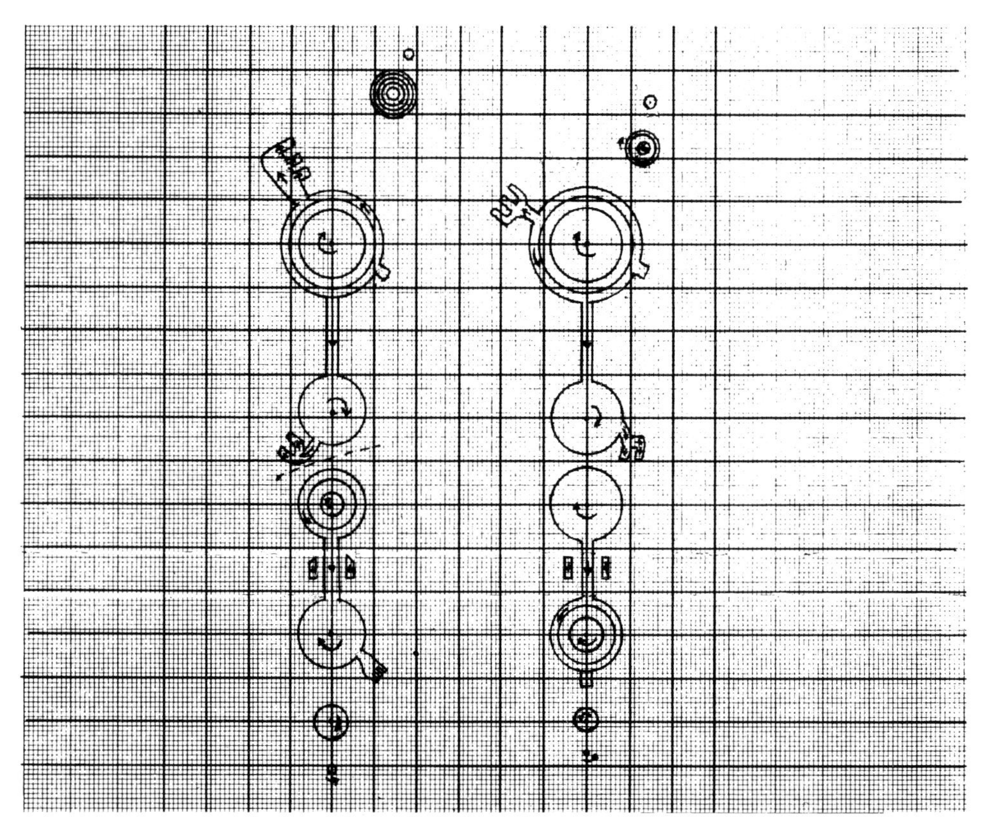

Fig. 26 Approximate scale drawings of the principal Alton Barnes circles (left) and the Stanton St. Bernard circles (right) arranged on a square grid using a nine-metre mesh. The Stanton circles were aligned along tractor lines but the centres of the Alton circles, although parallel to tractor lines, were offset by about 4.5 metres to the left. The centres of the five biggest Stanton circles fall upon 9-metre grid points within accuracy limits of +/− 3/4 metre.

ionisation activity and changes in agricultural practise. The latter embrace the uniformity of seed production and the evenness of crop height which results from identical stem-lengths, seed-planting in neat rows by today's well-designed agricultural machines, a level spread of fertilisers, and a lack of spurious weeds. All these factors help make for uniform field growth in which it is easier to detect small circles, narrow rings, narrow spurs, etc, than ever before. From the time of the Napoleonic wars until the Second World War much of Wessex was down to sheep farming. Cereal fields did exist but they were much smaller than today's fields. Only in the last 50 years has 'prairie' farming of cereal crops become widespread. Centuries and millennia ago the seeds were broadcast unevenly by hand, the manure scattered likewise. Until fifty years ago horses were pulling the plough in many areas. Now the tractors are heavier than ever before, and so is the farm machinery, especially the combine harvesters which follow the same tracks made by the tractors.

The chalk hills of Wessex are the home of the circles phenomenon, just as in the Neolithic and the Bronze Age they were the home of the sacred stone rings, timber rings and circular round-barrows. Our ancestors found simple circles and rings in their crops and in the grass, and they worshipped them. The results of the author's study into this fascinating facet of his research, begun in 1980, and put in writing from 1983 onwards is set out in considerable detail in two books published elsewhere this year, the first of which is *The Goddess of the Stones.*

Acknowledgements We wish to thank the very considerable number of people who by their participation as part of the CERES operation or in collaboration with CERES made possible this important collection of detailed scientific data on the circles effect.

NEW EYE-WITNESS REPORTS OF SOUND, LIGHT AND ELECTROSTATICS IN CONNECTION WITH CIRCLE-FORMATION

By G.T. MEADEN

The most direct and arresting evidence concerning the nature of circle formation comes from the testimony of eye-witnesses. Reported sightings are few to date and have been fortuitous observations by the non-scientific public. Every account is valuable and is to be cherished for its content however limited that may be, except that due regard has to be paid to the likely accuracy of the observations. This situation will prevail until an adequate number of sightings by trained scientists takes place and high-quality video film or cine film of circle-forming events becomes available.

It is therefore noteworthy that we have succeeded in acquiring fresh reports from eye-witnesses who were present when circles formed in fields close to them. Two are reported here, one from Gloucestershire and one from Cambridgeshire. One spectacular case involved an amazing display of electrostatics and plainly demonstrated the link between atmospheric vorticity and natural electricity. Some additional cases are referenced, and others have been introduced elsewhere in this book (pp35-39, 122-124, 130). In addition, new eye-witness reports of ionised vortices are provided for Allington, Alton Barnes and Avebury in Wiltshire. Two further cases were added (pp 196-9) just before this book went to press.

We begin with an interview with Tom Gwinnett, a builder and farmer living at Sunnybanks, Woodside, Woolaston some eight kilometres out of Chepstow (Gwent) along the Lydney road in Gloucestershire (grid reference ST 5898). This is a remarkable eye-witness account of the highest importance for circles research *because it brings together in a single sequence the primary elements of circle formation, self-luminous vortex, electrostatic development, sound, and a car-stop event.* The interview took place on 24 July 1990, almost two years after the event.

One weekday in July 1988 Mr. Gwinnett was driving home along a lane past his own wheatfield when the car stalled and the headlights cut out. It was dusk, the time around 10 p.m. BST., and just dark enough for headlights to be needed. The air was calm and the weather dry. The precise state of the sky is not known but the day had been rainless and the evening sunny. Both the wheat, which was an organically-grown crop ripe for harvesting, and the ground were definitely dry.

Mr. Gwinnett stepped from his car and immediately noticed that "the heads of the wheat seemed to be alive with electricity showing up as myriads of flashes of light, like wiggling glow-worm lights but coloured orange-yellow, and running inwards towards a point in the field about 50 metres away just above which a light-form consisting of numerous orangey-yellow lights was spinning". At the same time the witness could hear "a whirling, humming sound" which he likened to the sound of "an old Singer sewing machine". This continued for some time, certainly for more than a minute, whereupon all the lights vanished abruptly, as if a switch had been pulled, and the sound stopped. At this same moment, the car lights came back on.

Puzzled, Mr. Gwinnett got back into his car, a 1985 2.3 litre petrol-engined Vauxhall, and tried the starter motor. The engine fired and Mr. Gwinnett drove on home. Next morning when he looked across the field to see where he had viewed the spinning light he noticed that at the exact same spot there was a crop-circle! Investigation revealed this to be a spiral-bedded clockwise circle, eight metres in diameter, with a sharp perimeter. The witness was in no doubt that the luminous vortex was responsible for the circle, and that the electrical flow across the field was the cause of the temporary malfunction of motor-engine and lights. The site was not far from the Severn estuary with hills close by to the north and west.

Readers of *The circles effect and its mysteries* will recognise the importance of this case as cross-referencing itself to and thereby helping to substantiate similar car-stop cases cited therein. The electrostatic display was the consequence of the spinning vortex dragging into its orbit air filled wth static charge which had originated within the dry crop (cf the article by Gordon Garrould page 142). Doubtless, the motion of the electrical charges would lead to the whistling humming sound heard by Tom Gwinnett if not also the crackling sound reported by some field walkers and circles enthusiasts and the lady eye-witness in the story which follows.

This next statement describes a crop-circle event witnessed in Cambridgeshire in 1934. Attention was drawn to it by the publication in the London *Sunday Express* on 12 August 1990 of a letter to the editor by Miss Kathleen Skin of Cambridge.

I witnessed a corn circle being formed in 1934. I was gazing over a field of corn waiting to be harvested when I heard a crackling like fire and saw a whirlwind in the centre of the field, spinning stalks, seeds and dust up into the air for about 100 or more feet. I found a perfect circle of flattened corn, the stalks interlaced and their ears lying on top of each another (some even plaited) on the periphery. The circle was hot to the touch.

There was nothing to be seen in the sky - no wind, and no sound. Maybe on a windless day the corn stalks form an electric current which attracts an electric force in the atmosphere meeting with such pressure that the corn is pressed hard on to the ground in a circular motion, a sort of miniature tornado.

Further significant details resulted from an interview with Miss Skin. The event happened after lunch one afternoon in July 1934, before school term ended [which means before about the 20th of the month, probably on a Saturday]. The place was Eversden, ten kilometres from Cambridge. The weather was dry, windless, hot, sultry. Because of the heat and the sunshine

Kathleen, aged 14, was seated in the shade of a hedgerow facing a five-acre wheatfield. Mr. Hagger, the farmer, whom she knew well, stopped to chat before moving on.

Suddenly, Kathleen heard a crackling sound and saw there was a whirlwind in the centre of the field spinning out a circle in the corn and simultaneously spinning stalks and loose matter high into the air. She started running towards it, but within seconds the whirlwind had left its circle and was traversing the field. She reached the circle to find the straw lying clockwise, interlaced and plaited in the complex way now familiar to circles investigators. The air at the circle seemed hot, and she could feel the warmth of the corn through her shoes, so she touched the lying wheat with her hand and was amazed at how hot the fallen crop was. By this time the whirlwind had reached the corner of the field and created a second circle about four metres in diameter. The young lady did not enter the second circle but went home to tell her mother about it. She went back next day and found the farmer harvesting the field. He had seen such circles before, he said, adding that the circle was nothing unusual for him and that it was locally known that whirlwinds were able to make such circles in the crops.

From the physico-meteorological standpoint this could be an example of vortex breakdown of a 'thermal' whirlwind (cf H.J. Lugt, *Bull.Amer. Met. Soc.* vol. 70, 1526-1537, 1989 who discusses natural vortex breakdown for tornadoes, waterspouts, etc). The present status of the theory of crop-circle formation is that the presence of circles may intimate the occurrence of vortex breakdown (J. T. Snow, T. Kikuchi) or the descent of a spherical vortex (G.B. Bathurst). Certainly the majority of circles develop downwind of a topographical obstacle which is responsible for creating an eddy-induced vortex, and vortex breakdown or spherical-vortex descent may be the intermediary mechanism between high-level vortex and crop-circle. On the other hand it is apparent that the thermal-type of whirlwind (i.e. land-devil) is responsible for some circles, so, here too, a similar damaging-vortex mechanism may be the link. Land devils often appear in the absence of hills over flat countryside and near coasts, their rotation triggered by sea-breeze interactions. Vortex breakdown near coasts could be a factor in crop-circle development in these regions. Alternatively, there may be some means by which spherical vortices of Hill's type effect the damage, as George Bathurst is suggesting (pp 68-72), and also Dr. Karl L.E. Nickel (Freiburg University, Germany) in private correspondence.

Inland, whirlwinds have been known, or seen, to create crop-circles on several occasions (example, Malvern Hills, Herefordshire, 1981 (*J.Meteorology*, vol.8, 216-217, 1982) and 1986). They have also been known to flatten circles in grass (e.g. at Pucklechurch, Avon County 1989, P.D. Rendall, *J.Meteorology* 14, 414-415, 1989) and in the stubble of harvested crops (J.F. Pearson, Roundway Hill 1989, *J.Meteorology* 15, 219, 1990). The latter case, which happened on the Roundway plateau near Devizes, Wiltshire, was shaped like an orb, and considered by George Bathurst to be a spherical vortex of Hill's type (see pp 143-7).

Turning to examples of nocturnal cases we commence with a hovering orange light seen on the edge of Allington Down east of Devizes in Wiltshire. I learnt of this at the beginning of July 1990 when I received a letter and sketch from Mr. Fred J. Bailey of Melksham, Wiltshire, about a luminous phenomenon that he had seen below the hill-line from Allington, between Devizes and Alton Barnes in Wiltshire twenty years earlier. In this report I reproduce his letter and a summary of an interview I had with him a couple of weeks later.

Sir,

Having read so much about crop circles I wonder if it is caused by something I saw one evening on my way through the village of Allington near Devizes at about 10.30 p.m. one evening.

We saw what appeared to be a craft of some sort with some smaller objects circling around at about 200 feet (60 metres) above ground. It was a strange colour, a shining brown. We stopped the car and watched for about 30 seconds when all of a sudden it disappeared. I have three witnesses who saw this apparition. After reading so much about it, I have come to the conclusion that it is caused by a vacuum caused by the vicinity of the hills. This causes it to pick up the dirt into the air; this makes the object. It then twirls it around, then it disappears. It seems to appear where the hills have a funnel. You do not see it in a large grass field. I think it was the light that caused the glow. Also the four circles were caused by the smaller objects.

The interview was conducted at Mr. Bailey's house in the company of his wife. It was established that the night in question was a Saturday in August or July in 1970. The time was given as 10.30 p.m., i.e. "dusk". The witnesses were Mr and Mrs Bailey and John and Ursula. Their grandchild Albena, born in 1967, was three at the time. The light was described as a rusty-brown or orange. It was watched hovering close to the hill as seen from Allington, and was over land farmed by Mr. King-Forster. It was about half-a-mile away which would be slightly west of north as seen from the road. Its national grid reference would therefore be SU 065642 whereas that of the car was SU 068633.

The light was held in view for some 30 seconds, and was thought to be spinning. It disappeared by dissolving. Mr. Bailey, now aged 77, volunteered that the air in this region is often very dusty, the chalk dust from the dry light soil being easily picked up by wind movements. He was a milkman most of his life and knew the area well, travelling along this road for many years.

A rather similar observation was made after 2 a.m. B.S.T. on 15 July 1990 just above Walker's Hill (SU 112645) (and not far from Golden Ball Hill) which overlooks the fields of Alton Barnes in which the spectacular circles of 12 July had appeared (SU 115631). This was a "very big" low -level hovering light which was rhythmically pulsating between orangey-yellow and yellow-white, and was sufficiently transparent that stars could be seen through it. The witness said that for 3-4 beats lasting 2-3 seconds the colour was orange-yellow and then for 3-4 beats which took another 2-3 seconds it was yellow-white. He had pulled into a lay-by in order to observe the phenomenon but did not remain long enough to see what happened to the light-form; nor could he say whether there were similar apparitions in the vicinity at this or any other time that night. Next morning circles were found in wheatfields on the nearby chalkhill plateau (SU 116642, 124648). This account was reported to me by Gordon W.C. Garrould and Maxwell Woosnam who interviewed the witness.

We conclude this summary with a reported sighting of a low-level self-luminous object observed within Avebury henge (SU 102699) a few years ago. The witness was a resident in her middle years whose account of her experience was given by Paul Devereux in *Places of Power* and is reproduced by permission. "While walking her dog one October evening in 1983, around 10 o'clock, she saw what she momentarily took to be the moon over the south-west quadrant of the henge. She was on the road just inside the west entrance to the henge. The "moon" was, in fact, a soft, yellow-white orb of light that silently drifted over the bank and ditch of the henge, descended past the stones in the outer circle of the south-west quadrant, and settled like thistledown on to the grass just inside the arc of megaliths. "It just went out," the witness said. "It made no sound at all" ".

Avebury henge is two kilometres from Windmill Hill and would be in its lee for a light north-west wind. The top of Windmill Hill is the site of a Neolithic causewayed camp, an interrupted ditch enclosure which was in use from 4000 B.C. to around 3000/2500 B.C. The great henge and stone circles were built at Avebury about 2500 B.C., at a place seemingly well visited by mysterious lights and vortices. Silbury Hill predates the Avebury rings by a couple of centuries. The whole region close to Windmill Hill from the south-east to the south-west of the hill is a rich area for crop-circle formation, all of which adds to the evidence that the region owed something of its prehistoric spirituality, as displayed by the character and disposition of the sacred monuments, to a mystic vision of the much-admired but misunderstood forces of the natural elements. This realm of archaeological and prehistorical-religious research is extensive and hugely important. It is dealt with fully in a recently-completed study which the author started in 1980 and is to appear in three volumes to be published in 1991-1993. The first is entitled *The Goddess of the Stones.*

Crop-circles are not a new phenomenon. They have been appearing since crop planting began, and can be validated right back to the Neolithic of the ancient British. Even from mediaeval times eye-witness documentation exists of crop-circle formation, and in the next article Bob Skinner gives a report of what appears to be a genuine vortex case from Wiltshire – an example of an ionised vortex spinning at ground level. For this the date is 1633, probably early autumn. This is followed by the mowing devil story, originally published in August 1678 and first published with annotations in a crop-circle context in *J. Meteorology,* vol 14, 381-389, 1989).

A SEVENTEENTH-CENTURY REPORT OF AN ENCOUNTER WITH A PLASMA VORTEX?

By R.M. SKINNER

The following is an excerpt from John Aubrey's *Natural History of Wiltshire* with annotations.

"In the year 1633-4, soon after I had entered into my grammar at the Latin School at Yatton Keynal, our curate, Mr. Hart, was annoyd one night by these elves or fayries comming over the downes, it being nearly darke, and approaching one of the fairy dances as the common people call them in these parts, viz. the greene circles made by those sprites on the grasse, he all at once sawe an innumerable quantitie of pigmies or very small people dancing rounde and rounde, and singing and making all manner of small odd noyses. So being very greatly amaz'd, and yet not being able, as he says, to run away from them, being as he supposes kepte there in a kinde of enchantment. They no sooner perceave him but they surrounde him on all sides, and what betwixt feare and amazement, he fell downe scarcely knowing what he did; and thereupon these little creatures pinch'd him all over, and made a sorte of quick humming noyse all the time; but at length they left him, and when the sun rose he found himself exactly in the midst of one of these faery dances. This relation I had from him myselfe a few dayes after he was so tormented; but when I and my bedfellow Stump wente soon afterwards at night time to the dances on the downes, we sawe none of the elves or fairies. But indeed it is said they seldom appeare to any persons who go to seeke for them."

It is interesting to note the number of parallels in this account to the circumstances of crop circle formation, and witness statements of close contact with vortices:

1. *The topographical location* - on the downs, and in Wiltshire, where there have been numerous crop circles.

2. *The time of day* - dusk dawn, "it being nearly darke" ("the sun rose" later).

3. *Observation of vortex* "Dancing round and round" - the rotary movement of dust and vegetable matter in the vortex? Perhaps the witness's perception of the vortex could have been altered by electromagnetic effects, leading to a visionary aspect to report?

4. *The sounds* - "singing, and making all manner of small noyses", "a sort of quick humming noise all the time" - perhaps a combination of sound of vortex and electromagnetic sound.

5. *Changed state of consciousness?* The witness was "kept in a kinde of enchantment" – changed state of consciousness, due to electromagnetic effect? - leading to collapse.

6. *Physiological effect?* - The witness was "pinch'd him all over" - perhaps describing hairs standing on end, or another electromagnetic effect. Compare with the statement that "something stung my hands and cheeks" and of a

"prickling feeling" in Mr. Payne's account, (Meaden: *Circles Effect and It's Mysteries,* p.83), and of witnesses describing the sensation of hair standing on end when near supposed vortices (Randles and Fuller: *Crop Circles: A Mystery Solved?* p.146, 147, 148).

7. *Evidence of vortex in grass around him?* Is this perhaps stretching things too far! Aubrey uses the phrase "Fairy dance" - the local name for fairy ring or circle, and this cannot be equated with the 'crop circle' phenomenon. However, is it possible that the ring Mr. Hart found around him at dawn was not the usual fairy ring, but the swirled ring or circle effect caused by the vortex?

N.B. The elements of a buzzing sound and pricking sensation also appear in other folklore accounts of encounters with fairies. (see *Popular Romances of the West of England* - Robert Hunt (1881, 1908) pp. 101, 119). Whirlwinds themselves were in some places regarded as being fairies, or indicating the passage of fairies.

THE MOWING-DEVIL OR STRANGE NEWS OUT OF HARTFORD-SHIRE, 1678.

THE MOWING-DEVIL:
OR, STRANGE NEWS OUT OF
HARTFORD-SHIRE.

Being a True Relation of a Farmer, who Bargaining with a Poor Mower, about the Cutting down Three Half Acres of Oats: upon the Mower's asking too much, the Farmer swore *That the Devil should Mow it rather than He.* And so it fell out, that very Night, the Crop of Oat shew'd as if it had been all of a Flame; but next Morning appear'd so neatly mow'd by the Devil or some Infernal Spirit, that no Mortal Man was able to do the like.

Also, How the said Oats ly now in the Field, and the Owner has not Power to fetch them away.

Licensed, August 22nd, 1678.

Men may dally with Heaven, and criticise on Hell, as Wittily as they please, but that there are really such places, the wise Dispensations of Almighty Providence does not cease continually to evince. For if by those accumulated circumstances which generally induce us to the belief of anything beyond our senses, we may reasonably gather that there are certainly such things as DEVILS, we must necessarily conclude that these Devils have a Hell: and as there is a Hell, there must be a Heaven, and consequently a GOD: and so all the Duties of Christian Religion as indispensable subsequents necessarily follow.

The first of which Propositions, this ensuing Narrative does not a little help to Confirm.

For no longer ago, than within the compass of the present Month of August, there hapned so unusual an Accident in Hartfordshire as is not only the general Discourse, and Admiration of the whole Country: but may for its Rarity challenge any other event, which has for these many years been Product in any other Country whatsoever. The story thus.

In the said County lives a Rich industrious Farmer, who perceiving a small Crop of his (of about three Half-Acres of Land which he had Sowed with

Oats) to be Ripe and fit for Gathering, sent to a poor Neighbour whom he knew worked commonly in the Summer-time at harvest Labor to agree him about Mowing or Cutting the said Oats down. The poor Man as it behoov'd Him endeavour'd to sell the Sweat of his Brows and Marrow of his Bones at as dear a Rate as reasonably he might, and therefore askt a good round Price for his Labour, which the Farmer taking some exception at, bid him much more under the usual Rate than the poor Man askt for it: So that some sharp Words had past, when the Farmer told him he would Discourse with him no more about it. Whereupon the honest Mower recollecting with himself, that if he undertook not that little Spot of Work, he might thereby lose much more business which the Farmer had to imploy him in beside, ran after him, and told him, that, rather than displease him, he would do it at what rate in Reason he pleas'd: and as an instance of his willingness to serve him, propos'd to him a lower price, than he had Mowed for any time this Year before. The irretated Farmer with a stern look, and hasty gesture, told the poor man That the Devil himself should Mow his Oats before he should have anything to do with them, and upon this went his way, and left the sorrowful Yeoman, not a little troubled that he had disoblig'd one in whose Power it lay to do him many kindnesses.

But, however, in the happy series of an interrupted prosperity, we may strut and plume our selves over the miserable Indigencies of our necessitated Neighbours, yet there is a just God above, who weighs us not by our Bags, nor measures us by our Coffers: but looks upon all men indifferently, as the common Sons of Adam: so that he who carefully Officiates that Rank or Station wherein the Almighty has plac't him, tho' but a mean one, is truly more worthy the Estimation of all men, than he who is prefer'd to superior dignities, and abuses them: And what greater abuse than the contempt of Men below him: the relief of whose common neccessities is none of the least Conditions whereby he holds all his Good things: which when that Tenure is forfeited by his default, he may justly expect some Judgment to ensue: or else that those riches whereby he prizes himself so extravagantly may shortly be taken from him.

We will not attempt to fathom the cause, or reason of, Preternatural events: but certain we are, as the most Credible and General Relation can inform us, that same night this poor Mower and Farmer parted, his Field of Oats was publickly beheld by several Passengers to be all of a Flame, and so continued for some space, to the great consternation of those that beheld it.

Which strange news being by several carried to the Farmer next morning, could not but give him a great curiosity to go and see what was become of his Crop of Oats, which he could not imagine, but what was totally devour'd by those ravenous Flames which were observed to be so long resident on his Acre and half of Ground.

Certainly a reflection on his sudden and indiscreet expression (That the Devil should Mowe his Oats before the poor Man should have any thing to do with them) cold not but on this occasion come into his Memory. For if we will but allow our selves so much leisure, to consider how many hits of providence go to the production of one Crop of Corn, such as the aptitude of Soyl, the Seasonableness of Showers, Nourishing Solstices and Salubreous Winds, etc., we should rather welcome Maturity with Devout Acknowledgements than prevent our gathering of it by our profuse wishes.

But not to keep the curious Reader any longer in suspense, the inquisitive Farmer no sooner arriv'd at the place where his Oats grew, but to his admiration he found the Crop was cut down ready to his hands; and if the Devil had a mind to shew his dexterity in the art of Husbandry, and scorn'd to mow them after the usual manner, he cut them in round circles, and plac't every straw with that exactness that it would have taken up above an Age for any Man to perform what he did that one night: And the man that owns them is as yet afraid to remove them.

FINIS

A POSSIBLE MECHANISM FOR CROP-CIRCLE FORMATION – A SPECULATION

By GEORGE R. NEHLS Jr.

Although crop circles in the south central part of England have been directly observed for at least fifteen years[1], their reported frequency has grown exponentially during the last decade. Given the assumption that the reported increase is primarily due to an actual increase in the number of crop circle occurrences, not reporting vigilance, the question is raised regarding probable cause. The remainder of this article is dedicated to a possible explanation for the increase in the crop circle frequency, or at least suggests a line of enquiry.

Another natural phenomenon occurring coincidentally with the rise in crop circle frequency has been the rise to solar sunspot maximum activity, or "solar max". The sun's sunspot activity oscillates with a period of approximately eleven years. During periods of maximum activity, the sun experiences increases in the number and size of solar storms, which are electromagnetic phenomena. During solar storms, the sun ejects streams of high velocity charged particles, and other radio-active by-products, into surrounding space. It is important to note that, although the frequency of the solar max cycle appears to be relatively constant, the intensity of the maximum is definitely not. The approach to the maximum expected in 1991 suggests that this current cycle may find the greatest absolute maximum during historical record.

When the earth happens to lie in the path of a stream of charged particles flowing away from the sun, a number of phenomena are observed on the Earth. The most familiar is the aurora, or sheets of light that are occasionally viewed in the direction of the earth's poles. The aurorae are due to charged particles that get trapped in the earth's magnetosphere and eventually cause huge circling electric currents in the earth's ionosphere above the polar regions. A more recently noted effect is the disturbances that can occur to radio and television transmission during these "magnetic storms".

Perhaps the most recent observation of a terrestrial effect caused by solar storms is that large circulating electric currents are caused in the earth itself as a result of magnetic inductive coupling with the circulating electric currents in the ionosphere[2]. These circulating currents produce little observable phenomena on the surface of the earth except where regional geology resists the flow of electricity deep beneath the earth's surface. This condition can create large voltage differences between regions on the earth's surface. One well documented result of such a situation is the damage that can occur to a regional electric power grid[3].

1 Personal communication with local farmers in the vicinity of Bratton, Wiltshire, U.K.

2 *Bracing for the geomagnetic storms, IEEE Spectrum,* Kappenman & Albertson, 1990.

3 *The Geomagnetic Storm of March 13, 1989: Power System Effects,* Kappenman & Albertson.

It has been suggested[4] that electrical or electrical plasma-based phenomena may be part of the dynamo creating the crop circles. If this is the case, it would be worthwhile to determine what, in the electromagnetic environment, is providing the source of energy transfer. Although a number of atmospheric phenomena have been speculated, and may actually be intrinsic to the situation, it is possible that a ground-based phenomenon may also be involved.

Although this article is written without any knowledge of the geology in the crop circle's locale, it would seem reasonable to investigate whether a correlation exists between the chronological records of geomagnetic disturbances and known crop circle formation.

If such a correlation exists, further study may show some such mechanism as the following exists:

> During a period of electric field "distress", complex electric field potentials may be abundant in the locales in question. Additionally, electric field potentials could also exist between the earth and the atmosphere. As has been noted by others, the circles are known to occur in areas downwind of rapid ground elevation changes. It has also been noted by others that wind vortices can occur as a result of wind shear conditions associated with such elevation changes. The natural structure of such a wind vortex may encourage the build-up of some electrostatic potential in an axial or radial pattern. Upon contacting the ground, or perhaps in near proximity to the ground, a discharge of some pattern is released.

What may make the phenomenon difficult to observe could be due to its primary nature as a *ground-based* energy discharge – that is, while observers may be looking for some phenomenon that appears more "lightning-like", it could actually be occurring essentially at the earth's surface. Although the wind vortex would be necessary to provide the round patterns often observed, the energy required to allow the stalks to deform could be due primarily to the near instantaneous relaxation of distributed ground-based electric fields.

There is one more point to add to my speculation. The circulating currents that comprise the aurorae are deflected round to the night side of the planet. This may help to explain why the more extraordinary, special, circles effects seem to occur more often at night if the terrestrial superficial electric fields are more important then. Also, England should be far enough north to interact with the aurora borealis on a more regular basis than countries at more southerly latitudes (e.g. France and Germany, etc).

4 G. T. Meaden, *The Circles Effect and its Mysteries, ARTETECH,* 1990.

THE CIRCLES EFFECT IN THE RICE FIELDS OF JAPAN

By YOSHI-HIKO OHTSUKI

Abstract: Some of the circles known to have appeared in rice-fields in Japan since 1979 are reported. We have investigated at least 16 circles ourselves. There are some special characteristics in the Japanese cases compared with the crop circles in Britain.

INTRODUCTION

Recently it has become clear that many circles have appeared in Japanese rice-fields since 1979. At least 13 circles have been found for the period 1979-1989 and in 1990 there were at least twenty. The circles were very simple, i.e. they were either single circles or ringed circles. However we can find very interesting characteristics compared with crop circles in Britain. In some cases the bunched rice plants split into two at the circle edge, one part bending, the other not. Moreover, many of the rice-field circles appeared during the typhoon season between the start of September and the end of October. We have noted that the topographical and meteorological conditions were the same as for the crop-circle formation in Britain.

HISTORICAL SURVEY AND THE 1990 CIRCLES

The first-known circle appeared in a rice-field at Toyosato a few kilometres north of Tsukuba Science City, Ibaragi Prefecture from 29 June to 30 June 1979. The diameter was four metres but there was an untouched residual area in the centre of diameter 1.5 m (see Fig 1).

It is interesting to know that all the damaged rice straws 'disappeared' completely (neither bent nor cut). The owner of the field, Mr. S. Sawabe, said that there was only mud in the circle when he saw it first. However he recognised that all the straws and the roots of the rice were pressed deep into the mud.

In 1990 about ten circles appeared in a rice-field on Kyushu Island in the typhoon season (see Fig. 2). It was 17 September when two circles were found in the rice at Sasaguri near Fukuoka. One was 18 m in diameter, and the other 5.5 m with an outer ring 10.4 m diameter (see Fig. 2). All the straws were bent anticlockwise. It was also noted that a small hill of 100 m altitude was located to the north-west at a distance of 800 m from the circles, and that typhoon no. 19 was in the southern sea. The lee effect pointed out by Dr Meaden (1989) would be responsible for the creation of the circles.

A week later on 24 September two more, smaller, circles formed near the bigger circle, and on the same day a 10 m circle was found at another place, Ikuhashi, 40 km east of Sasaguri. The straw was bent clockwise. A small hill was located near the circle, a hundred metres to the north and typhoon no. 20 was in the southern sea.

On 1 October the first circle was found in Kanzaki, Saga Prefecture, on Kyushu Island, 40 km south of the Sasaguri circles when typhoon no. 20 was in

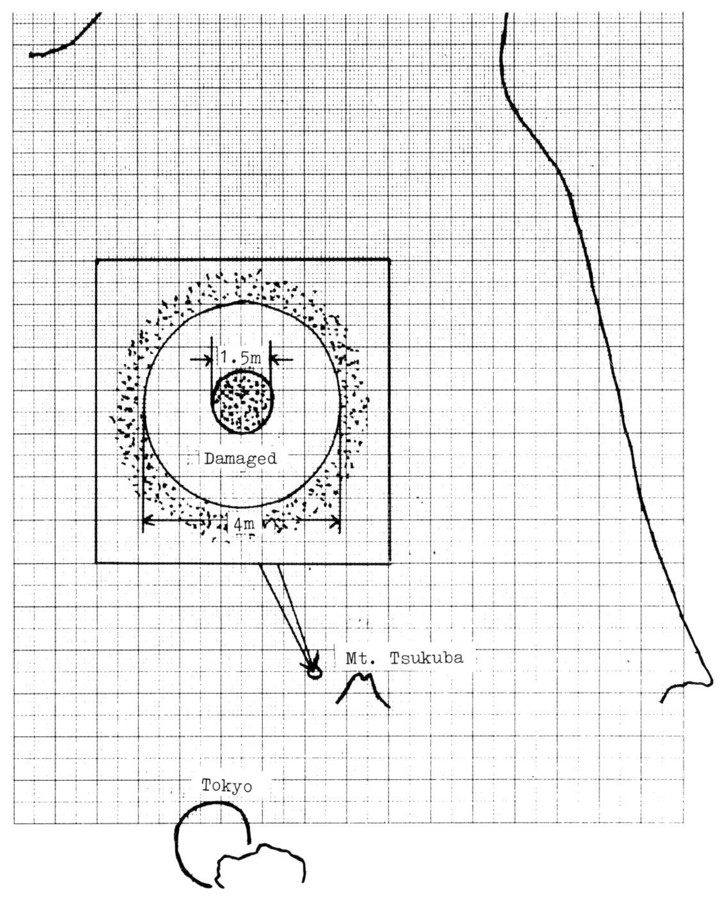

Fig. 1. The doughnut ring-circle which appeared in a rice-field in Tsukuba, Ibaragi Prefecture in 1979 (not to scale).

the eastern sea. Another five circles were found on 3 October at almost the same place (Mitagawa, Saga Prefecture) when typhoon no. 21 was in the Northern sea. All the straw was bent clockwise. On 11 October a 10 m circle was also found in Sasaguri.

Two circles and parts of circles like 'semi-circles' were found in the middle of October (formation date unclear) at Kuragasaki, Imaichi, (near Nikko, Tochigi Prefecture) in a wet grass field (Fig. 3). When the author arrived on 29 October he found that the grass had withered and it was then understood that the circles had formed a few weeks earlier.

SOME PROPERTIES OF RICE CIRCLES

The edge of the circles is very sharp (Fig. 4).

A part of the bunching of the rice (each about 5-6 cm in diameter) was bent

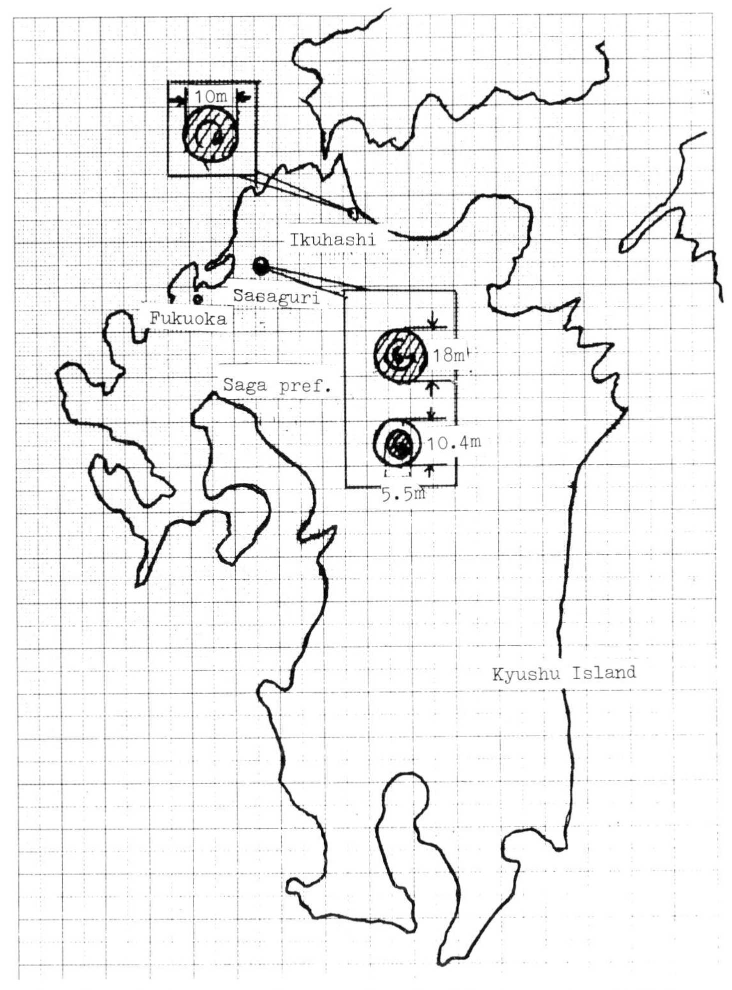

Fig. 2. Some of circles which appeared in Kyushu Island in September 1990 (not to scale).

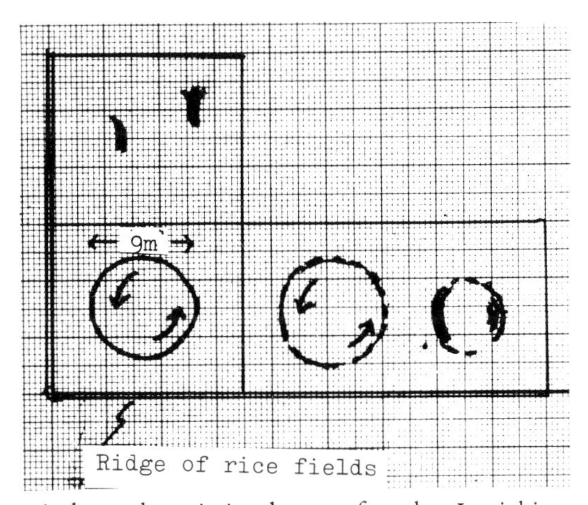

Fig. 3. Two circles and semi-circular arcs found at Imaichi near Nikko.

anticlockwise while the outer part was undamaged. So the sharpness was estimated to be within a centimetre (or less). This means the degree of sharpness is 1cm/900cm which is about 1 in 1000. It is very difficult to make such a very sharp edge by simple hoaxing.

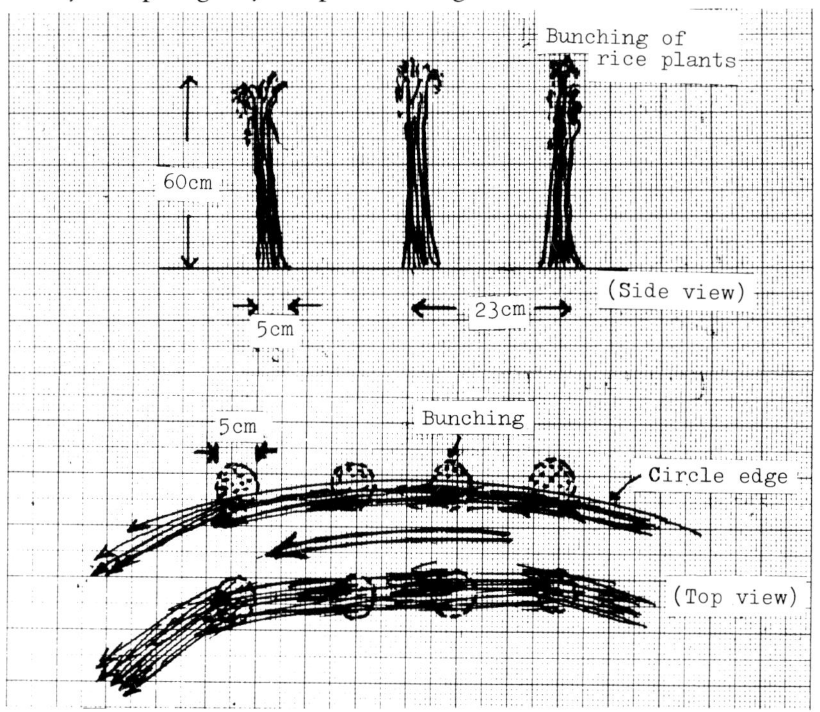

Fig. 4. The bunching of rice plants showing the circle edge cutting through some of the bunches.

At the edge of the bigger circle in Sasaguri three of the rice bunches had erupted-like bending in a radial direction. The erupted straw was damaged so much that this showed that there had been very high pressure directed from the centre of the circle.

CONCLUDING REMARKS

Investigations of the rice circles in 1990 showed that some kind of rotating elastic substance or quasi-solid substance came down into the rice-field. It is difficult to imagine that the air vortex or air plasma vortex formed such a sharp edge to the circle.

The air or air plasma has a shearing constant of 2×10^{-5}kg/m.s. The shearing viscosity strain will be 10^2 kg/m^2 for bending the straw completely. Because the shearing constant times the velocity gradient equals shearing viscosity strain the velocity gradient du/dy should be $10^2 / (2 \times 10^{-5})$ which is 5×10^{-7} m/s.m.

If the sharpness of the edge is of the order of 10^{-2} m, the velocity difference at the edge becomes about 5×10^5 which is tremendously high.

Therefore we need to make a suitable model for the creation of some quasi 'solid' or elastic state of the plasma vortex in the air. We will report on such a model in another paper.

Acknowledgement. The author thanks Mr K. Kasai of NHK (Japan Broadcasting) for helping him to carry out field works in the rice-fields on Kyushu Island during September 1990.

REFERENCES

MEADEN, G.T. (1989). *The Circles Effect and its Mysteries.* Artetech, England.
TAKANASHI, J. (1980). *Japan Flying Saucer Investigation.* No. 84, 12.

[Note by the editor: Sharp edges are noted in many of the British cropfield circles. I have presumed that this is possible because of a high velocity-gradient across the boundary between the ionized and non-ionized states, the boundary zone being a sort of 'plasma-pause'. It is logical to surmise that this boundary is thin. As a partial parallel one might reflect on the precision of detail obtained in Xerox-type photocopying machines by the controlled motion of electro-statically-charged carbon-dust particles].

CROP-CIRCLE EYE-WITNESSES CAUGHT IN A CIRCLE-MAKING VORTEX, MAY 1990, AND AN EYE-WITNESS ACCOUNT FROM THE 1940s

By G.T. MEADEN

Abstract: Two more eye-witness accounts of crop circles being formed by natural vortices are described. One happened in Surrey on 17 May 1990 when two circles were seen to form by the action of a spinning vortex which the witnesses described as a whirlwind that split in two. The noise of the approaching primary vortex came from above. The witnesses were affected not only by the buffetting from the spinning wind system but they found themselves inside one of the circles which resulted from the phenomenon. The other account dates from the late 1940's in South Wales. The witness was only a few metres from the whirling vortex as it spun out a typical sharp-edged circle. Crop circles had been found several times previously on the farm. These two splendid eye-witness accounts have major significance for the scientific advancement of circles research as a well-testified natural phenomenon.

CROP CIRCLES IN SURREY, MAY 1990

Late in the evening on Thursday 17 May 1990 at about 9 p.m. [B.S.T.] Mrs Vivian Tomlinson, 36, and her husband Gary, were following a public right-of-way across a wheatfield in Surrey when they found themselves in the midst of a commotion of wind which, preceded by a high-pitched sound from above them, soon developed into a 'large whirlwind' spinning where they stood. As they watched, the whirling wind pushed the corn down into a circle all around them, so not only did the witnesses see the vortex as it made a circle, they were inside the circle as it formed! The account is of the highest importance for all circles researchers, and it fully supports the scientific work and opinions expressed by professional physicists and meteorologists during the last ten years as to the basic nature of the crop-circles problem.

My attention was drawn to this event by a letter, dated 29 July 1990, from Mrs Tomlinson sent to Terry O'Hanlon of the *Sunday Mirror* who passed the letter on to me, with others, in February 1991. I promptly wrote to the lady asking additional questions and I followed up her instant reply with an interview. The present report commences with her first letter, in which I have changed, with her agreement, her mention of 7 p.m. to 9 p.m. because the occurrence was definitely at dusk, the sun having set at 20.48 B.S.T. on that day.

I'm writing about the corn circles that have baffled you all. I just could not believe my luck. My husband and I have actually witnessed the circles being made.

It was about 9 p.m. and we were returning from our walk across the cornfields out at Hambledon. Half way, we stopped to watch the wind blowing on the corn, sending wave after wave of ripples right across the corn, making it appear like a golden brown sea. I have always held a fascination for wind and sound, and can lose myself watching it. Suddenly, there was a change in wind pattern, it appeared to be pushing from both directions. At the centre point the wind gathered force pushing forward sending strong waves in the corn. The whistling grew stronger in the corn, almost like a high-pitched pan-pipe flute sound.

We both looked up to see if there was a helicopter above us. There was none, it felt strange. Suddenly there was a gush of strong wind pushing against us. The wind circled round us, looking down, we noticed corn being pushed down. It started with one large whirlwind. This broke into another one, pushing the offset one into the side, whirling away pushing down the corn.

The circle we were in was fast becoming interesting. Miniature whirlwinds were appearing one after another, rapidly whirling around the corn in small bunches, then gently falling down.

We stood watching in amazement, the corn swirled and then gently laid down. There was no feel of wind now or sound. It felt strange watching these ever-fast gathering whirlwinds. They just seemed to increase; they were enveloping around quickly. I panicked, grabbed my husband's hand and pulled him out of the circle.

It felt strange, perhaps because of the unknown answers that lay in the balance. I believe the answer lies in the current build-up of wind and force. Here is a diagram for you (Figure 1). I hope you understand it from my point of view. This we have seen two and a half months ago.

In diagram 3 there is a build up of force as wind meets at centre point causing the current flow of wind to push forward with great force. [The first three diagrams are side views while diagrams 4 and 5 are plan views – Ed.]

Mrs Tomlinson answered the queries in my letter as follows. The day of the week and date were Thursday 17 May 1990. The field was next to St Peter's Church, Hambledon, Surrey, and the site about a hundred metres from the summit of Byrony Hill. The cereal was wheat, light green and dryish, and two feet (0.6 metre) high. The circle was about two metres in diameter. The strong wind made the circle as a small spiral which appeared anticlockwise. The circle grew outwards from a centre. 'I think the whole event lasted about seven minutes, possibly longer, but the circle was made very quickly'.

As a result of the interview the following points can be added. In the evening Mr and Mrs Tomlinson had walked from the church along the public right of way across two fields of wheat to the top of Byrony Hill. Mrs Tomlinson thinks she underestimated the distance to the hilltop, saying she is not used to estimating distances. After the sun had set, they walked back down, and it was as they were crossing the second of the wheatfields, the one nearer the church, and were half way across it that the wind motion began. Until then there had been no significant wind.

As described above, the movement of the corn showed the development of two counterflowing winds, the noises of which intensified to a high pitch and caused the witnesses to look up to see the source of the noise. The violence of the wind rose very fast, and 'with a whoosh' Mr and Mrs Tomlinson found themselves 'pulled off the path and into the wheat'. They were then battered by the spinning wind which knocked the corn down as a typical spiral-centered circle, the sharp edge of which reached nearly to the edge of the path.

Something which impressed and puzzled Mrs Tomlinson was that she 'saw the air coming', i.e. the air was visible because it had cloud-vapour or mist in it; also, while the main whirlwind made a circle about two metres in diameter very swiftly, a second whirlwind peeled off from the first and ran to one side generating a second circle a little further out. The circle creation took only a couple of seconds or so, but lesser whirlwinds continued to form for a much longer time, possibly for seven minutes or so. Although the witnesses said they could not now feel the wind, they were able to watch a succession of small vortices, made visible by vapour condensation, appearing and running outwards from the circle into the wall of the circle. These minor vortices were perhaps four inches apart (0.1 metre) and taller than their breadth. Finally, the Tomlinsons got tired of watching them and left for home.

Mrs Tomlinson said she was glad to have the opportunity to write to the *Mirror* to tell them the truth about circle formation, in order that people should know that it is a natural happening, especially following some of the sensational stories which have been put around by publicity-seekers and fantasisers during the preceding weeks. She and her husband returned to the field at the beginning of August hoping to see the circles again and count them up, because she thought one or two other circles were in the field prior to the event she witnessed, but they found the crop had been harvested.

CROP CIRCLE EYE-WITNESS ACCOUNT FROM CILYCWM, SOUTH WALES

Another letter sent via the *Sunday Mirror* was from Mr William Cyril Williams of Brockworth, Gloucestershire. He wrote: 'With reference to the corn circles mystery, I actually witnessed one being made. I was standing in a cornfield one morning and saw a whirlwind touching the ground and forming a circle in the corn. It was just the strength of the wind in the whirlwind that formed the circle'.

I interviewed Mr Williams by telephone and learned that the event happened in the late 1940's when he worked on his father's farm, Penfedw Farm at Cilycwm, about six kilometres from Llandovery, Dyfed. He was then in his twenties. This area is surrounded by hills on all sides, and circles frequently form there, having been seen several times in the cornfields during the war years when much winter wheat was sown. The grid reference of Cilycwm is SN 7541.

On this occasion, a weekday in August, at about 10.30 to 11 in the morning [B.S.T.], Mr Williams had gone into the wheat field on harvesting day in advance of the cutting and binding machinery, and he was crossing the middle of the field when he heard the buzzing noise of a whirlwind starting up only a few metres away. He then saw the spinning whirlwind with dust in the air, and, as he watched, in a matter of only a couple of seconds or so the wheat fell down producing a sharp-edged circle three to four metres in diameter. It looked just like the other crop circles he had seen before except that this one was completely flat-bottomed whereas some of the earlier ones had stalks standing at their centres like a conical pyramid. The whirling vortex died out rapidly, but during its short life it remained stationary at the same place.

CONCLUSIONS

The list of perfectly good eye-witness descriptions assembled by CERES grows even longer. These additional reports confirm all previous accounts and fully support the generalised vortex explanation as the *fons et origo* of the crop circles. Both these new eye-witness accounts are important but the one from Surrey is unique because the circle-making vortex formed where the witnesses stood and the air was humid enough that the vortices were visible because of condensation effects.

[Note: This paper is a late addition to the book, inserted March 1991].

THE ARTIFICIAL PRODUCTION OF PLASMA-VORTEX QUINTUPLET CIRCLES

By SHELDON. L. WERNIKOFF

An important advance in experimental research on the circles effect has resulted from observations of the motion of vortices in a gas-filled glass chamber. The experiments concern the production of quintuplet circle sets by the impact of plasma vortices upon an anode in a commercially-made instrument.

The experiments are conducted using Tesla-generated high-voltage, low-frequency currents in an inert mixture of neon and argon. At certain frequencies around 150 khz plasma vortices form. The vortices are rendered luminous by the excitation of the neon-argon mixture. The anode is spherical in shape, approximately 40 mm in diameter, and is fabricated of carbon-steel alloy sheathed in a ceramic insulating capsule.

The vortices form spontaneously and glow brightly during their approach to the anode. Upon striking it each vortex gives rise to a regular set of five circles, the four satellite circles being located at equal distances in the four right-angle directions from the primary circle. The experiment has been repeated many times. The first colour photographs taken in October 1990 using 3200 ASA film suggest that the satellite circles are created at the moment of impact by the ejection of four subsidiary vortices from the primary one but the exact sequence will not be known until the process has been filmed by a high-speed video camera. Good photographs have subsequently been taken in monochrome at F1.2, 1/250 sec, pushed two stops to ASA 12500. The photograper was Mr. Richard Shapiro.

This work helps confirm the general ionized vortex ideas initiated by Dr. Meaden for crop-circle formation by natural vortex processes in the atmosphere, in combination with the theory of George Bathurst for quintuplet-formation by satellite vortex ejection (cf pp. 68-72 this book). Next it is hoped to film the life-cycle of the vortices using video film.

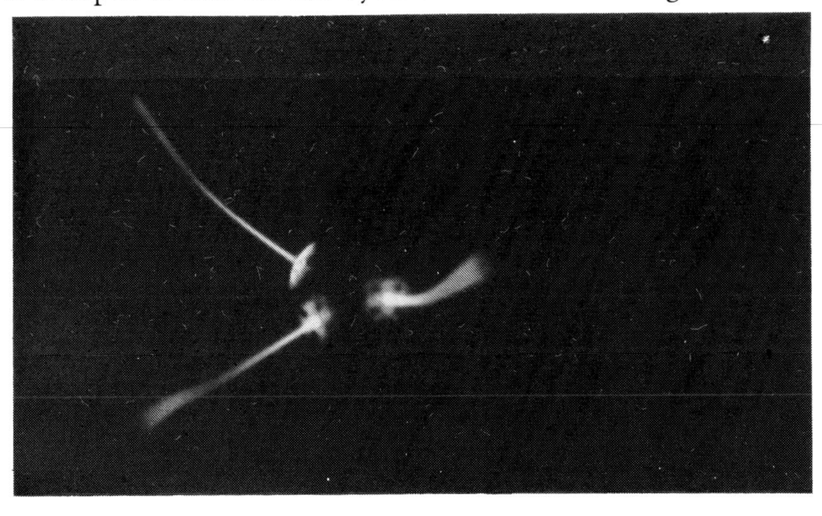

RECENT AND FORTHCOMING PAPERS ON CIRCLES RESEARCH

This is a list of major scientific papers on the circles effect published since December 1990 (other those by the editor than in *The Journal of Meteorology)* or known to be awaiting publication in scientific magazines or international conference proceedings and which are likely to be published in 1991.

BENNETT, M. (1990). The mechanics of crop circle formation. *Weather* (Roy. Meteorol. Soc.) vol. 45, 456.

ELIASSEN, Arnt (1991). Circles in h corn - a centrifugal pump?. *Weather* (Roy. Meteorol. Soc.) vol. 46, forthcoming.

KIKUCHI, Hiroshi (1991). EHD vortex in the atmospere with helical turbulence in electric and space-charge fields (12-page preprint received).

KIKUCHI, Tokio, SNOW, John, and MEADEN, G.T. (1991). Nanoburst: Microburst by a spiral vortex of micrometeorological scale. *Proc. Twentieth General Assembly of the International Union of Geodesy and Geophysics, Vienna, Austria, 11-24 August 1991.*

KIKUCHI, Tokio, SNOW, John, and MEADEN, G.T. (1991). Nanoburst, the microburst by spiral vortex, suggests the origin of circular crop damage.

LEWIS, Peter (1991). Angularity in the crop-markings made by vortices. *J. Meteorology,* vol. 16, forthcoming, May/June issue.

MEADEN, G.T. (1991). Discovery of a new electromagnetic phenomenon in the atmosphere: A vortex and its physical properties as revealed by patterned ground traces and radiofrequency, electromagnetic and luminous effects. *Proc. URSI [International Union of Radio Science] Conference held in Tokyo, Japan, September 1989.* Published by Springer Verlag, Germany.

MEADEN, G.T. (1991). A new proposal for the origin of the shapes of prehistoric stone circles.

MEADEN, G.T., and KIKUCHI, T. (1991). Simulated spiral-vortices do produce counter-rotating rings. *Weather* (Roy. Meteorol. Soc.) vol. 46, forthcoming.

* * *

LATEST NEWS: EXPERIMENTAL SUCCESS IN CREATING THE CIRCLES EFFECT IN THE LABORATORY

(From a letter to Dr. Meaden by Prof. Ohtsuki). Good news! On 17 March 1991 we succeeded in creating the circles effect on thin aluminium powder distributed over a metal plate set in our plasma chamber. These circles range from 2 to 10 mm with ring! You can see our photographs. So, your idea has been confirmed experimentally!

ANNOTATED CROP-CIRCLES BIBLIOGRAPHY

THE CIRCLES EFFECT AND ITS MYSTERIES. G.T. Meaden. Second edition 1990 (first edition June 1989 out of print). Updated to April 1990. A *scientific* appraisal of the mystery of crop circles using logic and the scientific method in an effort to reach a solution on the basis of available knowledge; includes some speculative interpretation, especially in the province of known and suggested electrical effects; clearly states the case for electromagnetic phenomena which lead to the known light and sound effects; argues that some light observations, previously unidentified and labelled UFOs by some witnesses, are in reality natural phenomena. £11.95, $35.00 U.S. incl. post ($40.00 air mail). Artetech Publishing, 54 Frome Road, Bradford-on-Avon, Wilts., BA15 1LD, England. [Japanese version by Maruzen Book Co., Tokyo, translated by Y.H. Ohtsuki].

CROP CIRCLES: A MYSTERY SOLVED. Jenny Randles and Paul Fuller. First edition, published August 1990, presents the circles situation as understood at April 1990; it provides a good historical account of crop-circle research from 1980 onwards, chiefly from the point of view of BUFORA. The approach is rational and scientific. Highly recommended. £13.95, Robert Hale, Clerkenwell Green, London, EC1R OHT, England.

THE CROP CIRCLE ENIGMA. Edited by Ralph Noyes. Published October 1990. A curious mixture of thought-provoking articles and varied viewpoints by several mostly non-scientific authors. Ideas range from the sound scientific to the sober psychological and the impetuous paranormal. A book for the general reader but not without some interest for the scientist, folklorist and psychologist. Most articles were submitted by mid-June 1990, but a short summary of the 1990 circles season (prepared by George Wingfield who claims a non-human 'intelligence' origin for the circles) was inserted before the September printing. Book authorised by the Centre for Crop Circles Studies, a new society formed in April 1990. £14.95, $25.95 U.S. Gateway Books, Wellow, Bath, Avon, BA2 8QJ, England.

CIRCULAR EVIDENCE. P. Delgado and C. Andrews. A much publicised book and a very bad one. Notable for its interesting colour photographs which are unhappily reproduced by an inferior 3-colour process instead of the conventional 4-colour method. A biassed, paranormal-flavoured overview of the circles effect written by opportunist non-scientists taking an anti-scientific stance and who had previously written chiefly for *Flying Saucer Review.* Loaded with errors, some of which are pointed out in a 2000-word book review (*J.Meteorology* vol. 14, 347-354, 1989) and many of which are discussed at length in the Randles-Fuller book above. Major falsities include statements that the fallen crop grows sideways, the circles effect is unrelated to topography and is not electromagetic, and that the circles appear only at night without light and sound. There is no index and no reference to the considerable research of others which preceded their work. Published July 1989. £14.95. Bloomsbury, London.

CROP CIRCLES - THE LATEST EVIDENCE. P. Delgado and C. Andrews. Published October 1990. 80pp, very good photographs. Openly supports a paranormal alien-intelligence origin for the circles. Not surprisingly these authors offer no proof for their contention although it is clear that such suggestions help to sell a lot of books to the credible. Since their 1989 book these authors have changed their original opinions when they declared that light and sound do not accompany circles formation. A second book which, because of its errors, will deceive readers who have no first-hand knowledge of circles research. These include insulting, incorrect, libellous remarks on pp 40-41 which should be withdrawn. £5.99 Bloomsbury, London.

CIRCLES RESEARCH 2: A geographical appraisal of the 1990 crop-circle season. Andrew Hewitt. Published summer 1991. 90pp + vii. Soft-back photocopy of original B.Sc. thesis. Demonstrates the unique geography of the 1990 season. Artetech Publishing, 54 Frome Road, Bradford-on-Avon, BA15 1LD. £20.

CIRCLES FROM THE SKY. Edited by G. Terence Meaden. Published June 1991. Contributions from 16 writers which make up the present volume. £14.99. Souvenir Press, 43 Great Russell Street, London WC1B 3PA.

THE GODDESS OF THE STONES: THE LANGUAGE OF THE MEGALITHS. G. Terence Meaden. Published June 1991. The writing of this book began in 1983 from ideas sown by the discovery of the first crop-circles in August 1980. It provides the missing archaeological link between the ancient circles of stone, timber and earth, and the ancient and modern views of crop circles. Proof is presented showing how our ancestors worshipped the ground hallowed by the descent of atmospheric vortices. For thousands of years stone circles and round barrows were raised over the spiral/circle marks made by crop-circle vortices. £18.99. Souvenir Press, 43 Great Russell Street, London WC1B 3PA.

MAGAZINES FREQUENTLY PUBLISHING CROP-CIRCLE PAPERS

The Journal of Meteorology. Founded 1975. This magazine has published crop-circle articles since first reporting the circles of 1980 in the March 1981 issue. 10 issues a year of which a few per year include several circles research papers chiefly of a scientific or general nature. In 1990 about 80 pages [of a total of 408 pages] were devoted to circles research and a further 100 to ball lightning or ball-of-light research. 1991 subscription rate £22 or $60.00 U.S. 1992 rate £24 or $65. Journal of Meteorology, 54 Frome Road Bradford-on-Avon, Wilts., England.

The Crop Watcher Ed. Paul Fuller, 3 Selborne Court, Tavistock Close, Romsey, Hants, S051 7TQ, England. 6 issues per year. Founded September 1990. Data reports, book reviews, news, humour, satire. A lively magazine which comes down fairly in support of logic and rationality. First year subscription £7.00

The Cereologist. Ed. John Michell, 11 Powis Gardens, London, W11 1JG. Three issues a year. First published August 1990. A non-scientific magazine formerly linked to CCCS, The Centre for Crop Circle Studies. Claims to be objective and all-embracing, but has a paranormal flavour. First year subscription £7.50.

The Circular Ed. Bob Kingsley, 58 Kings Road, West End, Woking, Surrey, GU24 9LW. Four issues a year. First published August 1990. Since March 1991 it has become the magazine of the CCCS. A magazine that ranges albeit superficially across all sides of the subject.

CIRCLES SOCIETIES

CERES. THE CIRCLES EFFECT RESEARCH GROUP. Named after the Graeco-Roman corn goddess Ceres, this international scientific research group was founded in 1987 to work on observational, experimental and theoretical crop-circles research. CERES is willing to collaborate with scientists and archaeologists from all countries, and needs more scientific volunteers who can join or organise circles watches and provide additional scientific instrumentation and cameras. Apply through Dr. Meaden or Peter Rendall. Always glad to receive circles reports for the central CERES data bank for serious scientific analysis. Please submit reports via Peter Rendall (46 Partridge Road, Pucklechurch, Bristol, BS17 3SP), Roger Davis (45 Whitcombe, Yate, Bristol BS17 4SX), David Reynolds (15 Pruden Avenue, Lanesfield, Wolverhampton, WV4 6PT), Dr. John Graham (Head of Agronomy, Shuttleworth College, Cranfield Institute of Technology, Biggleswade), Andrew Hewitt (23 Allenby Drive, Beeston, Leeds, LS11 5RX), Robert MacKenzie (Holly Cottage, Roberts Lane, Chalfont St. Peter, Bucks, SL9 0QR), Dr. Dennis Wheeler, Geography Department, Polytechnic, Sunderland, SR1 3SD), George Bathurst, Paul Fuller, or Terence Meaden.

CCCS. The Centre for Crop Circle Studies. A countrywide organisation formed in April 1990 which seeks cooperation with existing local groups on a friendly non-competitive basis. Wishes to be objective and impartial but most of its leaders have paranormal inclinations or susceptibilities. Details from P.O. Box 146, Guildford, Surrey, GU2 5JY.

CPR. Circles Phenomenon Research. Formed as a four-member group in 1987; disbanded 1989, then re-formed as a two-member group (C. Andrews and P. Delgado) and called British CPR; name reverted to CPR in 1990. Supports the 'unknown intelligence' idea. Not open to membership.

INTERNATIONAL WORKSHOP ON THE CIRCLES EFFECT: Organised by CERES in conjunction with visiting Professor Y.H. Ohtsuki a workshop on the science of the circles effect together with its archaeological and historical implications. July 1991.

Conference Organisers:

Dr. Derek M. Elsom, CERES-TORRO, Oxford Polytechnic, Headington, Oxford, OX3 0BP, U.K. (telephone 0865 819761; fax 0865 819073).

Dr.G. Terence Meaden, Circles Effect Research Unit, CERES-TORRO, 54 Frome Road, Bradford-on Avon, Wiltshire, BA14 1LD, U.K. (telephone 02216 2482; fax 02216 5601).

Addresses of Authors and Chairmen:

Hon. George B. Bathurst, CERES-TORRO, Hullasey House, Tarlton, Near Cirencester, Gloucestershire, GL7 6PA, U.K.

Prof. Christopher R. Church, Department of Aeronautics, Miami University, Oxford, Ohio 45056, U.S.A.

Mr. C. Paul Fuller, BUFORA, 3 Selbourne Court, Tavistock Close, Romsey, Hampshire, SP51 7TY, U.K.

Prof. Hiroshi Kikuchi, Nihon University, College of Science and Technology, 8 Kanda Surugadai, Chiyoda-ku, Tokyo, Japan.

Dr. Tokio Kikuchi, Department of Physics, Kochi University, Akebono-cho, Kochi 780, Japan.

Dr. Terence Meaden, Circles Effect Research Unit, CERES-TORRO, 54 Frome Road, Bradford-on-Avon, Wiltshire, BA15 1LD, U.K.

Prof. Y.H. Ohtsuki, Department of Physics, Waseda University, Okubo 3-4-1, Shinjuki-ku, Tokyo 160, Japan.

Miss Jenny Randles, BUFORA, 37 Heathbank, Stockport, Chesire, SK3 0UP, U.K.

Mr. David J. Reynolds, CERES-TORRO, 15 Pruden Avenue, Lanesfield, Wolverhampton, WV4 6PT, U.K.

Prof. John T. Snow, Department of Earth and Atmospheric Sciences, Purdue University, West Lafayette, Indiana 47907, U.S.A.

Mr. Frederick C. Taylor, Circles Investigation Group, 52 Appletree Grove, Andover, Hampshire, SP10 3RG, U.K.

Addresses of Additional Authors

Mr. Gordon W. C. Garrould, CERES-TORRO, Westport Granary, Gloucester Road, Malmesbury, Wiltshire

Dr. John A. Graham, Head of the Agronomy Department, Cranfield Institute of Technology, Shuttleworth College, Biggleswade, Bedfordshire, SG18 9DX.

Mr. Montague Keen, School Barn Farm, Pentlow, Sudbury, Suffolk, CO10 7JN

Mr. George Nehls, Jr., Minnesota Power, 30 West Superior Street, Duluth, Minnesota 55802, U.S.A.

Mr. Robert M. Skinner, 16 Hillside Lane, Heath End, Farnham, Surrey, GU9 0LB

Mr. Sheldon L. Wernikoff, CERES-TORRO, 9200 Niles Center Road, Skokie, Illinois, 60076-15481, U.S.A.

INDEX